Ren. Cartesius.

THE GEOMETRY
OF
RENÉ DESCARTES

TRANSLATED FROM THE FRENCH
AND LATIN

BY

DAVID EUGENE SMITH

AND

MARCIA L. LATHAM

WITH A FACSIMILE OF THE FIRST EDITION, 1637

LA SALLE, ILLINOIS
THE OPEN COURT PUBLISHING COMPANY
1952

Copyright by
THE OPEN COURT PUBLISHING COMPANY
1925

PRINTED IN THE UNITED STATES OF AMERICA

THE GEOMETRY OF RENÉ DESCARTES

Preface

If a mathematician were asked to name the great epoch-making works in his science, he might well hesitate in his decision concerning the product of the nineteenth century; he might even hesitate with respect to the eighteenth century; but as to the product of the sixteenth and seventeenth centuries, and particularly as to the works of the Greeks in classical times, he would probably have very definite views. He would certainly include the works of Euclid, Archimedes, and Apollonius among the products of the Greek civilization, while among those which contributed to the great renaissance of mathematics in the seventeenth century he would as certainly include *La Géométrie* of Descartes and the *Principia* of Newton.

But it is one of the curious facts in the study of historical material that although we have long had the works of Euclid, Archimedes, Apollonius, and Newton in English, the epoch-making treatise of Descartes has never been printed in our language, or, if so, only in some obscure and long-since-forgotten edition. Written originally in French, it was soon after translated into Latin by Van Schooten, and this was long held to be sufficient for any scholars who might care to follow the work of Descartes in the first printed treatise that ever appeared on analytic geometry. At present it is doubtful if many mathematicians read the work in Latin; indeed, it is doubtful if many except the French scholars consult it very often in the original language in which it appeared. But certainly a work of this kind ought to be easily accessible to American and British students of the history of mathematics, and in a language with which they are entirely familiar.

On this account, The Open Court Publishing Company has agreed with the translators that the work should appear in English, and with such notes as may add to the ease with which it will be read. To this organization the translators are indebted for the publication of the book, a labor of love on its part as well as on theirs.

As to the translation itself, an attempt has been made to give the meaning of the original in simple English rather than to add to the difficulty of the reader by making it a verbatim reproduction. It is believed that the student will welcome this policy, being content to go to the original in case a stricter translation is needed. One of the translators having used chiefly the Latin edition of Van Schooten, and the other the original French edition, it is believed that the meaning which Descartes had in mind has been adequately preserved.

Table of Contents[1]

BOOK I

Problems the Construction of which Requires Only Straight Lines and Circles

How the calculations of arithmetic are related to the operations of geometry.. 297
How multiplication, division, and the extraction of square root are performed geometrically 293
How we use arithmetic symbols in geometry............................. 299
How we use equations in solving problems............................... 300
Plane problems and their solution....................................... 302
Example from Pappus.. 304
Solution of the problem of Pappus...................................... 307
How we should choose the terms in arriving at the equation in this case...... 310
How we find that this problem is plane when not more than five lines are given 313

---

[1] It should be recalled that the first edition of this work appeared as a kind of appendix to the *Discours de la Methode,* and hence began on page 297. For convenience of reference, the original paging has been retained in the facsimile. A new folio number, appropriate to the present edition, will also be found at the foot of each page. For convenience of reference to the original, this table of contents follows the paging of the 1637 edition.

TABLE
Des matieres de la
GEOMETRIE.
Liure Premier.
DES PROBLESMES QU'ON PEUT
construire sans y employer que des cercles &
des lignes droites.

COMMENT le calcul d'Arithmetique se rapporte aux operations de Geometrie. 297
Comment se font Geometriquement la Multiplication, la Diuision, & l'extraction de la racine quarreé. 298
Comment on peut vser de chiffres en Geometrie. 299
Comment il faut venir aux Equations qui seruent a resoudre les problesmes. 300
Quels sont les problesmes plans; Et comment ils se resoluent. 302
Exemple tiré de Pappus. 304
Response a la question de Pappus. 307
Coment on doit poser les termes pour venir a l'Equation en cet exēple. 310

BOOK II

On the Nature of Curved Lines

What curved lines are admitted in geometry................................. 315
The method of distinguishing all curved lines of certain classes, and of knowing the ratios connecting their points on certain straight lines.......... 319
There follows the explanation of the problem of Pappus mentioned in the preceding book... 323
Solution of this problem for the case of only three or four lines............. 324
Demonstration of this solution... 332
Plane and solid loci and the method of finding them....................... 334
The first and simplest of all the curves needed in solving the ancient problem for the case of five lines..: 335
Geometric curves that can be described by finding a number of their points... 340
Those which can be described with a string................................. 340
To find the properties of curves it is necessary to know the relation of their points to points on certain straight lines, and the method of drawing other lines which cut them in all these points at right angles........... 341
General method for finding straight lines which cut given curves and make right angles with them.. 342
Example of this operation in the case of an ellipse and of a parabola of the second class... 343
Another example in the case of an oval of the second class.................. 344
Example of the construction of this problem in the case of the conchoid...... 351
Explanation of four new classes of ovals which enter into optics............. 352
The properties of these ovals relating to reflection and refraction............ 357
Demonstration of these properties... 360

viii

Table.

Comment on trouue que ce problesme est plan lorsqu'il n'est point proposé
en plus de 5 lignes. 313

Discours Second.
DE LA NATURE DES LIGNES COURBES.

Quelles sont les lignes courbes qu'on peut receuoir en Geometrie. 315
La façon de distinguer toutes ces lignes courbes en certains genres:
Et de connoistre le rapport qu'ont tous leurs poins a ceux des lignes
droites. 319
Suite de l'explication de la question de Pappus mise au liure preeedent. 323.
Solution de cete question quand elle n'est proposeé qu'en 3 ou 4 lignes. 324.
Demonstration de cete solution. 332
Quels sont les lieux plans & solides & la façon de les trouuer tous. 334
Quelle est la premiere & la plus simple de toutes les lignes courbes qui
seruent a la question des anciens quand elle est proposée en cinq lignes. 335.
Quelles sont les lignes courbes qu'on descrit en trouuant plusieurs de leurs
poins qui peuuent estre receuës en Geometrie. 340
Quelles sont aussy celles qu'on descrit auec vne chorde, qui peuuent y estre
receuës. 340
Que pour trouuer toutes les proprietez des lignes courbes, il suffit de sçauoir
le rapport qu'ont tous leurs poins a ceux des lignes droites; & la
façon de tirer a autres lignes qui les coupent en tous ces poins a angles
droits. 341
Façon generale pour trouuer des lignes droites qui couppent les courbes
donneés, ou leurs contingentes a angles droits. 342
Exemple de cete operation en vne Ellipse: Et en vne parabole du second
genre. 343
Autre exemple en vne ouale du second genre. 344
Exemple de la construction de ce problesme en la conchoide. 351
Explication de 4 nouueaux genres d'Ouales qui seruent a l'Optique. 352
Les proprietez de ces Ouales touchant les reflexions & les refractions. 357
Demonstration de ces proprietez. 360
Com-

TABLE OF CONTENTS

How it is possible to make a lens as convex or concave as we wish, in one of its surfaces, which shall cause to converge in a given point all the rays which proceed from another given point.............................. 363
How it is possible to make a lens which operates like the preceding and such that the convexity of one of its surfaces shall have a given ratio to the convexity or concavity of the other................................... 366
How it is possible to apply what has been said here concerning curved lines described on a plane surface to those which are described in a space of three dimensions, or on a curved surface............................ 368

BOOK III

ON THE CONSTRUCTION OF SOLID OR SUPERSOLID PROBLEMS

On those curves which can be used in the construction of every problem..... 369
Example relating to the finding of several mean proportionals............... 370
On the nature of equations.. 371
How many roots each equation can have.................................... 372
What are false roots.. 372
How it is possible to lower the degree of an equation when one of the roots is known 372
How to determine if any given quantity is a root........................... 373
How many true roots an equation may have................................. 373
How the false roots may become true, and the true roots false............... 373
How to increase or decrease the roots of an equation....................... 374
That by increasing the true roots we decrease the false ones, and vice versa.. 375
How to remove the second term of an equation............................. 376
How to make the false roots true without making the true ones false......... 377
How to fill all the places of an equation................................... 378
How to multiply or divide the roots of an equation......................... 379
How to eliminate the fractions in an equation.............................. 379
How to make the known quantity of any term of an equation equal to any given quantity 380

DE LA GEOMETRIE.

Comment on peut faire vn verre autant conuexe ou concaue en l'vne de ses superficies, qu'on voudra, qui rassemble a vn point donné tous les rayons qui vienent d'vn autre point donné. 363

Comment on en peut faire vn qui face le mesme, & que la connexité de l'vne de ses superficies ait la proportion donnée auec la conuexité ou concauité de l'autre. 366.

Comment on peut rapporter tout ce qui a esté dit des lignes courbes descrites sur vne superficie plate, a celles qui se descriuent dans vn espace qui a 3 dimensions, oubien sur vne superficie courbe. 368

Liure Troisiesme
DE LA CONSTRUCTION DES
problesmes solides, ou plusque solides.

DE quelles lignes courbes on peut se seruir en la construction de chasque problesme. 369

Exemple touchant l'inuention de plusieurs moyenes proportionelles. 370

De la nature des Equations. 371

Combien il peut y auoir de racines en chasque Equation. 372

Quelles sont les fausses racines. 372

Comment on peut diminuër le nombre des dimensions d'vne Equation, lorsqu'on connoist quelqu'vne de ses racines. 372

Comment on peut examiner si quelque quantité donnée est la valeur d'vne racine. 373

Combien il peut y auoir de vrayes racines en chasque Equation. 373

Comment on fait que les fausses racines deuienent vrayes, & les vrayes fausses. 373

Comment on peut augmenter ou diminuër les racines d'vne Equation. 374

Qu'en augmentant ainsi les vrayes racines on diminuë les fausses, ou au contraire. 375

Comment on peut oster le second terme d'vne Equation. 376

Comment on fait que les fausses racines deuienent vrayes sans que les vrayes deuienent fausses. 377

Comment on fait que toutes les places d'vne Equation soient remplies 378

Comment on peut multiplier ou diuiser les racines d'vne Equation. 379

Comment on oste les nombres rompus d'vne Equation. 379

Comment on rend la quantité connuë de l'vn des termes d'vne Equation esgale a telle autre qu'on veut. 380

Kkk 2   *Que*

TABLE OF CONTENTS

That both the true and the false roots may be real or imaginary............. 380
The reduction of cubic equations when the problem is plane................ 380
The method of dividing an equation by a binomial which contains a root..... 381
Problems which are solid when the equation is cubic....................... 383
The reduction of equations of the fourth degree when the problem is plane.
    Solid problems 383
Example showing the use of these reductions............................. 387
General rule for reducing equations above the fourth degree................ 389
General method for constructing all solid problems which reduce to an equation of the third or the fourth degree.............................. 389
The finding of two mean proportionals.................................... 395
The trisection of an angle.. 396
That all solid problems can be reduced to these two constructions............ 397
The method of expressing all the roots of cubic equations and hence of all
    equations extending to the fourth degree........................... 400
Why solid problems cannot be constructed without conic sections, nor those
    problems which are more complex without other lines that are also more
    complex 401
General method for constructing all problems which require equations of degree not higher than the sixth....................................... 402
The finding of four mean proportionals................................... 411

Table. De La Geometrie.

Que les racines tant vrayes que fausses peuuent estre reelles ou imaginaires. 380

La reduction des Equations cubiques lorsque le problesme est plan. 380

La façon de diuiser vne Equation par vn binome qui contient sa racine. 381.

Quels problesmes sont solides lorsque l'Equation est cubique. 383

La reduction des Equations qui ont quatre dimensions lorsque le problesme est plan. Et quels sont ceux qui sont solides. 383

Exemple de l'vsage de ces reductions. 387

Regle generale pour reduire toutes les Equations qui passent le quarré de quarré. 389

Façon generale pour construire tous les problesmes solides reduits a vne Equation de trois ou quatre dimensions. 389

L'inuention de deux moyenes proportionelles. 395

La diuision de l'angle en trois. 396

Que tous les problesmes solides se peuuent reduire a ces deux constructions. 397.

La façon d'exprimer la valeur de toutes les racines des Equations cubiques: Et en suite de toutes celles qui ne montent que iusques au quarré de quarré. 400

Pourquoy les problesmes solides ne peuuent estre construits sans les sections coniques, ny ceux qui sont plus composés sans quelques autres lignes plus compseés. 401

Façon generale pour construire tous les problesmes reduits a vne Equation qui n'a point plus de six dimensions. 402

L'inuention de quatre moyenes proportionelles. 411

F I N.

Les

BOOK FIRST

The Geometry of Rene Descartes

BOOK I

Problems the Construction of Which Requires Only Straight Lines and Circles

ANY problem in geometry can easily be reduced to such terms that a knowledge of the lengths of certain straight lines is sufficient for its construction.[1] Just as arithmetic consists of only four or five operations, namely, addition, subtraction, multiplication, division and the extraction of roots, which may be considered a kind of division, so in geometry, to find required lines it is merely necessary to add or subtract other lines; or else, taking one line which I shall call unity in order to relate it as closely as possible to numbers,[2] and which can in general be chosen arbitrarily, and having given two other lines, to find a fourth line which shall be to one of the given lines as the other is to unity (which is the same as multiplication); or, again, to find a fourth line which is to one of the given lines as unity is to the other (which is equivalent to division); or, finally, to find one, two, or several mean proportionals between unity and some other line (which is the same

---

[1] Large collections of problems of this nature are contained in the following works: Vincenzo Riccati and Girolamo Saladino, *Institutiones Analyticae,* Bologna, 1765; Maria Gaetana Agnesi, *Istituzioni Analitiche,* Milan, 1748; Claude Rabuel, *Commentaires sur la Géométrie de M. Descartes,* Lyons, 1730 (hereafter referred to as Rabuel); and other books of the same period or earlier.

[2] Van Schooten, in his Latin edition of 1683, has this note: "Per unitatem intellige lineam quandam determinatam, qua ad quamvis reliquarum linearum talem relationem habeat, qualem unitas ad certum aliquem numerum." *Geometria a Renato Des Cartes, una cum notis Florimondi de Beaune, opera atque studio Francisci à Schooten,* Amsterdam, 1683, p. 165 (hereafter referred to as Van Schooten).

In general, the translation runs page for page with the facing original. On account of figures and footnotes, however, this plan is occasionally varied, but not in such a way as to cause the reader any serious inconvenience.

LA GEOMETRIE.
LIVRE PREMIER.

Des problesmes qu'on peut construire sans y employer que des cercles & des lignes droites.

Ous les Problesmes de Geometrie se peuuent facilement reduire a tels termes, qu'il n'est besoin par aprés que de connoistre la longeur de quelques lignes droites, pour les construire.

Et comme toute l'Arithmetique n'est composée, que de quatre ou cinq operations, qui sont l'Addition, la Soustraction, la Multiplication, la Diuision, & l'Extraction des racines, qu'on peut prendre pour vne espece de Diuision : Ainsi n'at on autre chose a faire en Geometrie touchant les lignes qu'on cherche, pour les preparer a estre connuës, que leur en adiouster d'autres, ou en oster, Oubien en ayant vne, que ie nommeray l'vnité pour la rapporter d'autant mieux aux nombres, & qui peut ordinairement estre prise a discretion, puis en ayant encore deux autres, en trouuer vne quatriesme, qui soit à l'vne de ces deux, comme l'autre est a l'vnité, ce qui est le mesme que la Multiplication ; oubien en trouuer vne quatriesme, qui soit a l'vne de ces deux, comme l'vnité

Commēt le calcul d'Arithmetique se rapporte aux operations de Geometrie.

est

298   La Geometrie.

est a l'autre, ce qui est le mesme que la Diuision; ou enfin trouuer vne, ou deux, ou plusieurs moyennes proportionnelles entre l'vnité, & quelque autre ligne; ce qui est le mesme que tirer la racine quarrée, on cubique, &c. Et ie ne craindray pas d'introduire ces termes d'Arithmetique en la Geometrie, affin de me rendre plus intelligibile.

La Multiplication.   Soit par exemple A B l'vnité, & qu'il faille multiplier B D par B C, ie n'ay qu'a ioindre les poins A & C, puis tirer D E parallele a C A, & B E est le produit de cete Multiplication.

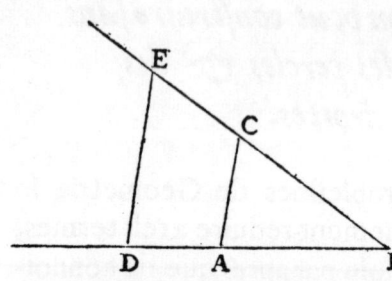

La Diuision.   Oubien s'il faut diuiser B E par B D, ayant ioint les poins E & D, ie tire A C parallele a D E, & B C est le produit de cete diuision.

l'Extraction de la racine quarrée.   Ou s'il faut tirer la racine quarrée de G H, ie luy adiouste en ligne droite F G, qui est l'vnité, & diuisant F H en deux parties esgales au point K, du centre K ie tire le cercle F I H, puis esleuant du point G vne ligne droite iusques à I, à angles droits sur F H, c'est G I la racine cherchée. Ie ne dis rien icy de la racine cubique, ny des autres, à cause que i'en parleray plus commodement cy aprés.

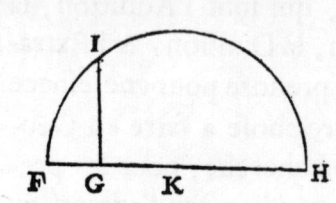

Commēt on peut   Mais souuent on n'a pas besoin de tracer ainsi ces ligne

as extracting the square root, cube root, etc., of the given line.[3] And I shall not hesitate to introduce these arithmetical terms into geometry, for the sake of greater clearness.

For example, let AB be taken as unity, and let it be required to multiply BD by BC. I have only to join the points A and C, and draw DE parallel to CA; then BE is the product of BD and BC.

If it be required to divide BE by BD, I join E and D, and draw AC parallel to DE; then BC is the result of the division.

If the square root of GH is desired, I add, along the same straight line, FG equal to unity; then, bisecting FH at K, I describe the circle FIH about K as a center, and draw from G a perpendicular and extend it to I, and GI is the required root. I do not speak here of cube root, or other roots, since I shall speak more conveniently of them later.

Often it is not necessary thus to draw the lines on paper, but it is sufficient to designate each by a single letter. Thus, to add the lines BD and GH, I call one a and the other b, and write $a+b$. Then $a-b$ will indicate that b is subtracted from a; ab that a is multiplied by b; $\frac{a}{b}$ that a is divided by b; aa or a^2 that a is multiplied by itself; a^3 that this result is multiplied by a, and so on, indefinitely.[4] Again, if I wish to extract the square root of a^2+b^2, I write $\sqrt{a^2+b^2}$; if I wish to extract the cube root of $a^3-b^3+ab^2$, I write $\sqrt[3]{a^3-b^3+ab^2}$, and similarly for other roots.[5] Here it must be observed that by a^2, b^3, and similar expressions, I ordinarily mean only simple lines, which, however, I name squares, cubes, etc., so that I may make use of the terms employed in algebra.[6]

[3] While in arithmetic the only exact roots obtainable are those of perfect powers, in geometry a length can be found which will represent exactly the square root of a given line, even though this line be not commensurable with unity. Of other roots, Descartes speaks later.

[4] Descartes uses a^3, a^4, a^5, a^6, and so on, to represent the respective powers of a, but he uses both aa and a^2 without distinction. For example, he often has $aabb$, but he also uses $\frac{3a^2}{4b^2}$.

[5] Descartes writes: $\sqrt{C.a^3-b^3+abb}$. See original, page 299, line 9.

[6] At the time this was written, a^2 was commonly considered to mean the surface of a square whose side is a, and b^3 to mean the volume of a cube whose side is b; while b^4, b^5, ... were unintelligible as geometric forms. Descartes here says that a^2 does not have this meaning, but means the line obtained by constructing a third proportional to 1 and a, and so on.

GEOMETRY

It should also be noted that all parts of a single line should always be expressed by the same number of dimensions, provided unity is not determined by the conditions of the problem. Thus, a^3 contains as many dimensions as ab^2 or b^3, these being the component parts of the line which I have called $\sqrt[3]{a^3-b^3+ab^2}$. It is not, however, the same thing when unity is determined, because unity can always be understood, even where there are too many or too few dimensions; thus, if it be required to extract the cube root of $a^2b^2 - b$, we must consider the quantity a^2b^2 divided once by unity, and the quantity b multiplied twice by unity.[7]

Finally, so that we may be sure to remember the names of these lines, a separate list should always be made as often as names are assigned or changed. For example, we may write, AB=1, that is AB is equal to 1;[8] GH $= a$, BD $= b$, and so on.

If, then, we wish to solve any problem, we first suppose the solution already effected,[9] and give names to all the lines that seem needful for its construction,—to those that are unknown as well as to those that are known.[10] Then, making no distinction between known and unknown lines, we must unravel the difficulty in any way that shows most natur-

[7] Descartes seems to say that each term must be of the third degree, and that therefore we must conceive of both a^2b^2 and b as reduced to the proper dimension.

[8] Van Schooten adds "seu unitati," p. 3. Descartes writes, AB ∞ 1. He seems to have been the first to use this symbol. Among the few writers who followed him, was Hudde (1633-1704). It is very commonly supposed that ∞ is a ligature representing the first two letters (or diphthong) of "æquare." See, for example, M. Aubry's note in W. W. R. Ball's *Recréations Mathématiques et Problèmes des Temps Anciens et Modernes*, French edition, Paris, 1909, Part III, p. 164.

[9] This plan, as is well known, goes back to Plato. It appears in the work of Pappus as follows: "In analysis we suppose that which is required to be already obtained, and consider its connections and antecedents, going back until we reach either something already known (given in the hypothesis), or else some fundamental principle (axiom or postulate) of mathematics." *Pappi Alexandrini Collectiones quae supersunt e libris manu scriptis edidit Latina interpellatione et commentariis instruxit Fredericus Hultsch*, Berlin, 1876-1878; vol. II, p. 635 (hereafter referred to as Pappus). See also Commandinus, *Pappi Alexandrini Mathematicae Collectiones*, Bologna, 1588, with later editions.

Pappus of Alexandria was a Greek mathematician who lived about 300 A.D. His most important work is a mathematical treatise in eight books, of which the first and part of the second are lost. This was made known to modern scholars by Commandinus. The work exerted a happy influence on the revival of geometry in the seventeenth century. Pappus was not himself a mathematician of the first rank, but he preserved for the world many extracts or analyses of lost works, and by his commentaries added to their interest.

[10] Rabuel calls attention to the use of $a, b, c, \ldots$ for known, and $x, y, z, \ldots$ for unknown quantities (p. 20).

LIVRE PREMIER. 299

gnes sur le papier, & il suffist de les designer par quelques lettres, chascune par vne seule. Comme pour adiouster la ligne B D a G H, ie nomme l'vne a & l'autre b, & escris $a + b$; Et $a - b$, pour soustraire b d' a; Et ab, pour les multiplier l'vne par l'autre; Et $\frac{a}{b}$, pour diuiser a par b; Et aa, ou a^2, pour multiplier a par soy mesme; Et a^3, pour le multiplier encore vne fois par a, & ainsi a l'infini; Et $\sqrt{a^2 + b^2}$, pour tirer la racine quarrée d' $a^2 + b^2$; Et $\sqrt{C. a^3 - b^3 + abb}$, pour tirer la racine cubique d' $a^3 - b^3 + abb$, & ainsi des autres.

vser de chiffres en Geometrie.

Où il est a remarquer que par a^2 ou b^3 ou semblables, ie ne conçoy ordinairement que des lignes toutes simples, encore que pour me seruir des noms vsités en l'Algebre, ie les nomme des quarrés ou des cubes, &c.

Il est aussy a remarquer que toutes les parties d'vne mesme ligne, se doiuent ordinairement exprimer par autant de dimensions l'vne que l'autre, lorsque l'vnité n'est point déterminée en la question, comme icy a^3 en contient autant qu' abb ou b^3 dont se compose la ligne que i'ay nommée $\sqrt{C. a^3 - b^3 + abb}$: mais que ce n'est pas de mesme lorsque l'vnité est déterminée, a cause qu'elle peut estre sousentendue par tout ou il y a trop ou trop peu de dimensions: comme s'il faut tirer la racine cubique de $aabb - b$, il faut penser que la quantité $aabb$ est diuisée vne fois par l'vnité, & que l'autre quantité b est multipliée deux fois par la mesme.

Au

LA GEOMETRIE.

Au reste affin de ne pas manquer a se souuenir des noms de ces lignes, il en faut tousiours faire vn registre separé, à mesure qu'on les pose ou qu'on les change, escriuant par exemple.

AB ∞ 1, c'est a dire, AB esgal à 1.
GH ∞ a
BD ∞ b, &c.

Commét il faut venir aux Equatiós qui seruent a resoudre les problesmes.

Ainsi voulant resoudre quelque problesme, on doit d'abord le considerer comme desia fait, & donner des noms a toutes les lignes, qui semblent necessaires pour le construire, aussy bien a celles qui sont inconnuës, qu'aux autres. Puis sans considerer aucune difference entre ces lignes connuës, & inconnuës, on doit parcourir la difficulté, selon l'ordre qui monstre le plus naturellement de tous en qu'elle sorte elles dependent mutuellement les vnes des autres, iusques a ce qu'on ait trouué moyen d'exprimer vne mesme quantité en deux façons: ce qui se nomme vne Equation; car les termes de l'vne de ces deux façons sont esgaux a ceux de l'autre. Et on doit trouuer autant de telles Equations, qu'on a supposé de lignes, qui estoient inconnuës. Oubien s'il ne s'en trouue pas tant, & que nonobstant on n'omette rien de ce qui est desiré en la question, cela tesmoigne qu'elle n'est pas entierement determinée. Et lors on peut prendre a discretion des lignes connuës, pour toutes les inconnuës ausqu'elles ne correspond aucune Equation. Aprés cela s'il en reste encore plusieurs, il se faut seruir par ordre de chascune des Equations qui restent aussy, soit en la considerant toute seule, soit en la comparant auec les autres, pour expliquer chascune de ces lignes inconnuës; & faire

ainsi

ally the relations between these lines, until we find it possible to express a single quantity in two ways.[11] This will constitute an equation, since the terms of one of these two expressions are together equal to the terms of the other.

We must find as many such equations as there are supposed to be unknown lines;[12] but if, after considering everything involved, so many cannot be found, it is evident that the question is not entirely determined. In such a case we may choose arbitrarily lines of known length for each unknown line to which there corresponds no equation.[13]

If there are several equations, we must use each in order, either considering it alone or comparing it with the others, so as to obtain a value for each of the unknown lines; and so we must combine them until there remains a single unknown line[14] which is equal to some known line, or whose square, cube, fourth power, fifth power, sixth power, etc., is equal to the sum or difference of two or more quantities,[15] one of which is known, while the others consist of mean proportionals between unity and this square, or cube, or fourth power, etc., multiplied by other known lines. I may express this as follows:

$$z = b,$$
$$\text{or } z^2 = -az + b^2,$$
$$\text{or } z^3 = az^2 + b^2z - c^3,$$
$$\text{or } z^4 = az^3 - c^3z + d^4, \text{ etc.}$$

That is, z, which I take for the unknown quantity, is equal to b; or, the square of z is equal to the square of b diminished by a multiplied by z; or, the cube of z is equal to a multiplied by the square of z, plus the square of b multiplied by z, diminished by the cube of c; and similarly for the others.

[11] That is, we must solve the resulting simultaneous equations.

[12] Van Schooten (p. 149) gives two problems to illustrate this statement. Of these, the first is as follows: Given a line segment AB containing any point C, required to produce AB to D so that the rectangle AD.DB shall be equal to the square on CD. He lets $AC = a$, $CB = b$, and $BD = x$. Then $AD = a + b + x$, and $CD = b + x$, whence $ax + bx + x^2 = b^2 + 2bx + x^2$ and $x = \dfrac{b^2}{a-b}$.

[13] Rabuel adds this note: "We may say that every indeterminate problem is an infinity of determinate problems, or that every problem is determined either by itself or by him who constructs it" (p. 21).

[14] That is, a line represented by x, x^2, x^3, x^4, ...

[15] In the older French, "le quarré, ou le cube, ou le quarré de quarré, ou le sursolide, ou le quarré de cube &c.," as seen on page 11 (original page 302).

9

GEOMETRY

Thus, all the unknown quantities can be expressed in terms of a single quantity,[16] whenever the problem can be constructed by means of circles and straight lines, or by conic sections, or even by some other curve of degree not greater than the third or fourth.[17]

But I shall not stop to explain this in more detail, because I should deprive you of the pleasure of mastering it yourself, as well as of the advantage of training your mind by working over it, which is in my opinion the principal benefit to be derived from this science. Because, I find nothing here so difficult that it cannot be worked out by any one at all familiar with ordinary geometry and with algebra, who will consider carefully all that is set forth in this treatise.[18]

[16] See line 20 on the opposite page.

[17] Literally, "Only one or two degrees greater."

[18] In the Introduction to the 1637 edition of *La Géométrie,* Descartes made the following remark: "In my previous writings I have tried to make my meaning clear to everybody; but I doubt if this treatise will be read by anyone not familiar with the books on geometry, and so I have thought it superfluous to repeat demonstrations contained in them." See *Oeuvres de Descartes,* edited by Charles Adam and Paul Tannery, Paris, 1897-1910, vol. VI, p. 368. In a letter written to Mersenne in 1637 Descartes says: "I do not enjoy speaking in praise of myself, but since few people can understand my geometry, and since you wish me to give you my opinion of it, I think it well to say that it is all I could hope for, and that in *La Dioptrique* and *Les Météores,* I have only tried to persuade people that my method is better than the ordinary one. I have proved this in my geometry, for in the beginning I have solved a question which, according to Pappus, could not be solved by any of the ancient geometers.

"Moreover, what I have given in the second book on the nature and properties of curved lines, and the method of examining them, is, it seems to me, as far beyond the treatment in the ordinary geometry, as the rhetoric of Cicero is beyond the a, b, c of children. . . .

"As to the suggestion that what I have written could easily have been gotten from Vieta, the very fact that my treatise is hard to understand is due to my attempt to put nothing in it that I believed to be known either by him or by any one else. . . . I begin the rules of my algebra with what Vieta wrote at the very end of his book, *De emendatione aequationum.* . . . Thus, I begin where he left off." *Oeuvres de Descartes, publiées par Victor Cousin,* Paris, 1824, Vol. VI, p. 294 (hereafter referred to as Cousin).

In another letter to Mersenne, written April 20, 1646, Descartes writes as follows: "I have omitted a number of things that might have made it (the geometry) clearer, but I did this intentionally, and would not have it otherwise. The only suggestions that have been made concerning changes in it are in regard to rendering it clearer to readers, but most of these are so malicious that I am completely disgusted with them." Cousin, Vol. IX, p. 553.

In a letter to the Princess Elizabeth, Descartes says: "In the solution of a geometrical problem I take care, as far as possible, to use as lines of reference parallel lines or lines at right angles; and I use no theorems except those which assert that the sides of similar triangles are proportional, and that in a right triangle the square of the hypotenuse is equal to the sum of the squares of the sides. I do not hesitate to introduce several unknown quantities, so as to reduce the question to such terms that it shall depend only on these two theorems." Cousin, Vol. IX, p. 143.

Livre Premier.

ainsi en les demeslant, qu'il n'en demeure qu'vne seule, esgale a quelque autre, qui soit connuë, oubien dont le quarré, ou le cube, ou le quarré de quarré, ou le sursolide, ou le quarré de cube, &c. soit esgal a ce, qui se produist par l'addition, ou soustraction de deux ou plusieurs autres quantités, dont l'vne soit connuë, & les autres soient composées de quelques moyennes proportionnelles entre l'vnité, & ce quarré, ou cube, ou quarré de quarré, &c. multipliées par d'autres connuës. Ce que i'escris en cete sorte.

$$z \infty\ b. \text{ ou}$$

$$z^2 \infty -az + bb. \text{ ou}$$

$$z^3 \infty + az^2 + bbz - c. \text{ ou}$$

$$z^4 \infty\ az^3 - cz + d. \text{ \&c.}$$

C'est a dire, z, que ie prens pour la quantité inconnuë, est esgalé a b, ou le quarré de z est esgal au quarré de b moins a multiplié par z. ou le cube de z est esgal à a multiplié par le quarre de z plus le quarré de b multiplié par z moins le cube de c. & ainsi des autres.

 Et on peut tousiours reduire ainsi toutes les quantités inconnuës à vne seule, lorsque le Problesme se peut construire par des cercles & des lignes droites, ou aussy par des sections coniques, ou mesme par quelque autre ligne qui ne soit que d'vn ou deux degrés plus composée. Mais ie ne m'areste point a expliquer cecy plus en detail, a cause que ie vous osterois le plaisir de l'apprendre de vous mesme, & l'vtilité de cultiuer vostre esprit en vous y exerceant, qui est a mon auis la principale, qu'on puisse

Pp 3   tirer

tirer de cete science. Aussy que ie n y remarque rien de si difficile, que ceux qui seront vn peu versés en la Geometrie commune, & en l'Algebre, & qui prendront garde a tout ce qui est en ce traité, ne puissent trouuer.

C'est pourquoy ie me contenteray icy de vous auertir, que pourvû qu'en demeslant ces Equations on ne manque point a se seruir de toutes les diuisions, qui seront possibles, on aura infailliblement les plus simples termes, ausquels la question puisse estre reduite.

Quels sont les problesmes plans

Et que si elle peut estre resolue par la Geometrie ordinaire, c'est à dire, en ne se seruant que de lignes droites & circulaires tracées sur vne superficie plate, lorsque la derniere Equation aura esté entierement demeslée, il n'y restera tout au plus qu'vn quarré inconnu, esgal a ce qui se produist de l'Addition, ou soustraction de sa racine multipliée par quelque quantité connue, & de quelque autre quantité aussy connue

Comment ils se resoluent.

Et lors cete racine, ou ligne inconnue se trouue aysement. Car si i'ay par exemple

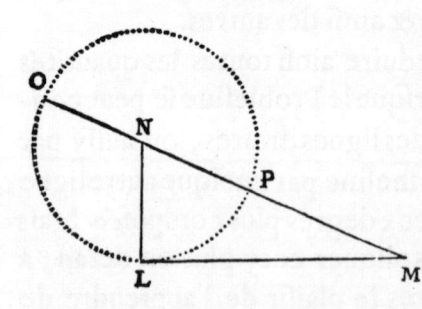

$$z \infty a z + bb$$

ie fais le triangle rectangle N L M, dont le costé L M est esgal à b racine quarrée de la quantité connue bb, & l'autre L N est $\frac{1}{2} a$, la moitié de l'autre quantité connue, qui estoit multipliée par z que ie suppose estre la ligne inconnue. puis prolongeant M N la baze de ce triangle,

I shall therefore content myself with the statement that if the student, in solving these equations, does not fail to make use of division wherever possible, he will surely reach the simplest terms to which the problem can be reduced.

And if it can be solved by ordinary geometry, that is, by the use of straight lines and circles traced on a plane surface,[19] when the last equation shall have entirely solved there will remain at most only the square of an unknown quantity, equal to the product of its root by some known quantity, increased or diminished by some other quantity also known.[20] Then this root or unknown line can easily be found. For example, if I have $z^2 = az + b^2$,[21] I construct a right triangle NLM with one side LM, equal to b, the square root of the known quantity b^2, and the other side, LN, equal to $\frac{1}{2}a$, that is, to half the other known quantity which was multiplied by z, which I supposed to be the unknown line. Then prolonging MN, the hypotenuse[22] of this triangle, to O, so that NO is equal to NL, the whole line OM is the required line z. This is expressed in the following way:[23]

$$z = \frac{1}{2}a + \sqrt{\frac{1}{4}a^2 + b^2}.$$

But if I have $y^2 = -ay + b^2$, where y is the quantity whose value is desired, I construct the same right triangle NLM, and on the hypote-

[19] For a discussion of the possibility of constructions by the compasses and straight edge, see Jacob Steiner, *Die geometrischen Constructionen ausgeführt mittelst der geraden Linie und eines festen Kreises*, Berlin, 1833. For briefer treatments, consult Enriques, *Fragen der Elementar-Geometrie*, Leipzig, 1907; Klein, *Problems in Elementary Geometry*, trans. by Beman and Smith, Boston, 1897; Weber und Wellstein, *Encyklopädie der Elementaren Geometrie*, Leipzig, 1907. The work by Mascheroni, *La geometria del compasso*, Pavia, 1797, is interesting and well known.

[20] That is, an expression of the form $z^2 = az \pm b$. "Esgal a ce qui se produit de l'Addition, ou soustraction de sa racine multipleé par quelque quantité connue, & de quelque autre quantité aussy connue," as it appears in line 14, opposite page.

[21] Descartes proposes to show how a quadratic may be solved geometrically.

[22] Descartes says "prolongeant MN la baze de ce triangle," because the hypotenuse was commonly taken as the base in earlier times.

[23] From the figure $\text{OM}\cdot\text{PM} = \overline{\text{LM}}^2$. If $\text{OM} = z$, $\text{PM} = z - a$, and since $\text{LM} = b$, we have $z(z-a) = b^2$ or $z^2 = az + b^2$. Again, $\text{MN} = \sqrt{\frac{1}{4}a^2 + b^2}$, whence $\text{OM} = z = \text{ON} + \text{MN} = \frac{1}{2}a + \sqrt{\frac{1}{4}a^2 + b^2}$. Descartes ignores the second root, which is negative.

nuse MN lay off NP equal to NL, and the remainder PM is y, the desired root. Thus I have

$$y = -\frac{1}{2}a + \sqrt{\frac{1}{4}a^2 + b^2}.$$

In the same way, if I had

$$x^4 = -ax^2 + b^2,$$

PM would be x^2 and I should have

$$x = \sqrt{-\frac{1}{2}a + \sqrt{\frac{1}{4}a^2 + b^2}},$$

and so for other cases.

Finally, if I have $z^2 = az - b^2$, I make NL equal to $\frac{1}{2}a$ and LM equal to b as before; then, instead of joining the points M and N, I draw MQR parallel to LN, and with N as a center describe a circle through L cutting MQR in the points Q and R; then z, the line sought, is either MQ or MR, for in this case it can be expressed in two ways, namely:[24]

$$z = \frac{1}{2}a + \sqrt{\frac{1}{4}a^2 - b^2},$$

and

$$z = \frac{1}{2}a - \sqrt{\frac{1}{4}a^2 - b^2}.$$

---

[24] Since $MR \cdot MQ = \overline{LM}^2$, then if $R = z$, we have $MQ = a - z$, and so $z(a-z) = b^2$ or $z^2 = az - b^2$. If, instead of this, $MQ = z$, then $MR = a - z$, and again, $z^2 = az - b^2$. Furthermore, letting O be the mid-point of QR,

$$MQ = OM - OQ = \frac{1}{2}a - \sqrt{\frac{1}{4}a^2 - b^2},$$

and

$$MR = MO + OR = \frac{1}{2}a + \sqrt{\frac{1}{4}a^2 - b^2}.$$

Descartes here gives both roots, since both are positive. If MR is tangent to the circle, that is, if $b = \frac{1}{2}a$, the roots will be equal; while if $b > \frac{1}{2}a$, the line MR will not meet the circle and both roots will be imaginary. Also, since $RM \cdot QM = \overline{LM}^2$, $z_1 z_2 = b^2$, and $RM + QM = z_1 + z_2 = a$.

angle, iufques a O, en forte qu'N O foit efgale a N L, la toute O M eft z la ligne cherchée. Et elle s'exprime en cete forte

$$z \infty \tfrac{1}{2} a + \sqrt{\tfrac{1}{4} aa + bb}.$$

Que fi iay $yy \infty -ay + bb$, & qu'y foit la quantité qu'il faut trouuer, ie fais le mefme triangle rectangle N L M, & de fa baze M N i'ofte N P efgale a N L, & le refte P M eft y la racine cherchée. De façon que iay $y \infty -\tfrac{1}{2} a + \sqrt{\tfrac{1}{4} aa + bb}$. Et tout de mefme fi i'auois $x^4 \infty -ax^2 + b^2$. P M feroit x^2. & i'aurois $x \infty \sqrt{-\tfrac{1}{2}a + \sqrt{\tfrac{1}{4}aa + bb}}$: & ainfi des autres.

Enfin fi i'ay

$$z^2 \infty az -bb:$$

ie fais N L efgale à $\tfrac{1}{2} a$, & L M efgale à b cóme deuãt, puis, au lieu de ioindre les poins M N, ie tire M Q R parallele a L N. & du centre N par L ayant defcrit vn cercle qui la couppe aux poins Q & R, la ligne cherchée z eft M Q, oubié M R, car en ce cas elle s'exprime en deux façons, a fçauoir $z \infty \tfrac{1}{2} a + \sqrt{\tfrac{1}{4} aa - bb}$, & $z \infty \tfrac{1}{2} a - \sqrt{\tfrac{1}{4} aa - bb}$.

Et fi le cercle, qui ayant fon centre au point N, paffe par le point L, ne couppe ny ne touche la ligne droite M Q R, il n'y a aucune racine en l'Equation, de façon qu'on peut affurer que la conftruction du problefme propofé eft impoffible.

Au

Au reſte ces meſmes racines ſe peuuent trouuer par vne infinité d'autres moyens , & i'ay ſeulement veulu mettre ceux cy, comme fort ſimples, affin de faire voir qu'on peut conſtruire tous les Problesmes de la Geometrie ordinaire, ſans faire autre choſe que le peu qui eſt compris dans les quatre figures que i'ay expliquées.   Ce que ie ne croy pas que les anciens ayent remarqué. car autrement ils n'euſſent pas pris la peine d'en eſcrire tant de gros liures, ou le ſeul ordre de leurs propoſitions nous fait connoiſtre qu'ils n'ont point eu la vraye methode pour les trouuer toutes, mais qu'ils ont ſeulement ramaſſé celles qu'ils ont rencontrées.

Exemple tiré de Pappus.

Et on le peut voir auſſy fort clairement de ce que Pappus a mis au commencement de ſon ſeptieſme liure, ou aprés s'eſtre areſté quelque tems a denombrer tout ce qui auoit eſté eſcrit en Geometrie par ceux qui l'auoient precedé, il parle enfin d vne queſtion , qu'il dit que ny Euclide, ny Apollonius, ny aucun autre n'auoient ſceu entierement reſoudre. & voycy ſes mots.

Ie cite plutoſt la verſion latine que le texte grec affin que chaſcun l'entende plus ayſement.

Quem autem dicit (Apollonius) in tertio libro locum ad tres, & quatuor lineas ab Euclide perfectum non eſſe , neque ipſe perficere poterat, neque aliquis alius : ſed neque paululum quid addere iis, quæ Euclides ſcripſit, per ea tantum conica , quæ uſque ad Euclidis tempora præmonſtrata ſunt, &c.

Et vn peu aprés il explique ainſi qu'elle eſt cete queſtion.

At locus ad tres, & quatuor lineas , in quo (Apollonius) magnifice ſe iactat, & oſtentat, nulla habita gratia ei , qui prius ſcripſerat , eſt hujuſmodi. Si poſitione datis tribus rectis

And if the circle described about N and passing through L neither cuts nor touches the line MQR, the equation has no root, so that we may say that the construction of the problem is impossible.

These same roots can be found by many other methods;[25] I have given these very simple ones to show that it is possible to construct all the problems of ordinary geometry by doing no more than the little covered in the four figures that I have explained.[26] This is one thing which I believe the ancient mathematicians did not observe, for otherwise they would not have put so much labor into writing so many books in which the very sequence of the propositions shows that they did not have a sure method of finding all,[27] but rather gathered together those propositions on which they had happened by accident.

This is also evident from what Pappus has done in the beginning of his seventh book,[28] where, after devoting considerable space to an enumeration of the books on geometry written by his predecessors,[29] he finally refers to a question which he says that neither Euclid nor Apollonius nor any one else had been able to solve completely;[30] and these are his words:

"Quem autem dicit (Apollonius) in tertio libro locum ad tres, & quatuor lineas ab Euclide perfectum non esse, neque ipse perficere poterat, neque aliquis alius; sed neque paululum quid addere iis, quæ

---

[25] For interesting contraction, see Rabuel, p. 23, et seq.

[26] It will be seen that Descartes considers only three types of the quadratic equation in z, namely, $z^2 + az - b^2 = 0$, $z^2 - az - b^2 = 0$, and $z^2 - az + b^2 = 0$. It thus appears that he has not been able to free himself from the old traditions to the extent of generalizing the meaning of the coefficients, — as negative and fractional as well as positive. He does not consider the type $z^2 + az + b^2 = 0$, because it has no positive roots.

[27] "Qu'ils n'ont point eu la vraye methode pour les trouuer toutes."

[28] See Note [9].

[29] See Pappus, Vol. II, p. 637. Pappus here gives a list of books that treat of analysis, in the following words: "Illorum librorum, quibus de loco, 'ἀναλυόμενος sive resoluto agitur, ordo hic est. Euclidis datorum liber unus, Apollonii de proportionis sectione libri duo, de spatii sectione duo, de sectione determinata duo, de tactionibus duo, Euclidis porismatum libri tres, Apollonii inclinationum libri duo, eiusdem locorum planorum duo, conicorum octo, Aristaei locorum solidorum libri duo." See also the Commandinus edition of Pappus, 1660 edition, pp. 240-252.

[30] For the history of this problem, see Zeuthen: *Die Lehre von den Kegelschnitten im Alterthum*, Copenhagen, 1886. Also, Adam and Tannery, *Oeuvres de Descartes*, vol. 6, p. 723.

GEOMETRY

Euclides scripsit, per ea tantum conica, quæ usque ad Euclidis tempora præmonstrata sunt, &c." [31]

A little farther on, he states the question as follows:

"At locus ad tres, & quatuor lineas, in quo (Apollonius) magnifice se jactat, & ostentat, nulla habita gratia ei, qui prius scripserat, est hujusmodi.[32] *Si positione datis tribus rectis lineis ab uno & eodem puncto, ad tres lineas in datis angulis rectæ lineæ ducantur, & data sit proportio rectanguli contenti duabus ductis ad quadratum reliquæ: punctum contingit positione datum solidum locum, hoc est unam ex tribus conicis sectionibus. Et si ad quatuor rectas lineas positione datas in datis angulis lineæ ducantur; & rectanguli duabus ductis contenti ad contentum duabus reliquis proportio data sit; similiter punctum datum coni sectionem positione continget. Si quidem igitur ad duas tantum locus planus ostensus est. Quod si ad plures quam quatuor, punctum continget locos non adhuc cognitos, sed lineas tantum dictas; quales autem sint, vel quam habeant proprietatem, non constat: earum unam, neque primam, & quæ manifestissima videtur, composuerunt ostendentes utilem esse. Propositiones autem ipsarum hæ sunt.*

"Si ab aliquo puncto ad positione datas rectas lineas quinque ducantur rectæ lineæ in datis angulis, & data sit proportio solidi parallelepipedi rectanguli, quod tribus ductis lineis continetur ad solidum parallelepipedum rectangulum, quod continetur reliquis duabus, & data quapiam linea, punctum positione datam lineam continget. Si autem ad sex, & data sit proportio solidi tribus lineis contenti ad solidum, quod tribus reliquis continetur; rursus punctum continget positione datam lineam. Quod si ad plures quam sex, non adhuc habent dicere, an data sit proportio cujuspiam contenti quatuor lineis ad id quod reliquis continetur,

---

[31] Pappus, Vol. II, pp. 677, et seq., Commandinus edition of 1660, p. 251. Literally, "Moreover, he (Apollonius) says that the problem of the locus related to three or four lines was not entirely solved by Euclid, and that neither he himself, nor any one else has been able to solve it completely, nor were they able to add anything at all to those things which Euclid had written, by means of the conic sections only which had been demonstrated before Euclid." Descartes arrived at the solution of this problem four years before the publication of his geometry, after spending five or six weeks on it. See his letters, Cousin, Vol. VI, p. 294, and Vol. VI, p. 224.

[32] Given as follows in the edition of Pappus by Hultsch, previously quoted: "Sed hic ad tres et quatuor lineas locus quo magnopere gloriatur simul addens ei qui conscripserit gratiam habendam esse, sic se habet."

rectis lineis ab uno & eodem puncto, ad tres lineas in datis angulis rectæ lineæ ducantur, & data sit proportio rectanguli contenti duabus ductis ad quadratum reliquæ: punctum contingit positione datum solidum locum, hoc est unam ex tribus conicis sectionibus. Et si ad quatuor rectas lineas positione datas in datis angulis lineæ ducantur; & rectanguli duabus ductis contenti ad contentum duabus reliquis proportio data sit: similiter punctum datum coni sectionem positione continget. Si quidem igitur ad duas tantum locus planus ostensus est. Quod si ad plures quam quatuor, punctum continget locos non adhuc cognitos, sed lineas tantum dictas; quales autem sint, vel quam habeant proprietatem, non constat: earum unam, neque primam, & quæ manifestissima videtur, composuerunt ostendentes utilem esse. propositiones autem ipsarum hæ sunt.

Si ab aliquo puncto ad positione datas rectas lineas quinque ducantur rectæ lineæ in datis angulis, & data sit proportio solidi parallelepipedi rectanguli, quod tribus ductis lineis continetur ad solidum parallelepipedum rectangulum, quod continetur reliquis duabus, & data quapiam linea, punctum positione datam lineam continget. Si autem ad sex, & data sit proportio solidi tribus lineis contenti ad solidam, quod tribus reliquis continetur; rursus punctum continget positione datam lineam. Quod si ad plures quam sex, non adhuc habent dicere, an data sit proportio cuiuspiã contenti quatuor lineis ad id quod reliquis continetur, quoniam non est aliquid contentum pluribus quam tribus dimensionibus.

Ou ie vous prie de remarquer en passant, que le scrupule, que faisoient les anciens d'vser des termes de l'Arithmetique en la Geometrie, qui ne pouuoit proceder,

que de ce qu'ils ne voyoient pas assés clairement leur rapport, causoit beaucoup d'obscurité, & d'embaras, en la façon dont ils s'expliquoient. car Pappus poursuit en cete sorte.

Acquiescunt autem his, qui paulo ante talia interpretati sunt. neque unum aliquo pacto comprehensibile significantes quod his continetur. Licebit autẽ per coniunctas proportiones hæc, & dicere, & demonstrare universe in dictis proportionibus, atque his in hunc modum. Si ab aliquo puncto ad positione datas rectas lineas ducantur rectæ lineæ in datis angulis, & data sit proportio coniuncta ex ea, quam habet una ductarum ad unam, & altera ad alteram, & alia ad aliam, & reliqua ad datam lineam, si sint septem; si vero octo, & reliqua ad reliquam: punctum continget positione datas lineas. Et similiter quotcumque sint impares vel pares multitudine, cum hæc, ut dixi, loco ad quatuor lineas respondeant, nullum igitur posuerunt ita ut linea nota sit, &c.

La question donc qui auoit esté commencée a resoudre par Euclide, & poursuiuie par Apollonius, sans auoir esté acheuée par personne, estoit telle. Ayant trois ou quatre ou plus grand nombre de lignes droites données par position, premierement on demande vn point, duquel on puisse tirer autant d'autres lignes droites, vne sur chascune des données, qui façent auec elles des angles donnés, & que le rectangle contenu en deux de celles, qui seront ainsi tirées d'vn mesme point, ait la proportion donnée auec le quarré de la troisiesme, s'il n'y en a que trois; oubien auec le rectangle des deux autres, s'il y en a quatre; oubien, s'il y en a cinq, que le parallelepipede composé de trois ait la proportion donnée auec le parallelepipede

quoniam non est aliquid contentum pluribus quam tribus dimensionibus." [33]

Here I beg you to observe in passing that the considerations that forced ancient writers to use arithmetical terms in geometry, thus making it impossible for them to proceed beyond a point where they could see clearly the relation between the two subjects, caused much obscurity and embarrassment, in their attempts at explanation.

Pappus proceeds as follows:

"Acquiescunt autem his, qui paulo ante talia interpretati sunt; neque unum aliquo pacto comprehensibile significantes quod his continetur. Licebit autem per conjunctas proportiones hæc, & dicere & demonstrare universe in dictis proportionibus, atque his in hunc modum. Si ab aliquo puncto ad positione datas rectas lineas ducantur rectæ lineæ in datis angulis, & data sit proportio conjuncta ex ea, quam habet una ductarum ad unam, & altera ad alteram, & alia ad aliam, & reliqua ad datam lineam, si sint septem; si vero octo, & reliqua ad reliquam: punctum continget positione datas lineas. Et similiter quotcumque sint

[33] This may be somewhat freely translated as follows: "The problem of the locus related to three or four lines, about which he (Apollonius) boasts so proudly, giving no credit to the writer who has preceded him, is of this nature: If three straight lines are given in position, and if straight lines be drawn from one and the same point, making given angles with the three given lines; and if there be given the ratio of the rectangle contained by two of the lines so drawn to the square of the other, the point lies on a solid locus given in position, namely, one of the three conic sections.

"Again, if lines be drawn making given angles with four straight lines given in position, and if the rectangle of two of the lines so drawn bears a given ratio to the rectangle of the other two; then, in like manner, the point lies on a conic section given in position. It has been shown that to only two lines there corresponds a plane locus. But if there be given more than four lines, the point generates loci not known up to the present time (that is, impossible to determine by common methods), but merely called 'lines'. It is not clear what they are, or what their properties. One of them, not the first but the most manifest, has been examined, and this has proved to be helpful. (Paul Tannery, in the *Oeuvres de Descartes,* differs with Descartes in his translation of Pappus. He translates as follows: Et on n'a fait la synthèse d' aucune de ces lignes, ni montré qu'elle servit pour ces lieux, pas même pour celle qui semblerait la première et la plus indiquée.) These, however, are the propositions concerning them.

"If from any point straight lines be drawn making given angles with five straight lines given in position, and if the solid rectangular parallelepiped contained by three of the lines so drawn bears a given ratio to the solid rectangular parallelepiped contained by the other two and any given line whatever, the point lies on a 'line' given in position. Again, if there be six lines, and if the solid contained by three of the lines bears a given ratio to the solid contained by the other three lines, the point also lies on a 'line' given in position. But if there be more than six lines, we cannot say whether a ratio of something contained by four lines is given to that which is contained by the rest, since there is no figure of more than three dimensions."

GEOMETRY

impares vel pares multitudine, cum hæc, ut dixi, loco ad quatuor lineas respondeant, nullum igitur posuerunt ita ut linea nota sit, &c.[34]

The question, then, the solution of which was begun by Euclid and carried farther by Apollonius, but was completed by no one, is this:

Having three, four or more lines given in position, it is first required to find a point from which as many other lines may be drawn, each making a given angle with one of the given lines, so that the rectangle of two of the lines so drawn shall bear a given ratio to the square of the third (if there be only three); or to the rectangle of the other two (if there be four), or again, that the parallelepiped[35] constructed upon three shall bear a given ratio to that upon the other two and any given line (if there be five), or to the parallelepiped upon the other three (if there be six); or (if there be seven) that the product obtained by multiplying four of them together shall bear a given ratio to the product of the other three, or (if there be eight) that the product of four of them shall bear a given ratio to the product of the other four. Thus the question admits of extension to any number of lines.

Then, since there is always an infinite number of different points satisfying these requirements, it is also required to discover and trace the curve containing all such points.[36] Pappus says that when there are only three or four lines given, this line is one of the three conic sections, but he does not undertake to determine, describe, or explain the nature of the line required[37] when the question involves a greater number of lines. He only adds that the ancients recognized one of them which they had shown to be useful, and which seemed the sim-

---

[34] This rather obscure passage may be translated as follows: "For in this are agreed those who formerly interpreted these things (that the dimensions of a figure cannot exceed three) in that they maintain that a figure that is contained by these lines is not comprehensible in any way. This is permissible, however, both to say and to demonstrate generally by this kind of proportion, and in this manner: If from any point straight lines be drawn making given angles with straight lines given in position; and if there be given a ratio compounded of them, that is the ratio that one of the lines drawn has to one, the second has to a second, the third to a third, and so on to the given line if there be seven lines, or, if there be eight lines, of the last to a last, the point lies on the lines that are given in position. And similarly, whatever may be the odd or even number, since these, as I have said, correspond in position to the four lines; therefore they have not set forth any method so that a line may be known." The meaning of the passage appears from that which follows in the text.

[35] That is, continued product.

[36] It is here that the essential feature of the work of Descartes may be said to begin.

[37] See line 19 on the opposite page.

lelepipede composé des deux qui restent, & d'vne autre ligne donnée. Ou s'il y en a six, que le parallelepipede cõposé de trois ait la proportion donnée auec le parallelepipede des trois autres. Ou s'il y en a sept, que ce qui se produist lorsqu'on en multiplie quatre l'vne par l'autre, ait la raison donnée auec ce qui se produist par la multiplication des trois autres, & encore d'vne autre ligne donnée; Ou s'il y en a huit, que le produit de la multiplication de quatre ait la proportion donnée auec le produit des quatre autres. Et ainsi cete question se peut estendre a tout autre nombre de lignes. Puis a cause qu'il y a tousiours vne infinité de diuers poins qui peuuent satisfaire a ce qui est icy demandé, il est aussy requis de connoistre, & de tracer la ligne, dans laquelle ils doiuent tous se trouuer. & Pappus dit que lorsqu'il n'y a que trois ou quatre lignes droites données, c'est en vne des trois sections coniques. mais il n'entreprend point de la determiner, ny de la descrire. non plus que d'expliquer celles ou tous ces poins se doiuent trouuer, lorsque la question est proposée en vn plus grand nombre de lignes. Seulement il aiouste que les anciens en auoient imaginé vne qu'ils monstroient y estre vtile , mais qui sembloit la plus manifeste, & qui n'estoit pas toutefois la premiere. Ce qui m'a donné occasion d'essayer si par la methode dont ie me sers on peut aller aussy loin qu'ils ont esté.

Et premierement i'ay connu que cete question n'estant proposée qu'en trois, ou quatre, ou cinq lignes , on peut tousiours trouuer les poins cherchés par la Geometrie simple; c'est a dire en ne se seruant que de la reigle & du compas, *Responce à la question de Pappus.*

compas, ny ne faisant autre chose, que ce qui a desia esté dit; excepté seulement lorsqu'il y a cinq lignes données, si elles sont toutes paralleles. Auquel cas, comme aussy lorsque la question est proposée en six, ou 7, ou 8, ou 9 lignes, on peut tousiours trouuer les poins cherchés par la Geometrie des solides; c'est a dire en y employant quelqu'vne des trois sections coniques. Excepté seulement lorsqu'il y a neuf lignes données, si elles sont toutes paralleles. Auquel cas derechef, & encore en 10, 11, 12, ou 13 lignes on peut trouuer les poins cherchés par le moyen d'vne ligne courbe qui soit d'vn degré plus composée que les sections coniques. Excepté en treize si elles sont toutes paralleles, auquel cas, & en quatorze, 15, 16, & 17 il y faudra employer vne ligne courbe encore d'vn degré plus composée que la precedente. & ainsi a l'infini.

Puis iay trouué aussy, que lorsqu'il n'y a que trois ou quatre lignes données, les poins cherchés se rencontrent tous, non seulement en l'vne des trois sections coniques, mais quelquefois aussy en la circonference d'vn cercle, ou en vne ligne droite. Et que lorsqu'il y en a cinq, ou six, ou sept, ou huit, tous ces poins se rencontrent en quelque vne des lignes, qui sont d'vn degré plus composées que les sections coniques, & il est impossible d'en imaginer aucune qui ne soit vtile a cete question; mais ils peuuent aussy derechef se rencontrer en vne section conique, ou en vn cercle, ou en vne ligne droite. Et s'il y en a neuf, ou 10, ou 11, ou 12, ces poins se rencontrent en vne ligne, qui ne peut estre que d'vn degré plus composée que les precedentes; mais toutes celles

qui

plest, and yet was not the most important.[38] This led me to try to find out whether, by my own method, I could go as far as they had gone.[39]

First, I discovered that if the question be proposed for only three, four, or five lines, the required points can be found by elementary geometry, that is, by the use of the ruler and compasses only, and the application of those principles that I have already explained, except in the case of five parallel lines. In this case, and in the cases where there are six, seven, eight, or nine given lines, the required points can always be found by means of the geometry of solid loci,[40] that is, by using some one of the three conic sections. Here, again, there is an exception in the case of nine parallel lines. For this and the cases of ten, eleven, twelve, or thirteen given lines, the required points may be found by means of a curve of degree next higher than that of the conic sections. Again, the case of thirteen parallel lines must be excluded, for which, as well as for the cases of fourteen, fifteen, sixteen, and seventeen lines, a curve of degree next higher than the preceding must be used; and so on indefinitely.

Next, I have found that when only three or four lines are given, the required points lie not only all on one of the conic sections but sometimes on the circumference of a circle or even on a straight line.[41]

When there are five, six, seven, or eight lines, the required points lie on a curve of degree next higher than the conic sections, and it is impossible to imagine such a curve that may not satisfy the conditions of the problem; but the required points may possibly lie on a conic section, a circle, or a straight line. If there are nine, ten, eleven, or twelve lines, the required curve is only one degree higher than the preceding, but any such curve may meet the requirements, and so on to infinity.

---

[38] See lines 5-10 from the foot of page 23.

[39] Descartes gives here a brief summary of his solution, which he amplifies later.

[40] This term was commonly applied by mathematicians of the seventeenth century to the three conic sections, while the straight line and circle were called plane loci, and other curves linear loci. See Fermat, *Isagoge ad Locos Planos et Solidos*, Toulouse, 1679.

[41] Degenerate or limiting forms of the conic sections.

Finally, the first and simplest curve after the conic sections is the one generated by the intersection of a parabola with a straight line in a way to be described presently.

I believe that I have in this way completely accomplished what Pappus tells us the ancients sought to do, and I will try to give the demonstration in a few words, for I am already wearied by so much writing.

Let AB, AD, EF, GH, ... be any number of straight lines given in position,[42] and let it be required to find a point C, from which straight lines CB, CD, CF, CH, ... can be drawn, making given angles CBA, CDA, CFE, CHG, ... respectively, with the given lines, and

---

[42] It should be noted that these lines are given in position but not in length. They thus become lines of reference or coördinate axes, and accordingly they play a very important part in the development of analytic geometry. In this connection we may quote as follows: "Among the predecessors of Descartes we reckon, besides Apollonius, especially Vieta, Oresme, Cavalieri, Roberval, and Fermat, the last the most distinguished in this field; but nowhere, even by Fermat, had any attempt been made to refer several curves of different orders simultaneously to one system of coördinates, which at most possessed special significance for one of the curves. It is exactly this thing which Descartes systematically accomplished." Karl Fink, *A Brief History of Mathematics*, trans. by Beman and Smith, Chicago, 1903, p. 229.

Heath calls attention to the fact that "the essential difference between the Greek and the modern method is that the Greeks did not direct their efforts to making the fixed lines of a figure as few as possible, but rather to expressing their equations between areas in as short and simple a form as possible." For further discussion see D. E. Smith, *History of Mathematics*, Boston, 1923-25, Vol. II, pp. 316-331 (hereafter referred to as Smith).

Livre Premier.

qui font d'vn degré plus compofées y peuuent feruir, & ainfi a l'infini.

 Au refte la premiere, & la plus fimple de toutes aprés les fections coniques, eft celle qu'on peut defcrire par l'interfection d'vne Parabole, & d'vne ligne droite, en la façon qui fera tantoft expliquée. En forte que ie penfe auoir entierement fatisfait a ceque Pappus nous dit auoir efté chetché en cecy par les anciens. & ie tafcheray d'en mettre la demonftration en peu de mots. car il m'ennuie defia d'en tant efcrire.

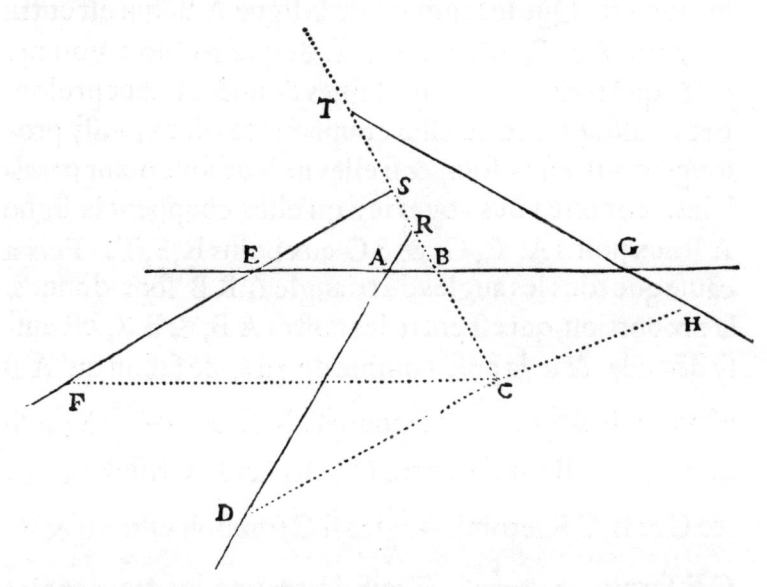

 Soient A B, A D, E F, G H, &c. plufieurs lignes données par pofition, & qu'il faille trouuer vn point, comme C, duquel ayant tiré d'autres lignes droites fur les données, comme C B, C D, C F, & C H, en forte que les angles C B A, C D A, C F E, C H G, &c. foient donnés,

310 LA GEOMETRIE.

& que ce qui est produit par la multiplication d'vne partie de ces lignes, soit esgal a ce qui est produit par la multiplication des autres, oubien qu'ils ayent quelque autre proportion donnée, car cela ne rend point la question plus difficile.

Commēt on doit poser les termes pour venir à l'Equation en cet exemple.

Premierement ie suppose la chose comme desia faite, & pour me demesler de la cōfusion de toutes ces lignes, ie considere l'vne des données, & l'vne de celles qu'il faut trouuer, par exemple A B, & C B, comme les principales, & ausquelles ie tasche de rapporter ainsi toutes les autres. Que le segment de la ligne A B, qui est entre les poins A & B, soit nommé x. & que B C soit nommé y. & que toutes les autres lignes données soient prolongées, iusques a ce qu'elles couppent ces deux, aussy prolongées s'il est besoin, & si elles ne leur sont point paralleles. comme vous voyés icy qu'elles couppent la ligne A B aux poins A, E, G, & B C aux poins R, S, T. Puis a cause que tous les angles du triangle A R B sont donnés, la proportion, qui est entre les costés A B, & B R, est aussy donnée, & ie la pose comme de z à b, de façon qu' A B estant x, R B sera $\frac{bx}{z}$, & la toute C R sera $y + \frac{bx}{z}$, à cause que le point B tombe entre C & R; car si R tomboit entre C & B, C R seroit $y - \frac{bx}{z}$; & si C tomboit entre B & R, C R seroit $-y + \frac{bx}{z}$. Tout de mesme les trois angles du triangle D R C sont donnés, & par consequent aussy la proportion qui est entre les costés C R, & C D, que ie pose comme de z à c: de façon que C R estant $y + \frac{bx}{z}$,

CD

such that the product of certain of them is equal to the product of the rest, or at least such that these two products shall have a given ratio, for this condition does not make the problem any more difficult.

First, I suppose the thing done, and since so many lines are confusing, I may simplify matters by considering one of the given lines and one of those to be drawn (as, for example, AB and BC) as the principal lines, to which I shall try to refer all the others. Call the segment of the line AB between A and B, x, and call BC, y. Produce all the other given lines to meet these two (also produced if necessary) provided none is parallel to either of the principal lines. Thus, in the figure, the given lines cut AB in the points A, E, G, and cut BC in the points R, S, T.

Now, since all the angles of the triangle ARB are known,[43] the ratio between the sides AB and BR is known.[44] If we let $AB : BR = z : b$, since $AB = x$, we have $RB = \frac{bx}{z}$; and since B lies between C and R [45], we have $CR = y + \frac{bx}{z}$. (When R lies between C and B, CR is equal to $y - \frac{bx}{z}$, and when C lies between B and R, CR is equal to $-y + \frac{bx}{z}$.) Again, the three angles of the triangle DRC are known,[46] and therefore the ratio between the sides CR and CD is determined. Calling this ratio $z : c$, since $CR = y + \frac{bx}{z}$, we have $CD = \frac{cy}{z} + \frac{bcx}{z^2}$. Then, since

---

[43] Since BC cuts AB and AD under given angles.
[44] Since the ratio of the sines of the opposite angles is known.
[45] In this particular figure, of course.
[46] Since CB and CD cut AD under given angles.

GEOMETRY

the lines AB, AD, and EF are given in position, the distance from A to E is known. If we call this distance k, then $EB = k + x$; although $EB = k - x$ when B lies between E and A, and $E = -k + x$ when E lies between A and B. Now the angles of the triangle ESB being given, the ratio of BE to BS is known. We may call this ratio $z : d$. Then $BS = \dfrac{dk + dx}{z}$ and $CS = \dfrac{zy + dk + dx}{z}$.[47] When S lies between B and C we have $CS = \dfrac{zy - dk - dx}{z}$, and when C lies between B and S we have $CS = \dfrac{-zy + dk + dx}{z}$. The angles of the triangle FSC are known, and hence, also the ratio of CS to CF, or $z : e$. Therefore, $CF = \dfrac{ezy + dek + dex}{z^2}$. Likewise, AG or l is given, and $BG = l - x$. Also, in triangle BGT, the ratio of BG to BT, or $z : f$, is known. Therefore, $BT = \dfrac{fl - fx}{z}$ and $CT = \dfrac{zy + fl - fx}{z}$. In triangle TCH, the ratio of TC to CH, or $z : g$, is known,[48] whence $CH = \dfrac{gzy + fgl - fgx}{z^2}$.

[47] We have
$$CS = y + BS$$
$$= y + \frac{dk + dx}{z}$$
$$= \frac{zy + dk + dx}{z},$$

and similarly for the other cases considered below.

The translation covers the first eight lines on the original page 312 (page 32 of this edition.

[48] It should be noted that each ratio assumed has z as antecedent.

Livre Premier.

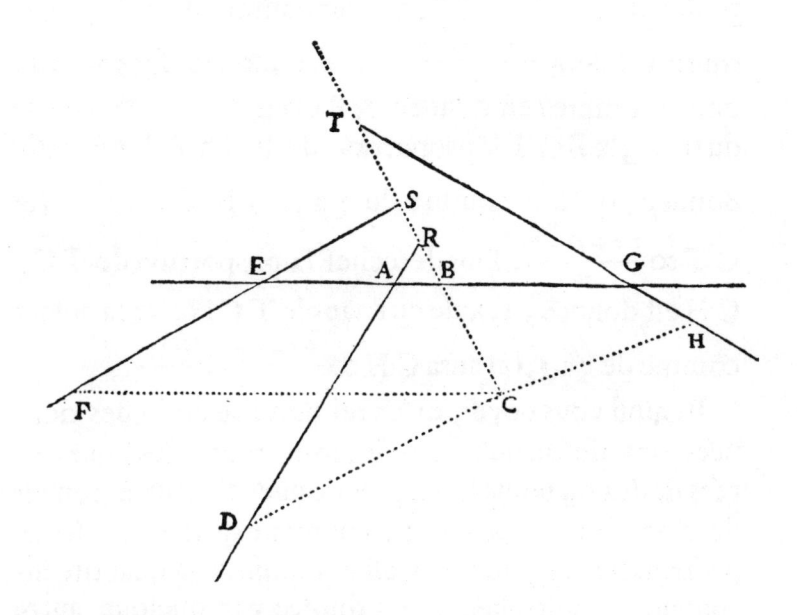

CD sera $\frac{cy}{z} + \frac{bcx}{zz}$. Aprés cela pourceque les lignes AB, AD, & EF sont données par position, la distance qui est entre les poins A & E est aussy donnée, & si on la nomme K, on aura E B esgal a $k + x$; mais ce seroit $k - x$, si le point B tomboit entre E & A; & $-k + x$, si E tomboit entre A & B. Et pourceque les angles du triangle E S B sont tous donnés, la proportion de BE a BS est aussy donnée, & ie la pose comme z à d, si bien que BS est $\frac{dk + dx}{z}$, & là toute C S est $\frac{zy + dk + dx}{z}$; mais ce seroit $\frac{zy - dk - dx}{z}$, si le point S tomboit entre B & C; & ce seroit $\frac{-zy + dk + dx}{z}$, si C tomboit entre B & S. De plus les trois angles du triangle F S C sont donnés, & en suite la pro-

proportion de C S à C F, qui soit comme de z à e, & la toute C F sera $\frac{ezy \mp dek \mp dex}{zz}$. En mesme façon A G que ie nomme l est donnée, & B G est $l -- x$, & a cause du triangle B G T la proportion de B G a B T est aussy donnée, qui soit comme de z à f. & B T sera $\frac{fl -- fx}{z}$, & C T ∞ $\frac{zy \mp fl -- fx}{z}$. Puis derechef la proportion de T C a C H est donnée, a cause du triangle T C H, & la posant comme de z à g, on aura C H ∞ $\frac{\mp gzy \mp fgl -- fgx}{zz}$.

Et ainsi vous voyés, qu'en tel nombre de lignes données par position qu'on puisse auoir, toutes les lignes tirées dessus du point C a angles donnés suiuant la teneur de la question, se peuuent tousiours exprimer chascune par trois termes; dont l'vn est composé de la quantité inconnue y, multipliée, ou diuisée par quelque autre connue; & l'autre de la quantité inconnue x, aussy multipliée ou diuisée par quelque autre connuë, & le trosiesme d'vne quantité toute connuë. Excepté seulement si elles sont paralleles; oubien a la ligne A B, auquel cas le terme composé de la quantité x sera nul ; oubien a la ligne C B, auquel cas celuy qui est composé de la quantité y sera nul; ainsi qu'il est trop manifeste pour que ie m'areste a l'expliquer. Et pour les signes $+$, & $--$, qui se ioignent à ces termes, ils peuuent estre changés en toutes les façons imaginables.

Puis vous voyés aussy, que multipliant plusieurs de ces lignes l'vne par l'autre, les quantités x & y, qui se trouuent dans le produit, n'y peuuent auoir que chascune autant de dimensions, qu'il y a eu de lignes, a l'explication

FIRST BOOK

And thus you see that, no matter how many lines are given in position, the length of any such line through C making given angles with these lines can always be expressed by three terms, one of which consists of the unknown quantity y multiplied or divided by some known quantity; another consisting of the unknown quantity x multiplied or divided by some other known quantity; and the third consisting of a known quantity.[49] An exception must be made in the case where the given lines are parallel either to AB (when the term containing x vanishes), or to CB (when the term containing y vanishes). This case is too simple to require further explanation.[50] The signs of the terms may be either $+$ or $-$ in every conceivable combination.[51]

You also see that in the product of any number of these lines the degree of any term containing x or y will not be greater than the number of lines (expressed by means of x and y) whose product is found. Thus, no term will be of degree higher than the second if two lines be multiplied together, nor of degree higher than the third, if there be three lines, and so on to infinity.

[49] That is, an expression of the form $ax + by + c$, where a, b, c, are any real positive or negative quantities, integral or fractional (not zero, since this exception is considered later).

[50] The following problem will serve as a very simple illustration: Given three parallel lines AB, CD, EF, so placed that AB is distant 4 units from CD, and CD is distant 3 units from EF; required to find a point P such that if PL, PM, PN

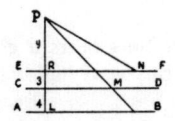

be drawn through P, making angles of 90°, 45°, 30°, respectively, with the parallels. Then $\overline{PM}^2 = PL \cdot PN$.

Let $PR = y$, then $PN = 2y$, $PM = \sqrt{2}(y+3)$, $PL = y+7$. If $\overline{PM}^2 = PN \cdot PL$, we have $\left[\sqrt{2}(y+3)\right]^2 = 2y(y+7)$, whence $y = 9$. Therefore, the point P lies on the line XY parallel to EF and at a distance of 9 units from it. Cf. Rabuel, p. 79.

[51] Depending, of course, upon the relative positions of the given lines.

Furthermore, to determine the point C, but one condition is needed, namely, that the product of a certain number of lines shall be equal to, or (what is quite as simple), shall bear a given ratio to the product of certain other lines. Since this condition can be expressed by a single equation in two unknown quantities,[52] we may give any value we please to either x or y and find the value of the other from this equation. It is obvious that when not more than five lines are given, the quantity x, which is not used to express the first of the lines can never be of degree higher than the second.[53]

Assigning a value to y, we have $x^2 = \pm ax \pm b^2$, and therefore x can be found with ruler and compasses, by a method already explained.[54] If then we should take successively an infinite number of different values for the line y, we should obtain an infinite number of values for the line x, and therefore an infinity of different points, such as C, by means of which the required curve could be drawn.

This method can be used when the problem concerns six or more lines, if some of them are parallel to either AB or BC, in which case

[52] That is, an indeterminate equation. "De plus, à cause que pour determiner le point C, il n'y a qu'une seule condition qui soit requise, à sçavoir que ce qui est produit par la multiplication d'un certain nombre de ces lignes soit égal, ou (ce qui n'est de rien plus mal-aisé) ait la proportion donnee, à ce qui est produit par la multiplication des autres; on peut prendre à discretion l'une des deux quantitez inconnuës x ou y, & chercher l'autre par cette Equation." Such variations in the texts of different editions are of no moment, but are occasionally introduced as matters of interest.

[53] Since the product of three lines bears a given ratio to the product of two others and a given line, no term can be of higher degree than the third, and therefore, than the second in x.

[54] See pages 13, et seq.

LIVRE PREMIER. 313

cation desquelles elles feruent, qui ont esté ainsi multipliées: en sorte qu'elles n'auront iamais plus de deux dimensions, en ce qui ne sera produit que par la multiplication de deux lignes; ny plus de trois, en ce qui ne sera produit que par la multiplication de trois, & ainsi a l'infini.

De plus, a cause que pour determiner le point C, il n'y a qu'vne seule condition qui soit requise, à sçauoir que ce qui est produit par la multiplication d'vn certain nombre de ces lignes soit esgal, ou (ce qui n'est de rien plus malaysé) ait la proportion donnée, à ce qui est produit par la multiplication des autres; on peut prendre a discretion l'vne des deux quantités inconnues x ou y, & chercher l'autre par cete Equation. en laquelle il est euident que lorsque la question n'est point proposée en plus de cinq lignes, la quantité x qui ne sert point a l'expression de la premiere peut tousiours n'y auoir que deux dimensions. de façon que prenant vne quantité connuë pour y, il ne restera que $xx \infty + $ ou $-- ax + $ ou $-- bb$. & ainsi on pourra trouuer la quantité x auec la reigle & le compas, en la façon tantost expliquée. Mesme prenant successiuement infinies diuerses grandeurs pour la ligne y, on en trouuera aussy infinies pour la ligne x, & ainsi on aura vne infinité de diuers poins, tels que celuy qui est marqué C, par le moyen desquels on descrira la ligne courbe demandée.

Il se peut faire aussy, la question estant proposée en six, ou plus grand nombre de lignes; s'il y en a entre les données, qui soient paralleles a BA, ou BC, que l'vne des deux quantités x ou y n'ait que deux dimensions en

Comment on trouue que ce problesme est plan, lorsqu'il n'est point proposé en plus de 5 lignes.

Rr   l'Equa-

l'Equation, & ainsi qu'on puisse trouuuer le point C auec la reigle & le compas. Mais au contraire si elles sont toutes paralleles, encore que la question ne soit proposée qu'en cinq lignes, ce point C ne pourra ainsi estre trouué, a cause que la quantité x ne se trouuant point en toute l'Equation, il ne sera plus permis de prendre vne quantité connuë pour celle qui est nommée y, mais ce sera elle qu'il faudra chercher. Et pource quelle aura trois dimensions, on ne la pourra trouuer qu'en tirant la racine d'vne Equation cubique. ce qui ne se peut generalement faire sans qu'on y employe pour le moins vne section conique. Et encore qu'il y ait iusques a neuf lignes données, pourvû qu'elles ne soient point toutes paralleles, on peut tousiours faire que l'Equation ne monte que iusques au quarré de quarré. au moyen dequoy on la peut aussy tousiours resoudre par les sections coniques, en la façon que i'expliqueray cy aprés. Et encore qu'il y en ait iusques a treize, on peut tousiours faire qu'elle ne monte que iusques au quarré de cube. en suite de quoy on la peut resoudre par le moyen d'vne ligne, qui n'est que d'vn degré plus composée que les sections coniques, en la façon que i'expliqueray aussy cy aprés. Et cecy est la premiere partie de ce que i'auois icy a demonstrer; mais auant que ie passe a la seconde il est besoin que ie die quelque chose en general de la nature des lignes courbes.

LA

either x or y will be of only the second degree in the equation, so that the point C can be found with ruler and compasses.

On the other hand, if the given lines are all parallel even though a question should be proposed involving only five lines, the point C cannot be found in this way. For, since the quantity x does not occur at all in the equation, it is no longer allowable to give a known value to y. It is then necessary to find the value of y.[55] And since the term in y will now be of the third degree, its value can be found only by finding the root of a cubic equation, which cannot in general be done without the use of one of the conic sections.[56]

And furthermore, if not more than nine lines are given, not all of them being parallel, the equation can always be so expressed as to be of degree not higher than the fourth. Such equations can always be solved by means of the conic sections in a way that I shall presently explain.[57]

Again, if there are not more than thirteen lines, an equation of degree not higher than the sixth can be employed, which admits of solution by means of a curve just one degree higher than the conic sections by a method to be explained presently.[58]

This completes the first part of what I have to demonstrate here, but it is necessary, before passing to the second part, to make some general statements concerning the nature of curved lines.

[55] That is, to solve the equation for y.
[56] See page 84.
[57] See page 107.
[58] This line of reasoning may be extended indefinitely. Briefly, it means that for every two lines introduced the equation becomes one degree higher and the curve becomes correspondingly more complex.

BOOK SECOND

Geometry

BOOK II

On the Nature of Curved Lines

THE ancients were familiar with the fact that the problems of geometry may be divided into three classes, namely, plane, solid, and linear problems.[59] This is equivalent to saying that some problems require only circles and straight lines for their construction, while others require a conic section and still others require more complex curves.[60] I am surprised, however, that they did not go further, and distinguish between different degrees of these more complex curves, nor do I see why they called the latter mechanical, rather than geometrical.[61]

If we say that they are called mechanical because some sort of instrument[62] has to be used to describe them, then we must, to be consistent,

---

[59] Cf. Pappus, Vol. I, p. 55, Proposition 5, Book III: "The ancients considered three classes of geometric problems, which they called plane, solid, and linear. Those which can be solved by means of straight lines and circumferences of circles are called plane problems, since the lines or curves by which they are solved have their origin in a plane. But problems whose solutions are obtained by the use of one or more of the conic sections are called solid problems, for the surfaces of solid figures (conical surfaces) have to be used. There remains a third class which is called linear because other 'lines' than those I have just described, having diverse and more involved origins, are required for their construction. Such lines are the spirals, the quadratrix, the conchoid, and the cissoid, all of which have many important properties." See also Pappus, Vol. I, p. 271.

[60] Rabuel (p. 92) suggests dividing problems into classes, the first class to include all problems that can be constructed by means of straight lines, that is, curves whose equations are of the first degree; the second, those that require curves whose equations are of the second degree, namely, the circle and the conic sections, and so on.

[61] Cf. Encyclopédie ou Dictionnaire Raisonné des Sciences, des Arts et des Metiers, par une Société de gens de lettres, mis en ordre et publiées par M. Diderot, et quant à la Partie Mathematique par M. d'Alembert, Lausanne and Berne, 1780. In substance as follows: "Mechanical is a mathematical term designating a construction not geometric, that is, that cannot be accomplished by geometric curves. Such are constructions depending upon the quadrature of the circle.

The term, mechanical curve, was used by Descartes to designate a curve that cannot be expressed by an algebraic equation." Leibniz and others call them transcendental.

[62] "Machine."

LA GEOMETRIE.
LIVRE SECOND.

De la nature des lignes courbes.

LEs anciens ont fort bien remarqué, qu'entre les Problefmes de Geometrie, les vns font plans, les autres folides,&les autres lineaires, c'eft a dire, que les vns peuuent eftre conftruits, en ne traçant que des lignes droites, & des cercles; au lieu que les autres ne le peuuent eftre, qu'on n'y employe pour le moins quelque fection conique; ni enfin les autres, qu'on n'y employe quelque autre ligne plus compofée. Mais ie m'eftonne de ce qu'ils n'ont point outre cela diftingué diuers degrés entre ces lignes plus compofées, & ie ne fçaurois comprendre pourquoy ils les ont nommées mechaniques, plutoft que Geometriques. Car de dire que ç'ait efté, a caufe qu'il eft befoin de fe feruir de quelque machine pour les defcrire, il faudroit reietter par mefme raifon les cercles & les lignes droites; vû qu'on ne les defcrit fur le papier qu'auec vn compas, & vne reigle, qu'on peut auffy nommer des machines. Ce n'eft pas non plus, a caufe que les inftrumens, qui feruent a les tracer, eftant plus compofés que la reigle & le compas, ne peuuent eftre fi iuftes; car il faudroit pour cete raifon les reietter des Mechaniques, où la iufteffe des ouurages qui fortent de la main eft defirée; plutoft que de la Geometrie, ou c'eft feulement la iufteffe du raifonnemēt qu'on recherche,

Quelles font les lignes courbes qu'on peut receuoir en Geometrie.

che, & qui peut sans doute estre aussy parfaite touchant ces lignes, que touchant les autres. Ie ne diray pas aussy, que ce soit a cause qu'ils n'ont pas voulu augmenter le nombre de leurs demandes, & qu'ils se sont contentés qu'on leur accordast, qu'ils pussent ioindre deux poins donnés par vne ligne droite, & descrire vn cercle d'vn centre donné, qui passast par vn point donné. car ils n'ont point fait de scrupule de supposer outre cela, pour traiter des sections coniques, qu'on pust coupper tout cone donné par vn plan donné. & il n'est besoin de rien supposer pour traçer toutes les lignes courbes, que ie pretens icy d'introduire; sinon que deux ou plusieurs lignes puissent estre meuës l'vne par l'autre, & que leurs intersections en marquent d'autres; ce qui ne me paroist en rien plus difficile. Il est vray qu'ils n'ont pas aussy entierement receu les sections coniques en leur Geometrie, & ie ne veux pas entreprendre de changer les noms qui ont esté approuués par l'vsage; mais il est, ce me semble, tres clair, que prenant comme on fait pour Geometrique ce qui est precis & exact, & pour Mechanique ce qui ne l'est pas; & considerant la Geometrie comme vne science, qui enseigne generalement a connoistre les mesures de tous les cors, on n'en doit pas plutost exclure les lignes les plus composées que les plus simples, pourvû qu'on les puisse imaginer estre descrites par vn mouuement continu, ou par plusieurs qui s'entresuiuent & dont les derniers soient entierement reglés par ceux qui les precedent. car par ce moyen on peut tousiours auoir vne connoissance exacte de leur mesure. Mais peutestre que ce qui a empesché les anciens Geometres de receuoir

reject circles and straight lines, since these cannot be described on paper without the use of compasses and a ruler, which may also be termed instruments. It is not because the other instruments, being more complicated than the ruler and compasses, are therefore less accurate, for if this were so they would have to be excluded from mechanics, in which accuracy of construction is even more important than in geometry. In the latter, exactness of reasoning alone[63] is sought, and this can surely be as thorough with reference to such lines as to simpler ones.[64] I cannot believe, either, that it was because they did not wish to make more than two postulates, namely, (1) a straight line can be drawn between any two points, and (2) about a given center a circle can be described passing through a given point. In their treatment of the conic sections they did not hesitate to introduce the assumption that any given cone can be cut by a given plane. Now to treat all the curves which I mean to introduce here, only one additional assumption is necessary, namely, two or more lines can be moved, one upon the other, determining by their intersection other curves. This seems to me in no way more difficult.[65]

It is true that the conic sections were never freely received into ancient geometry,[66] and I do not care to undertake to change names confirmed by usage; nevertheless, it seems very clear to me that if we make the usual assumption that geometry is precise and exact, while mechanics is not;[67] and if we think of geometry as the science which furnishes a general knowledge of the measurement of all bodies, then we have no more right to exclude the more complex curves than the simpler ones, provided they can be conceived of as described by a continuous motion or by several successive motions, each motion being completely determined by those which precede; for in this way an exact knowledge of the magnitude of each is always obtainable.

[63] An interesting question of modern education is here raised, namely, to what extent we should insist upon accuracy of construction even in elementary geometry.
[64] Not only ancient writers but later ones, up to the time of Descartes, made the same distinction; for example, Vieta. Descartes's view has been universally accepted since his time.
[65] That is, in no way less obvious than the other postulates.
[66] Because the ancients did not believe that the so-called constructions of the conic sections on a plane surface could be exact.
[67] Since it is not possible to construct an ideal line, plane, and so on.

GEOMETRY

Probably the real explanation of the refusal of ancient geometers to accept curves more complex than the conic sections lies in the fact that the first curves to which their attention was attracted happened to be the spiral,[68] the quadratrix,[69] and similar curves, which really do belong only to mechanics, and are not among those curves that I think should be included here, since they must be conceived of as described by two separate movements whose relation does not admit of exact determination. Yet they afterwards examined the conchoid,[70] the cissoid,[71] and a few others which should be accepted; but not knowing much about their properties they took no more account of these than of the others. Again, it may have been that, knowing as they did only a little about the conic sections,[72] and being still ignorant of many of the possibilities of the ruler and compasses, they dared not yet attack a matter of still greater difficulty. I hope that hereafter those who are clever enough to make use of the geometric methods herein suggested will find no great difficulty in applying them to plane or solid problems. I therefore think it proper to suggest to such a more extended line of investigation which will furnish abundant opportunities for practice.

Consider the lines AB, AD, AF, and so forth (page 46), which we may suppose to be described by means of the instrument YZ. This instrument consists of several rulers hinged together in such a way that YZ being placed along the line AN the angle XYZ can be increased or decreased in size, and when its sides are together the points B, C, D, E, F, G, H, all coincide with A; but as the size of the angle is increased,

[68] See Heath, *History of Greek Mathematics* (hereafter referred to as Heath), Cambridge, 2 vols., 1921. Also Cantor, *Vorlesungen über Geschichte der Mathematik*, Leipzig, Vol. I (2), p. 263, and Vol. II (1), pp. 765 and 781 (hereafter referred to as Cantor).

[69] See Heath, I, 225; Smith, Vol. II, pp. 300, 305.

[70] See Heath, I, 235, 238; Smith, Vol. II, p. 298.

[71] See Heath, I, 264; Smith, Vol. II, p. 314.

[72] They really knew much more than would be inferred from this statement. In this connection, see Taylor, *Ancient and Modern Geometry of Conics*, Cambridge, 1881.

LIVRE SECOND.

uoir celles qui estoient plus composées que les sections coniques, c'est que les premieres qu'ils ont considerées, ayant par hasard esté la Spirale, la Quadratrice, & semblables, qui n'appartienent veritablement qu'aux Mechaniques, & ne sont point du nombre de celles que ie pense deuoir icy estre receues, a cause qu'on les imagine descrites par deux mouuemens separés, & qui n'ont entre eux aucun raport qu'on puisse mesurer exactement, bienqu'ils ayent aprés examiné la Conchoide, la Cissoide, & quelque peu d'autres qui en sont, toutefois a cause qu'ils n'ont peuteftre pas assés remarqué leurs proprietés, ils n'en ont pas fait plus d'estat que des premieres. Oubien c'est que voyant, qu'ils ne connoissoient encore, que peu de choses touchant les sections coniques, & qu'il leur en restoit mesme beaucoup, touchant ce qui se peut faire auec la reigle & le compas, qu'ils ignoroient, ils ont creu ne deuoir point entamer de matiere plus difficile. Mais pourceque i'espere que d'orenauant ceux qui auront l'adresse de se seruir du calcul Geometrique icy proposé, ne trouueront pas assés dequoy s'arester touchant les problesmes plans, ou solides; ie croy qu'il est a propos que ie les inuite a d'autres recherches, où ils ne manqueront iamais d'exercice.

Voyés les lignes AB, AD, AF, & semblables que ie suppose auoir esté descrites par l'ayde de l'instrument YZ, qui est composé de plusieurs reigles tellement iointes, que celle qui est marquée YZ estant arestée sur la ligne AN, on peut ouurir & fermer l'angle XYZ; & que lorsqu'il est tout fermé, les poins B, C, D, F, G, H sont tous assemblés au point A ; mais qu'a mesure qu'on l'ouure,

l'ouure, la reigle B C, qui eſt iointe a angles droits auec X Y au point B, pouſſe vers Z la reigle C D, qui coule ſur Y Z en faiſant touſiours des angles droits auec elle, & C D pouſſe D E, qui coule tout de meſme ſur Y X en demeurant parallele a B C, D E pouſſe E F, E F pouſſe F G, cellecy pouſſe G H. & on en peut conceuoir vne infinité d'autres, qui ſe pouſſent conſequutiuement en meſme façon, & dont les vnes facent touſiours les meſmes angles auec Y X, & les autres auec Y Z. Or pendant qu'on ouure ainſi l'angle X Y Z, le point B deſcrit la ligne A B, qui eſt vn cercle, & les autres poins D, F, H, ou ſe font les interſections des autres reigles, deſcriuent d'autres lignes courbes A D, A F, A H, dont les dernieres ſont par ordre plus cõpoſées que la premiere, & cellecy plus que le cercle. mais ie ne voy pas ce qui peut empeſcher, qu'on ne conçoiue auſſy nettement, & auſſy diſtinctement la deſcription de cete premiere, que du cercle, ou

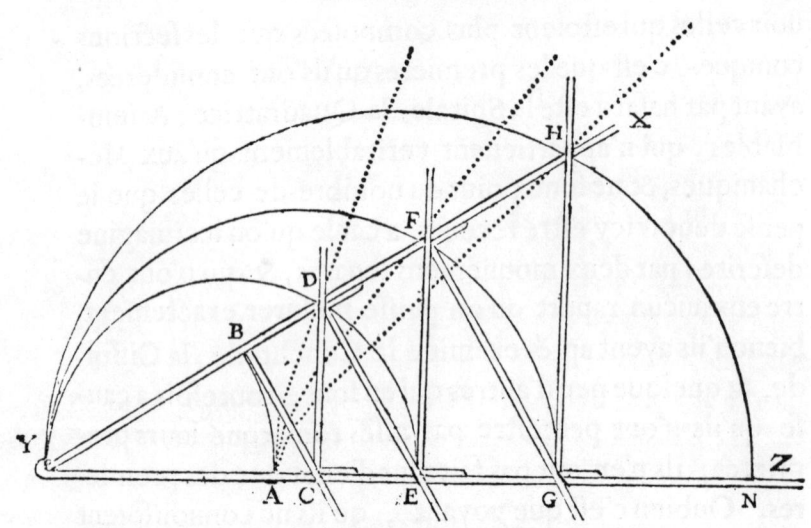

du

SECOND BOOK

the ruler BC, fastened at right angles to XY at the point B, pushes toward Z the ruler CD which slides along YZ always at right angles. In like manner, CD pushes DE which slides along YX always parallel to BC; DE pushes EF; EF pushes FG; FG pushes GH, and so on. Thus we may imagine an infinity of rulers, each pushing another, half of them making equal angles with YX and the rest with YZ.

Now as the angle XYZ is increased the point B describes the curve AB, which is a circle; while the intersections of the other rulers, namely, the points D, F, H describe other curves, AD, AF, AH, of which the latter are more complex than the first and this more complex than the circle. Nevertheless I see no reason why the description of the first[73] cannot be conceived as clearly and distinctly as that of the circle, or at least as that of the conic sections; or why that of the second, third,[74] or any other that can be thus described, cannot be as clearly conceived of as the first; and therefore I see no reason why they should not be used in the same way in the solution of geometric problems.[75]

[73] That is, AD.
[74] That is, AF and AH.
[75] The equations of these curves may be obtained as follows: (1) Let $YA = YB = a$, $YC = x$, $CD = y$, $YD = z$; then $z : x = x : a$, whence $z = \frac{x^2}{a}$. Also $z^2 = x^2 + y^2$; therefore the equation of AD is $x^4 = a^2(x^2 + y^2)$. (2) Let $YA = YB = a$, $YE = x$, $EF = y$, $YF = z$. Then $z : x = x : YD$, whence $YD = \frac{x^2}{z}$. Also

$$x : YD = YD : YC, \text{ whence } YC = \frac{x^4}{z^2} \div x = \frac{x^3}{z^2}.$$

But $YD : YC = YC : a$, and therefore

$$\frac{ax^2}{z} = \left(\frac{x^3}{z^2}\right)^2, \text{ or } z = \sqrt[3]{\frac{x^4}{a}}.$$

Also, $z^2 = x^2 + y^2$. Thus we get, as the equation of AF,

$$\sqrt[3]{\frac{x^8}{a^2}} = x^2 + y^2, \text{ or } x^8 = a^2(x^2 + y^2)^3.$$

(3) In the same way, it can be shown that the equation of AH is
$$x^{12} = a^2(x^2 + y^2)^5.$$
See Rabuel, p. 107.

GEOMETRY

I could give here several other ways of tracing and conceiving a series of curved lines, each curve more complex than any preceding one,[76] but I think the best way to group together all such curves and then classify them in order, is by recognizing the fact that all points of those curves which we may call "geometric," that is, those which admit of precise and exact measurement, must bear a definite relation[77] to all points of a straight line, and that this relation must be expressed by means of a single equation.[78] If this equation contains no term of higher degree than the rectangle of two unknown quantities, or the square of one, the curve belongs to the first and simplest class,[79] which contains only the circle, the parabola, the hyperbola, and the ellipse; but when the equation contains one or more terms of the third or fourth degree[80] in one or both of the two unknown quantities[81] (for it requires two unknown quantities to express the relation between two points) the curve belongs to the second class; and if the equation contains a term of the fifth or sixth degree in either or both of the unknown quantities the curve belongs to the third class, and so on indefinitely.

[76] "Qui seroient de plus en plus composées par degrez à l'infini." The French quotations in the footnotes show a few variants in style in different editions.

[77] That is, a relation exactly known, as, for example, that between two straight lines in distinction to that between a straight line and a curve, unless the length of the curve is known.

[78] It will be recognized at once that this statement contains the fundamental concept of analytic geometry.

[79] "Du premier & plus simple genre," an expression not now recognized. As now understood, the order or degree of a plane curve is the greatest number of points in which it can be cut by any arbitrary line, while the class is the greatest number of tangents that can be drawn to it from any arbitrary point in the plane.

[80] Grouped together because an equation of the fourth degree can always be transformed into one of the third degree.

[81] Thus Descartes includes such terms as x^2y, x^2y^2, . . as well as x^3, y^4 . . . . .

LIVRE SECOND. 319

du moins que des sections coniques, ny ce qui peut empescher, qu'on ne conçoiue la seconde, & la troisiesme, & toutes les autres, qu'on peut descrire, aussy bien que la premiere; ny par consequent qu'on ne les reçoiue toutes en mesme façon, pour seruir aux speculations de Geometrie.

Ie pourrois mettre icy plusieurs autres moyens pour tracer & conçeuoir des lignes courbes, qui seroient de plus en plus composées par degrés a l'infini. mais pour comprendre ensemble toutes celles, qui sont en la nature, & les distinguer par ordre en certains genres; ie ne sçache rien de meilleur que de dire que tous les poins, de celles qu'on peut nommer Geometriques, c'est a dire qui tombent sous quelque mesure precise & exacte, ont necessairement quelque rapport a tous les poins d'vne ligne droite, qui peut estre exprimé par quelque equation, en tous par vne mesme. Et que lorsque cete equation ne monte que iusques au rectangle de deux quantités indeterminées, oubien au quarré d'vne mesme, la ligne courbe est du premier & plus simple genre, dans lequel il n'y a que le cercle, la parabole, l'hyperbole, & l'Ellipse qui soient comprises. mais que lorsque l'equation monte iusques a la trois ou quatriesme dimension des deux, ou de l'vne des deux quantités indeterminées, car il en faut deux pour expliquer icy le rapport d'vn point a vn autre, elle est du second: & que lorsque l'equation monte iusques a la 5 ou sixiesme dimension, elle est du troisiesme; & ainsi des autres a l'infini.

La façon de distinguer toutes les lignes courbes en certains genres. Et de connoistre le rapport qu'ont tous leurs poins a ceux des lignes droites.

Comme si ie veux sçauoir de quel genre est la ligne E C, que i'imagine estre descrite par l'intersection de la reigle

320 LA GEOMETRIE.

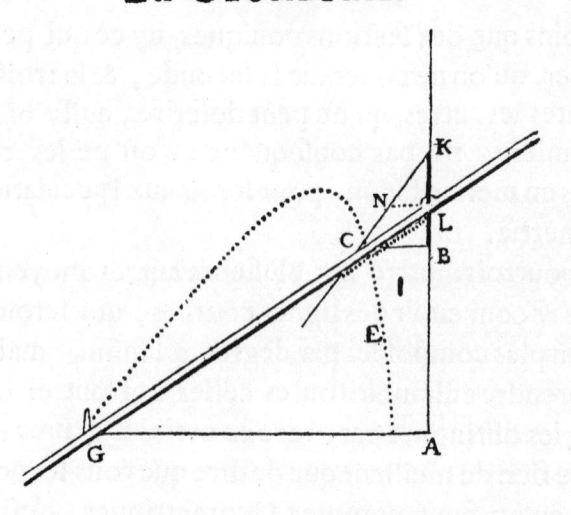

reigle G L, & du plan rectiligne C N K L, dont le costé
K N est indefiniement prolongé vers C , & qui estant
meu sur le plan de dessous en ligne droite, c'est a dire en
telle sorte que son diametre K L se trouue tousiours appliqué sur quelque endroit de la ligne B A prolongée de
part & d'autre, fait mouuoir circulairement cete reigle
G L autour du point G, a cause quelle luy est tellement
iointe quelle passe tousiours par le point L. Ie choisis
vne ligne droite, comme A B, pour rapporter a ses diuers
poins tous ceux de cete ligne courbe E C, & en cete ligne A B ie choisis vn point, comme A, pour commencer
par luy ce calcul. Ie dis que ie choisis & l'vn & l'autre, a
cause qu'il est libre de les prendre tels qu'on veult. car
encore qu'il y ait beaucoup de choix pour rendre l'equation plus courte, & plus aysée; toutefois en quelle façon
qu'on les prene, on peut tousiours faire que la ligne pa-
roisse de mesme genre, ainsi qu'il est aysé a demonstrer.

Aprés

SECOND BOOK

Suppose the curve EC to be described by the intersection of the ruler GL and the rectilinear plane figure CNKL, whose side KN is produced indefinitely in the direction of C, and which, being moved in the same plane in such a way that its side[82] KL always coincides with some part of the line BA (produced in both directions), imparts to the ruler GL a rotary motion about G (the ruler being hinged to the figure CNKL at L).[83] If I wish to find out to what class this curve belongs, I choose a straight line, as AB, to which to refer all its points, and in AB I choose a point A at which to begin the investigation.[84] I say "choose this and that," because we are free to choose what we will, for, while it is necessary to use care in the choice in order to make the equation as short and simple as possible, yet no matter what line I should take instead of AB the curve would always prove to be of the same class, a fact easily demonstrated.[85]

[82] "Diametre."

[83] The instrument thus consists of three parts, (1) a ruler AK of indefinite length, fixed in a plane; (2) a ruler GL, also of indefinite length, fastened to a pivot, G, in the same plane, but not on AK; and (3) a rectilinear figure BKC, the side KC being indefinitely long, to which the ruler GL is hinged at L, and which is made to slide along the ruler GL.

[84] That is, Descartes uses the point A as origin, and the line AB as axis of abscissas. He uses parallel ordinates, but does not draw the axis of ordinates.

[85] That is, the nature of a curve is not affected by a transformation of coördinates.

Then I take on the curve an arbitrary point, as C, at which we will suppose the instrument applied to describe the curve. Then I draw through C the line CB parallel to GA. Since CB and BA are unknown and indeterminate quantities, I shall call one of them y and the other x. To the relation between these quantities I must consider also the known quantities which determine the description of the curve, as GA, which I shall call a; KL, which I shall call b; and NL parallel to GA, which I shall call c. Then I say that as NL is to LK, or as c is to b, so CB, or y, is to BK, which is therefore equal to $\frac{b}{c}y$. Then BL is equal to $\frac{b}{c}y - b$, and AL is equal to $x + \frac{b}{c}y - b$. Moreover, as CB is to LB, that is, as y is to $\frac{b}{c}y - b$, so AG or a is to LA or $x + \frac{b}{c}y - b$. Multiplying the second by the third, we get $\frac{ab}{c}y - ab$ equal to

$$xy + \frac{b}{c}y^2 - by,$$

which is obtained by multiplying the first by the last. Therefore, the required equation is

$$y^2 = cy - \frac{cx}{b}y + ay - ac.$$

LIVRE SECOND.

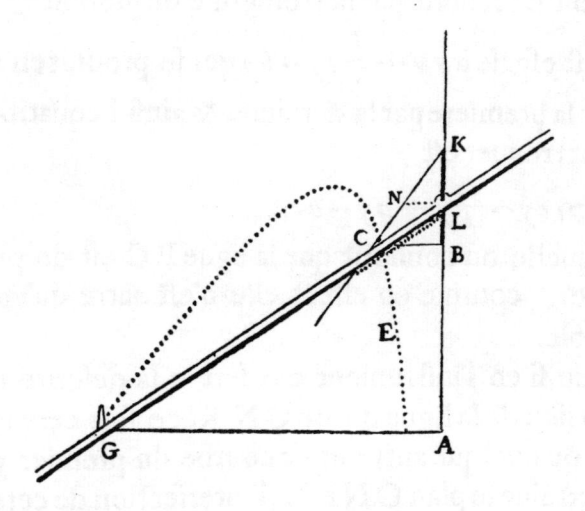

Aprés cela prenant vn point a difcretion dans la courbe, comme C, fur lequel ie fuppofe que l'inftrument qui fert a la defcrire eft appliqué, ie tire de ce point C la ligne CB parallele a GA, & pourceque CB & BA font deux quantités indeterminées & inconnuës, ie les nomme l'vne *y* & l'autre *x*. mais affin de trouuer le rapport de l'vne à l'autre ; ie confidere auffy les quantités connuës qui determinent la defcription de céte ligne courbe, comme GA que ie nomme *a*, KL que ie nomme *b*, & NL parallele a GA que ie nomme *c*. puis ie dis, comme NL eft à LK, ou *c* à *b*, ainfi CB, ou *y*, eft à BK, qui eft par confequent $\frac{b}{c}y$: & BL eft $\frac{b}{c}y - b$, & AL eft $x + \frac{b}{c}y - b$. de plus comme CB eft à LB, ou *y* à $\frac{b}{c}y - b$, ainfi *a*, ou GA, eft à LA, ou $x + \frac{b}{c}y - b$. de façon que mul-

tipliant

tipliant la seconde par la troisiesme on produit $\frac{ab}{c}y - ab$, qui est esgale à $xy + \frac{b}{c}yy - by$ qui se produit en multipliant la premiere par la derniere. & ainsi l'equation qu'il falloit trouuer est

$$yy \infty cy - \frac{cx}{b}y + ay - ac.$$

de laquelle on connoist que la ligne E C est du premier genre, comme en effect elle n'est autre qu'vne Hyperbole.

Que si en l'instrument qui sert a la descrire on fait qu'au lieu de la ligne droite C N K, ce soit cete Hyperbole, ou quelque autre ligne courbe du premier genre, qui termine le plan C N K L; l'intersection de cete ligne & de la reigle G L descrira, au lieu de l'Hyperbole E C, vne autre ligne courbe, qui sera du second genre. Comme si C N K est vn cercle, dont L soit le centre, on descrira la premiere Conchoide des anciens; & si c'est vne Parabole dont le diametre soit K B, on descrira la ligne courbe, que i'ay tantost dit estre la premiere, & la plus simple pour la question de Pappus, lorsqu'il n'y a que cinq lignes droites données par position. Mais si au lieu d'vne de ces lignes courbes du premier genre, c'en est vne du second, qui termine le plan C N K L, on en descrira par son moyen vne du troisiesme, ou si c'en est vne du troisiesme, on en descrira vne du quatriesme, & ainsi a l'infini. comme il est fort aysé a connoistre par le calcul. Et en quelque autre façon, qu'on imagine la description d'vne ligne courbe, pourvû qu'elle soit du nombre de celles que ie nomme Geometriques, on pourra tousiours trouuer

SECOND BOOK

From this equation we see that the curve EC belongs to the first class, it being, in fact, a hyperbola.[86]

If in the instrument used to describe the curve we substitute for the rectilinear figure CNK this hyperbola or some other curve of the first class lying in the plane CNKL, the intersection of this curve with the ruler GL will describe, instead of the hyperbola EC, another curve, which will be of the second class.

Thus, if CNK be a circle having its center at L, we shall describe the first conchoid of the ancients,[87] while if we use a parabola having KB as axis we shall describe the curve which, as I have already said, is the first and simplest of the curves required in the problem of Pappus, that is, the one which furnishes the solution when five lines are given in position.[88]

[86] Cf. Briot and Bouquet, *Elements of Analytical Geometry of Two Dimensions*, trans. by J. H. Boyd, New York, 1896, p. 143.
The two branches of the curve are determined by the position of the triangle CNKL with respect to the directrix AB. See Rabuel, p. 119.
Van Schooten, p. 171, gives the following construction and proof: Produce AG to D, making DG = EA. Since E is a point of the curve obtained when GL coincides with GA, L with A, and C with N, then EA = NL. Draw DF parallel to KC. Now let GCE be a hyperbola through E whose asymptotes are DF and FA. To prove that this hyperbola is the curve given by the instrument described above, produce BC to cut DF in I, and draw DH parallel to AF

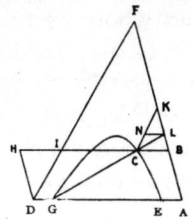

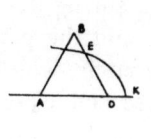

meeting BC in H. Then KL : LN = DH : HI. But DH = AB = x, so we may write $b : c = x :$ HI, whence HI $= \frac{cx}{b}$, IB $= a+c-\frac{cx}{b}$, IC $= a+c-\frac{cx}{b}-y$. But in any hyperbola IC.BC = DE.EA, whence we have $(a+c-\frac{cx}{b}-y)y = ac$, or $y^2 = cy - \frac{cxy}{b} + ay - ac$. But this is the equation obtained above, which is therefore the equation of a hyperbola whose asymptotes are AF and FD.

Van Schooten, p. 172, describes another similar instrument: Given a ruler AB pivoted at A, and another BD hinged to AB at B. Let AB rotate about A so that D moves along LK; then the curve generated by any point E of BE will be an ellipse whose semi-major axis is AB + BE and whose semi-minor axis is AB — BE.

[87] See notes 59 and 70.
[88] For a discussion of the elliptic, parabolic, and hyperbolic conchoids see Rabuel, pp. 123, 124.

GEOMETRY

If, instead of one of these curves of the first class, there be used a curve of the second class lying in the plane CNKL, a curve of the third class will be described; while if one of the third class be used, one of the fourth class will be obtained, and so on to infinity.[80] These statements are easily proved by actual calculation.

Thus, no matter how we conceive a curve to be described, provided it be one of those which I have called geometric, it is always possible to find in this manner an equation determining all its points. Now I shall place curves whose equations are of the fourth degree in the same class with those whose equations are of the third degree; and those whose equations are of the sixth degree[90] in the same class with those whose equations are of the fifth degree[91] and similarly for the rest. This classification is based upon the fact that there is a general rule for reducing to a cubic any equation of the fourth degree, and to an equation of the fifth degree[92] any equation of the sixth degree, so that the latter in each case need not be considered any more complex than the former.

It should be observed, however, with regard to the curves of any one class, that while many of them are equally complex so that they may be employed to determine the same points and construct the same problems, yet there are certain simpler ones whose usefulness is more limited. Thus, among the curves of the first class, besides the ellipse, the hyperbola, and the parabola, which are equally complex, there is also found the circle, which is evidently a simpler curve; while among those of the second class we find the common conchoid, which is described by means of the circle, and some others which, though less

---

[80] Rabuel (p. 125), illustrates this, substituting for the curve CNKL the semi-cubical parabola, and showing that the resulting equation is of the fifth degree, and therefore, according to Descartes, of the third class. Rabuel also gives (p. 119), a general method for finding the curve, no matter what figure is used for CNKL. Let $GA = a$, $KL = b$, $AB = x$, $CB = y$ and $KB = z$; then $LB = z - b$, and $AL = x + z - b$. Now $GA : AL = CB : BL$, or $a : x + z - b = y : z - b$, whence $z = \dfrac{xy - by + ab}{a - y}$.

This value of z is independent of the nature of the figure CNKL. But given any figure CNKL it is possible to obtain a second value for z from the nature of the curve. Equating these values of z we get the equation of the curve.

[90] "Celles dont l'équation monte au quarré de cube."
[91] "Celles dont elle ne monte qu'au sursolide."
[92] "Au sursolide."

Livre Second.

uer vne equation pour déterminer tous ſes poins en cete ſorte.

Au reſte ie mets les lignes courbes qui font monter cete equation iuſques au quarré de quarré, au meſme genre que celles qui ne la font monter que iuſques au cube. & celles dont l'equation monte au quarré de cube, au meſme genre que celles dont elle ne monte qu'au ſurſolide. & ainſi des autres. Dont la raiſon eſt, qu'il y a reigle generale pour reduire au cube toutes les difficultés qui vont au quarré de quarré, & au ſurſolide toutes celles qui vont au quarré de cube, de façon qu'on ne les doit point eſtimer plus compoſées.

Mais il eſt a remarquer qu'entre les lignes de chaſque genre, encore que la plus part ſoient eſgalement compoſées, en ſorte qu'elles peuuent ſeruir a déterminer les meſmes poins, & conſtruire les meſmes problesmes, il y en a toutefois auſſy quelques vnes, qui ſont plus ſimples, & qui n'ont pas tant d'eſtendue en leur puiſſance. comme entre celles du premier genre outre l'Ellipſe l'Hyperbole & la Parabole qui ſont eſgalement compoſées, le cercle y eſt auſſy compris, qui manifeſtement eſt plus ſimple. & entre celles du ſecond genre il y a la Conchoide vulgaire, qui a ſon origine du cercle; & il y en a encore quelques autres, qui bien qu'elles n'ayent pas tant d'eſtendue que la plus part de celles du meſme genre, ne peuuent toutefois eſtre miſes dans le premier.

Or aprés auoir ainſi reduit toutes les lignes courbes a certains genres, il m'eſt ayſé de pourſuiure en la demonſtration de la reſponſe, que i'ay tantoſt faite a la queſtion de Pappus. Car premierement ayant fait voir cy deſſus,

Suite de l'explication de la queſtion de Pappus miſe au liure precedent

324 　　　La Geometrie.

deſſus , que lorſqu'il n'y a que trois ou 4 lignes droites données, l'equation qui ſert a determiner les poins cherchés, ne monte que iuſques au quarré; il eſt euident, que la ligne courbe ou ſe trouuent ces poins, eſt neceſſairement quelqu'vne de celles du premier genre : a cauſe que cete meſme equation explique le rapport, qu'ont tous les poins des lignes du premier genre a ceux d'vne ligne droite. Et que lorſqu'il n'y a point plus de 8 lignes droites données , cete equation ne monte que iuſques au quarré de quarré tout au plus , & que par conſequent la ligne cherchée ne peut eſtre que du ſecond genre, ou au deſſous. Et que lorſqu'il n'y a point plus de 12 lignes données , l'equation ne monte que iuſques au quarré de cube, & que par conſequent la ligne cherchée n'eſt que du troiſieſme genre, ou au deſſous. & ainſi des autres. Et meſme a cauſe que la poſition des lignes droites données peut varier en toutes ſortes, & par conſequent faire chãger tant les quantités connuës, que les ſignes + & — de l'equation, en toutes les façons imaginables ; il eſt euident qu'il n'y a aucune ligne courbe du premier genre, qui ne ſoit vtile a cete queſtion, quand elle eſt propoſée en 4 lignes droites; ny aucune du ſecond qui n y ſoit vtile, quand elle eſt propoſée en huit ; ny du troiſieſme, quand elle eſt propoſée en douze: & ainſi des autres. En ſorte qu'il n'y a pas vne ligne courbe qui tombe ſous le calcul & puiſſe eſtre receüe en Geometrie , qui n'y ſoit vtile pour quelque nombre de lignes.

Solution de cete queſtion quandelle n'eſt propoſée qu'en 3 ou 4 lignes.

Mais il faut icy plus particulierement que ie determine, & donne la façon de trouuer la ligne cherchée ; qui ſert en chaſque cas, lorſqu'il ny a que 3 ou 4 lignes droites

complicated[93] than many curves of the same class, cannot be placed in the first class.[94]

Having now made a general classification of curves, it is easy for me to demonstrate the solution which I have already given of the problem of Pappus. For, first, I have shown that when there are only three or four lines the equation which serves to determine the required points[95] is of the second degree. It follows that the curve containing these points must belong to the first class, since such an equation expresses the relation between all points of curves of Class I and all points of a fixed straight line. When there are not more than eight given lines the equation is at most a biquadratic, and therefore the resulting curve belongs to Class II or Class I. When there are not more than twelve given lines, the equation is of the sixth degree or lower, and therefore the required curve belongs to Class III or a lower class, and so on for other cases.

Now, since each of the given lines may have any conceivable position, and since any change in the position of a line produces a corresponding change in the values of the known quantities as well as in the signs $+$ and $-$ of the equation, it is clear that there is no curve of Class I that may not furnish a solution of this problem when it relates to four lines, and that there is no curve of Class II that may not furnish a solution when the problem relates to eight lines, none of Class III when it relates to twelve lines, etc. It follows that there is no geometric curve whose equation can be obtained that may not be used for some number of lines.[96]

It is now necessary to determine more particularly and to give the method of finding the curve required in each case, for only three or

[93] "Pas tant d'étenduë." Cf. Rabuel, p. 113. "Pas tant d'étendue en leur puissance."

[94] Various methods of tracing curves were used by writers of the seventeenth century. Among these there were not only the usual method of plotting a curve from its equation and that of using strings, pegs, etc., as in the popular construction of the ellipse, but also the method of using jointed rulers and that of using one curve from which to derive another, as for example the usual method of describing the cissoid. Cf. Rabuel, p. 138.

[95] That is, the equation of the required locus.

[96] "En sorte qu'il n'y a pas une ligne courbe qui tombe sous le calcul & puisse être receuë en Geometrie, qui n'y soit utile pour quelque nombre de lignes."

four given lines. This investigation will show that Class I contains only the circle and the three conic sections.

Consider again the four lines AB, AD, EF, and GH, given before, and let it be required to find the locus generated by a point C, such that, if four lines CB, CD, CF, and CH be drawn through it making given angles with the given lines, the product of CB and CF is equal to the product of CD and CH. This is equivalent to saying that if

$$CB = y,$$
$$CD = \frac{czy + bcx}{z^2},$$
$$CF = \frac{ezy + dek + dex}{z^2},$$

and
$$CH = \frac{gzy + fgl - fgx}{z^2}.$$

then the equation is

$$y^2 = \frac{(cfglz - dckz^2)y - (dez^2 + cfgz - bcgz)xy + bcfglx - bcfgx^2}{ez^3 - cgz^2}.$$

Livre Second.

tes données, & on verra par mesme moyen que le premier genre des lignes courbes n'en contient aucunes autres, que les trois sections coniques, & le cercle.

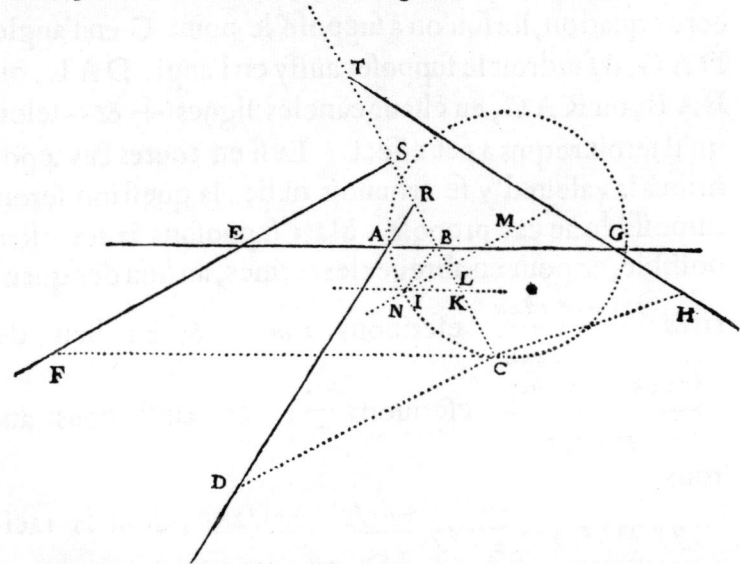

Reprenons les 4 lignes AB, AD, EF, & GH données cy dessus, & qu'il faille trouuer vne autre ligne, en laquelle il se rencontre vne infinité de poins tels que C, duquel ayant tiré les 4 lignes CB, CD, CF, & CH, a angles donnés, sur les données, CB multipliée par CF, produist une somme esgale a CD, multipliée par CH. c'est a dire ayant fait $CB \infty y$, $CD \infty \frac{czy + bcx}{zz}$

$CF \infty \frac{ezy + dek + dex}{zz}$ & $CH \infty \frac{gzy + fgl - fgx}{zz}$ l'equatiõ est

$$yy \infty \begin{Bmatrix} -dekzz \\ +cfglz \end{Bmatrix} y \begin{Bmatrix} -dezzx \\ -cfgzx \\ +bcgzx \end{Bmatrix} y \begin{Bmatrix} +bcfglx \\ -bcfgxx \end{Bmatrix}$$

$ezzz - cgzz$.

LA GEOMETRIE.

au moins en suppoſant ez plus grand que eg. car s'il eſtoit moindre, il faudroit changer tous les ſignes $+$ & $-$. Et ſi la quantité y ſe trouuoit nulle, ou moindre que rien en cete equation, lorſqu'on a ſuppoſé le point C en l'angle D A G, il faudroit le ſuppoſer auſſy en l'angle D A E, ou E A R, ou R A G, en changeant les lignes $+$ & $-$ ſelon qu'il ſeroit requis a cet effect. Et ſi en toutes ces 4 poſitions la valeur d'y ſe trouuoit nulle, la queſtion ſeroit impoſſible au cas propoſé. Mais ſuppoſons la icy eſtre poſſible, & pour en abreger les termes, au lieu des quantités $\dfrac{cfglz - dekzz}{ez - cgzz}$ eſcriuons $2m$, & au lieu de $\dfrac{dezz + cfgz - bcgz}{ez - cgzz}$ eſcriuons $\dfrac{2n}{z}$; & ainſi nous aurons

$$yy \infty 2my - \dfrac{2n}{z}xy \dfrac{+ bcfglx - bcfgxx}{ez - cgzz}, $$ dont la racine eſt

$$y \infty m - \dfrac{nx}{z} + \sqrt{mm - \dfrac{2mnx}{z} + \dfrac{nnxx}{zz} + \dfrac{bcfglx - bcfgxx}{ez - cgzz}}.$$

& derechef pour abreger, au lieu de $-\dfrac{2mn}{z} + \dfrac{bcfgl}{ez - cgzz}$ eſcriuons o, & au lieu de $\dfrac{nn}{zz} - \dfrac{bcfg}{e - cgzz}$ eſcriuons $\dfrac{p}{m}$. car ces quantités eſtant toutes données, nous les pouuons nommer comme il nous plaiſt. & ainſi nous auons

$$y \infty m - \dfrac{n}{z}x + \sqrt{mm + ox - \dfrac{p}{m}xx},$$ qui doit eſtre la longeur de la ligne B C, en laiſſant A B, ou x indeterminée.

SECOND BOOK

It is here assumed that ez is greater than cg; otherwise the signs $+$ and $-$ must all be changed.[97] If y is zero or less than nothing in this equation,[98] the point C being supposed to lie within the angle DAG, then C must be supposed to lie within one of the angles DAE, EAR, or RAG, and the signs must be changed to produce this result. If for each of these four positions y is equal to zero, then the problem admits of no solution in the case proposed.

Let us suppose the solution possible, and to shorten the work let us write $2m$ instead of $\dfrac{cflgz - dekz^2}{ez^3 - cgz^2}$, and $\dfrac{2n}{z}$ instead of $\dfrac{dez^2 + cfgz - bcga}{ez^3 - cgz^2}$. Then we have

$$y^2 = 2my - \frac{2n}{z}xy + \frac{bcfglx - bcfgx^2}{ez^3 - cgz^2},$$

of which the root[99] is

$$y = m - \frac{nx}{z} + \sqrt{m^2 - \frac{2mnx}{z} + \frac{n^2x^2}{z^2} + \frac{bcfglx - bcfgx^2}{ez^3 - cgz^2}}.$$

Again, for the sake of brevity, put $-\dfrac{2mn}{z} + \dfrac{bcfgl}{ez^3 - cgz^2}$ equal to o, and $\dfrac{n^2}{z^2} - \dfrac{bcfg}{ez^3 - cgz^2}$ equal to $\dfrac{p}{m}$; for these quantities being given, we can represent them in any way we please.[100] Then we have

$$y = m - \frac{n}{z}x + \sqrt{m^2 + ox + \frac{p}{m}x^2}.$$

This must give the length of the line BC, leaving AB or x undeter-

---

[97] When ez is greater than cg, then $ez^3 - cgz^2$ is positive and its square root is therefore real.

[98] Descartes uses "moindre que rien" for "negative."

[99] Descartes mentions here only one root; of course the other root would furnish a second locus.

[100] In a letter to Mersenne (Cousin, Vol. VII, p. 157), Descartes says: "In regard to the problem of Pappus, I have given only the construction and demonstration without putting in all the analysis; . . . in other words, I have given the construction as architects build structures, giving the specifications and leaving the actual manual labor to carpenters and masons."

mined. Since the problem relates to only three or four lines, it is obvious that we shall always have such terms, although some of them may vanish and the signs may all vary.[101]

After this, I make KI equal and parallel to BA, and cutting off on BC a segment BK equal to m (since the expression for BC contains $+ m$; if this were $- m$, I should have drawn IK on the other side of AB,[102] while if m were zero, I would not have drawn IK at all). Then I draw IL so that IK : KL $= z : n$; that is, so that if IK is equal to x, KL is equal to $\frac{n}{z} x$. In the same way I know the ratio of KL to IL, which I may call $n : a$, so that if KL is equal to $\frac{n}{z} x$, IL is equal to $\frac{a}{z} x$. I take the point K between L and C, since the equation contains $- \frac{n}{z} x$; if this were $+ \frac{n}{z} x$, I should take L between K and C;[103] while if $\frac{n}{z} x$ were equal to zero, I should not draw IL.

This being done, there remains the expression

$$LC = \sqrt{m^2 + ox + \frac{p}{m} x^2},$$

from which to construct LC. It is clear that if this were zero the point

---

[101] Having obtained the value of BC algebraically, Descartes now proceeds to construct the length BC geometrically, term by term. He considers BC equal to BK + KL + LC, which is equal to BK − LK + LC which in turn is equal to

$$m - \frac{n}{z} x + \sqrt{m^2 + ox + \frac{p}{m} x^2}.$$

[102] That is, take I on CB produced.
[103] That is, on KB produced. C is not yet determined.

LIVRE SECOND. 327

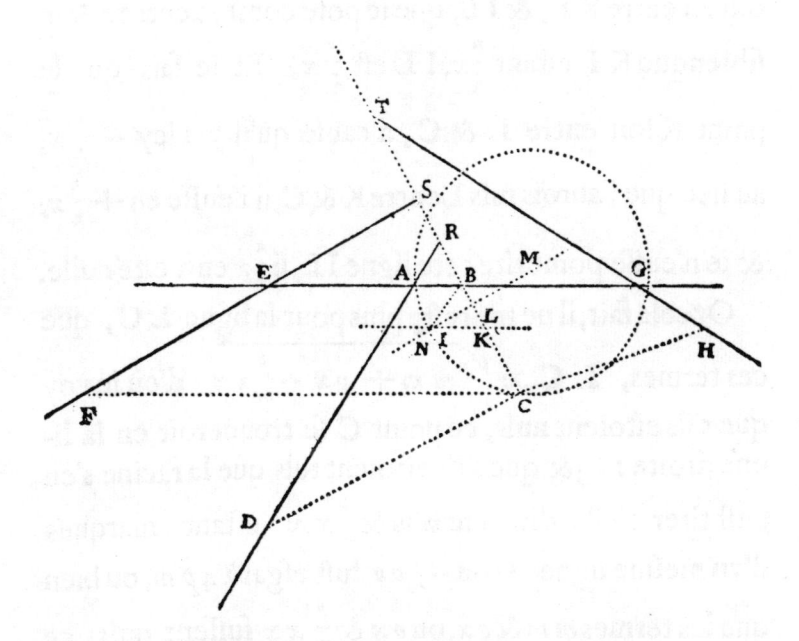

minée. Et il est euident que la question n'estant proposée qu'en trois ou quatre lignes, on peut tousiours auoir de tels termes. excepté que quelques vns d'eux peuuent estre nuls, & que les signes $+$ & $-$ peuuent diuersement estre changés.

Aprés cela ie fais K I esgale & parallele à B A, en sorte qu'elle couppe de B C la partie B K esgale à m ; à cause qu'il y a icy $+m$; & ie l'aurois adioustée en tirant cete ligne I K de l'autre costé, s'il y auoit eu $-m$; & ie ne l'aurois point du tout tirée, si la quantité m eust esté nulle. Puis ie tire aussy I L, en sorte que la ligne I K est à K L, comme Z est à n. c'est a dire que I K estant x, K L est $\frac{n}{z}x$. Et par mesme moyen ie connois aussy la proportion

qui

328   La Geometrie.

qui est entre K L, & I L, que ie pose comme entre n & a: si bien que K L estant $\frac{n}{z}x$, I L est $\frac{a}{z}x$; Et ie fais que le point K soit entre L & C, a cause qu'il y a icy $-\frac{n}{z}x$; au lieu que i'aurois mis L entre K & C, si i'eusse eu $+\frac{n}{z}x$; & ie n'eusse point tiré cete ligne I L, si $\frac{n}{z}x$ eust esté nulle.

Or cela fait, il ne me reste plus pour la ligne L C, que ces termes, L C $\infty \sqrt{mm + ox - \frac{p}{m}xx}$. d'où ie voy que s'ils estoient nuls, ce point C se trouueroit en la ligne droite I L; & que s'ils estoient tels que la racine s'en pust tirer, c'est a dire que mm & $\frac{p}{m}xx$ estant marqués d'vn mesme signe $+$ ou $-$, oo fust esgal à $4pm$, ou bien que les termes mm & ox, ou ox & $\frac{p}{m}xx$ fussent nuls, ce point C se trouueroit en vne autre ligne droite qui ne seroit pas plus malaysée a trouuer qu' I L. Mais lorsque cela n'est pas, ce point C est tousiours en l'une des trois sections coniques, ou en vn cercle, dont l'vn des diametres est en la ligne I L, & la ligne L C est l'vne de celles qui s'appliquent par ordre à ce diametre; ou au contraire L C est parallele au diametre, auquel celle qui est en la ligne I L est appliquée par ordre. A sçavoir si le terme $\frac{p}{m}xx$, est nul cete section conique est vne Parabole; & s'il est marqué du signe $+$, c'est vne Hyperbole; & enfin s'il est marqué du signe $-$ c'est vne Ellipse. Excepté seulement si la quantité aam est esgale à pzz & que l'angle I L C soit droit: auquel cas on à vn cercle au lieu d'vne

66

SECOND BOOK

C would lie on the straight line IL;[104] that if it were a perfect square, that is if m^2 and $\frac{p}{m} x^2$ were both $+$[105] and o^2 was equal to $4pm$, or if m^2 and ox, or ox and $\frac{p}{m} x^2$, were zero, then the point C would lie on another straight line, whose position could be determined as easily as that of IL.[106]

If none of these exceptional cases occur,[107] the point C always lies on one of the three conic sections, or on a circle having its diameter in the line IL and having LC a line applied in order to this diameter,[108] or, on the other hand, having LC parallel to a diameter and IL applied in order.

In particular, if the term $\frac{p}{m} x^2$ is zero, the conic section is a parabola; if it is preceded by a plus sign, it is a hyperbola; and, finally, if it is preceded by a minus sign, it is an ellipse.[109] An exception occurs when

[104] The equation of IL is $y = m - \frac{n}{z} x$.

[105] There is considerable diversity in the treatment of this sentence in different editions. The Latin edition of 1683 has "Hoc est, ut, mm & $\frac{p}{m} xx$ signo $+$ notalis." The French edition, Paris, 1705, has "C'est à dire que mm et $\frac{p}{m} xx$ étant marquez d'un même signe $+$ ou $-$." Rabuel gives "C'est a dire que mm and $\frac{p}{m} xx$ étant marquez d'un même signe $+$." He adds the following note: "Il y a dans les Editions Françoises de Leyde, 1637, et de Paris, 1705, 'un meme signe $+$ ou $-$', ce qui est une faute d'impression." The French edition, Paris, 1886, has "Etant marqués d'un meme signe $+$ ou $-$."

[106] Note the difficulty in generalization experienced even by Descartes. Cf. Briot and Bouquet, p. 72.

[107] "Mais lorsque cela n'est pas." In each case the equation giving the value of y is linear in x and y, and therefore represents a straight line. If the quantity under the radical sign and $\frac{n}{z} x$ are both zero, the line is parallel to AB. If the quantity under the radical sign and m are both zero, C lies in AL.

[108] "An ordinate." The equivalent of "ordination application" was used in the 16th century translation of Apollonius. Hutton's Mathematical Dictionary, 1796, gives "applicate." "Ordinate applicate," was also used.

[109] Cf. Briot and Bouquet, p. 143.

GEOMETRY

a^2m is equal to pz^2 and the angle ILC is a right angle,[110] in which case we get a circle instead of an ellipse.[111]

If the conic section is a parabola, its latus rectum is equal to $\dfrac{oz}{a}$ and its axis always lies along the line IL.[112] To find its vertex, N, make IN equal to $\dfrac{am^2}{oz}$, so that the point I lies between L and N if m^2 is positive and ox is positive; and L lies between I and N if m^2 is positive and ox negative; and N lies between I and L if m^2 is negative and ox positive. It is impossible that m^2 should be negative when the terms are arranged as above. Finally, if m^2 is equal to zero, the points N and I must coincide. It is thus easy to determine this parabola, according to the first problem of the first book of Apollonius[113].

If, however, the required locus is a circle, an ellipse, or a hyperbola,[114] the point M, the center of the figure, must first be found. This

[110] Rabuel (p. 167) adds "If $a^2m = pz^2$ or if $m = p$ the hyperbola is equilateral."

[111] In this case the triangle ILK is a right triangle, whence $\overline{IK}^2 = \overline{LK}^2 + \overline{IC}^2$; but by hypothesis IL : IK : KL $= a : z : n$; then $a^2 + n^2 = z^2$. Now the equation of the curve is
$$y = m - \frac{n}{z} + x\sqrt{m^2 + oz - \frac{p}{m}x^2},$$
and therefore the term in x^2 is
$$\left(\frac{n^2}{z^2} + \frac{p}{m}\right)x^2;$$
and if $a^2m = pz^2$, then $\dfrac{p}{m} = \dfrac{a^2}{z^2}$, and this term in x^2 becomes $\dfrac{a^2 + n^2}{z^2}x^2 = x^2$.

Therefore, the coefficients of x^2 and y^2 are unity and the locus is a circle.

[112] This may be seen as follows: From the figure, and by the nature of the parabola $\overline{LC}^2 = LN \cdot p$ and $LN = IL + IN$. Let $IN = \phi$; then since $IL = \dfrac{a}{z}x$, we have $LN = \dfrac{a}{z}x + \phi$ and $LC = y - m + \dfrac{n}{z}x$; whence $(y - m + \dfrac{n}{z}x)^2 = (\dfrac{a}{z}x + \phi)p$. But $(y - m + \dfrac{n}{z}x)^2 = m^2 + ox$ from the equation of the parabola; therefore $\dfrac{a}{z}xp + \phi p = m^2 + ox$. Equating coefficients, we have $\dfrac{a}{z}p = o$; $p = \dfrac{oz}{a}$; $\phi p = m^2$; $\phi\dfrac{oz}{a} = m^2$; $\phi = \dfrac{am^2}{oz}$.

[113] *Apollonii Pergaeii Quae Graece exstant* edidit I. L. Heiberg, Leipzig, 1891. Vol. I, p. 159, Liber I, Prop. LII. Hereafter referred to as Apollonius. This may be freely translated as follows: To describe in a plane a parabola, having given the parameter, the vertex, and the angle between an ordinate and the corresponding abscissa.

[114] Central conics are thus grouped together by Descartes, the circle being treated as a special form of the ellipse, but being mentioned separately in all cases.

LIVRE SECOND. 329

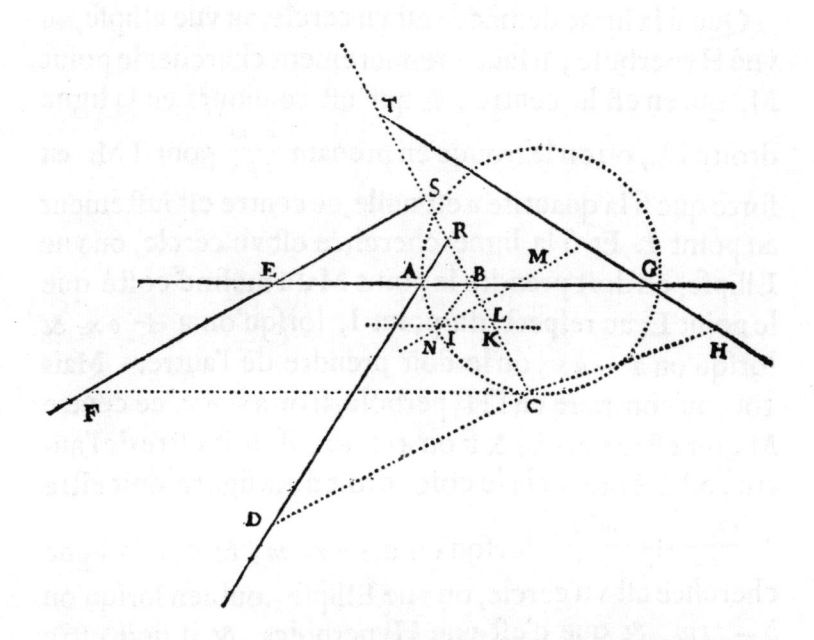

d'vne Ellipſe. Que ſi cete ſection eſt vne Parabole, ſon coſté droit eſt eſgal à $\frac{oz}{a}$, & ſon diametre eſt touſiours en la ligne IL. & pour trouuer le point N, qui en eſt le ſommet, il faut faire IN eſgale à $\frac{amm}{oz}$; & que le point I ſoit entre L & N, ſi les termes ſont $+ mm + ox$; oubien que le point L ſoit entre I & N, s'ils ſont $+ mm - ox$; oubien il faudroit qu'N fuſt entre I & L, s'il y auoit $- mm + ox$. Mais il ne peut iamais y auoir $- mm$, en la façon que les termes ont icy eſté poſés. Et enfin le point N ſeroit le meſme que le point I ſi la quantité mm eſtoit nulle. Au moyen dequoy il eſt ayſé de trouuer cete Parabole par le 1er. Probleſme du 1er. liure d'Apollonius.

Tt

Que

330   LA GEOMETRIE.

Que si la ligne demandée est vn cercle, ou vne ellipse, ou vne Hyperbole, il faut premierement chercher le point M, qui en est le centre, & qui est tousiours en la ligne droite I L, ou on le trouue en prenant $\frac{aom}{2pz}$ pour I M. en sorte que si la quantité o est nulle, ce centre est iustement au point I. Et si la ligne cherchée est vn cercle, ou vne Ellipse; on doit prendre le point M du mesme costé que le point L, au respect du point I, lorsqu'on a $+ox$; & lorsqu'on à $--ox$, on le doit prendre de l'autre. Mais tout au contraire en l'Hyperbole, si on a $--ox$, ce centre M doit estre vers L; & si on a $+ox$, il doit estre de l'autre costé. Aprés cela le costé droit de la figure doit estre

$$\sqrt{\frac{oozz}{aa} + \frac{4mpzz}{aa}}$$ lorsqu'on a $+mm$, & que la ligne cherchée est vn cercle, ou vne Ellipse; oubien lorsqu'on à $--mm$, & que c'est vne Hyperbole. & il doit estre

$$\sqrt{\frac{oozz}{aa} - \frac{4mpzz}{aa}}$$ si la ligne cherchée estant vn cercle, ou vne Ellipse, on à $--mm$; oubien si estant vne Hyperbole & la quantité oo estant plus grande que $4mp$, on à $+mm$. Que si la quantité mm est nulle, ce costé droit est $\frac{oz}{a}$, & si ox est nulle, il est $\sqrt{\frac{4mpzz}{aa}}$. Puis pour le costé trauersant, il faut trouuer vne ligne, qui soit a ce costé droit, cõme aam est à pzz, à sçauoir si ce costé droit est

$$\sqrt{\frac{oozz}{aa} + \frac{4mpzz}{aa}}$$ le trauersant est $$\sqrt{\frac{aaoomm}{ppzz} + \frac{4aam}{pzz}}.$$

Et en tous ces cas le diametre de la section est en la ligne I M, & L C est l'vne de celles qui luy est appliquée par ordre. Sibienque faisant M N esgale a la moitié du costé

trauer-

will always lie on the line IL and may be found by taking IM equal to $\frac{aom}{2pz}$.[115] If o is equal to zero M coincides with I. If the required locus is a circle or an ellipse, M and L must lie on the same side of I when the term ox is positive and on opposite sides when ox is negative. On the other hand, in the case of the hyperbola, M and L lie on the same side of I when ox is negative and on opposite sides when ox is positive.

The latus rectum of the figure must be

$$\sqrt{\frac{o^2z^2}{a^2} + \frac{4mpz^2}{a^2}}$$

if m^2 is positive and the locus is a circle or an ellipse, or if m^2 is negative and the locus is a hyperbola. It must be

$$\sqrt{\frac{o^2z^2}{a^2} - \frac{4mpz^2}{a^2}}$$

if the required locus is a circle or an ellipse and m^2 is negative, or if it is an hyperbola and o^2 is greater than $4mp$, m^2 being positive.

But if m^2 is equal to zero, the latus rectum is $\frac{oz}{a}$; and if oz is equal to zero[116], it is

$$\sqrt{\frac{4mpz^2}{a^2}}.$$

For the corresponding diameter a line must be found which bears the ratio $\frac{a^2m}{pz^2}$ to the latus rectum; that is, if the latus rectum is

$$\sqrt{\frac{o^2z^2}{a^2} + \frac{4mpz^2}{a^2}}$$

the diameter is

$$\sqrt{\frac{a^2o^2m^2}{p^2z^2} + \frac{4a^2m^3}{pz^2}}.$$

In every case, the diameter of the section lies along IM, and LC is one of its lines applied in order.[117] It is thus evident that, by making MN equal to half the diameter and taking N and L on the same side of M,

---

[115] Cf. Briot and Bouquet, p. 156.
[116] Some editions give, incorrectly, ox for oz.
[117] See note 108.

GEOMETRY

the point N will be the vertex of this diameter.[118] It is then a simple matter to determine the curve, according to the second and third problems of the first book of Apollonius.[119]

When the locus is a hyperbola[120] and m^2 is positive, if o^2 is equal to zero or less than $4pm$ we must draw the line MOP from the center M parallel to LC, and draw CP parallel to LM, and take MO equal to

$$\sqrt{m^2 - \frac{o^2 m}{4p}};$$

while if ox is equal to zero, MO must be taken equal to m. Then considering O as the vertex of this hyperbola, the diameter being OP and the line applied in order being CP, its latus rectum is

$$\sqrt{\frac{4a^4 m^4}{p^2 z^4} - \frac{a^4 o^2 m^3}{p^3 z^4}}$$

and its diameter[121] is

$$\sqrt{4m^2 - \frac{o^2 m}{p}}.$$

[118] If the equation contains $-m^2$ and $+nx$, then n^2 must be greater than $4mp$, otherwise the problem is impossible.

[119] Cf. Apollonius, Vol. I, p. 173, Lib. I, Prop. LV: To describe a hyperbola, given the axis, the vertex, the parameter, and the angle between the axes. Also see Prop. LVI: To describe an ellipse, etc.

[120] Cf. Letters of Descartes, Cousin, Vol. VIII, p. 142.

[121] "Côté traversant."

LIVRE SECOND.

trauerſant & le prenant du meſme coſté du point M, qu'eſt le point L, on a le point N pour le ſommet de ce diametre. en ſuite dequoy il eſt ayſé de trouuer la ſection par le ſecond & 3 prob. du 1er. liu. d'Apollonius.

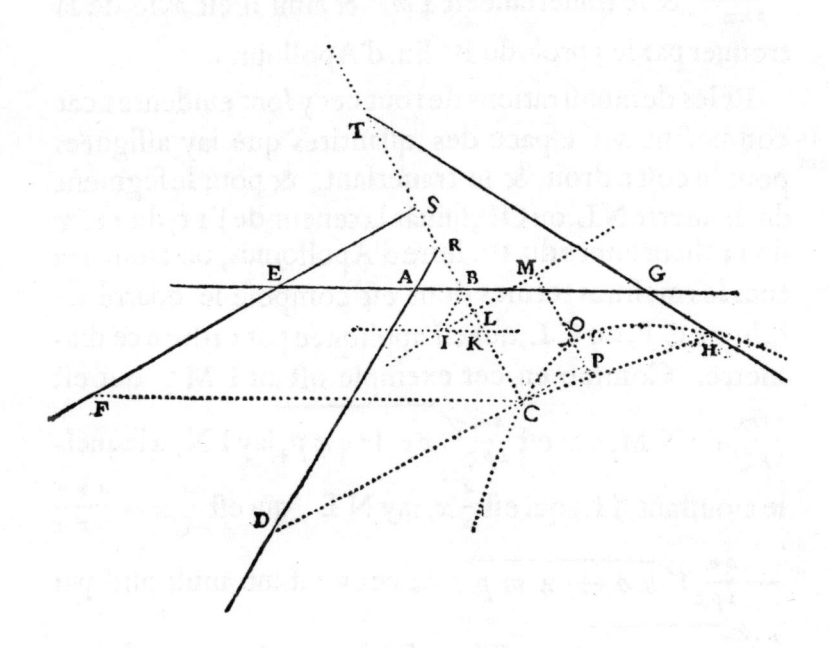

Mais quand cete ſection eſtant vne Hyperbole, on à $+mm$; & que la quantité oo eſt nulle ou plus petite que $4pm$, on doit tirer du centre M la ligne M O P parallele a L C, & C P parallele à L M: & faire M O eſgale a $\sqrt{mm - \frac{oom}{4p}}$; oubien la faire eſgale à m ſi la quantité ox eſt nulle. Puis conſiderer le point O, côme le ſommet de cete Hyperbole; dont le diametre eſt O P, & C P la

Tt 2   ligne

332 LA GEOMETRIE.

ligne qui luy est appliquée par ordre, & son costé droit est
$\sqrt{\frac{4 d^4 m^4}{p p z^4} - \frac{a^4 oo m^3}{p^3 z^4}}$ & son costé trauersāt est $\sqrt{4 m m - \frac{oo m}{p}}$.
Excepté quand ox est nulle. car alors le costé droit est
$\frac{2 a a m m}{p z z}$, & le trauersant est $2m$. & ainsi il est aysé de la
trouuer par le 3 prob. du 1er. liu. d'Apollonius.

Demonstration de tout ce qui vient d'estre expliqué.

Et les demonstrations de tout cecy sont euidentes. car composant vn espace des quantités que iay assignées pour le costé droit, & le trauersant, & pour le segment du diametre NL, ou OP, suiuāt la teneur de l'11, du 12, & du 13 theoresmes du 1er. liure d'Apollonius, on trouuera tous les mesmes termes dont est composé le quarré de la ligne CP, ou CL, qui est appliquée par ordre a ce diametre. Comme en cet exemple ostant I M, qui est
$\frac{aom}{2 p z}$, de NM, qui est $\frac{am}{2 p z}\sqrt{oo + 4 m p}$, iay IN, à laquelle aioustant IL, qui est $\frac{a}{z}x$, iay NL, qui est $\frac{a}{z}x - \frac{aom}{2 p z}$
$+ \frac{a m}{2 p z}\sqrt{oo + 4 m p}$, & cecy estant multiplié par
$\frac{z}{a}\sqrt{oo + 4 m p}$, qui est le costé droit de la figure, il vient
$x\sqrt{oo + 4 m p} - \frac{om}{2 p}\sqrt{oo + 4 m p} + \frac{m oo}{2 p} + 2 m m$
pour le rectangle. duquel il faut oster vn espace qui soit au quarré de NL comme le costé droit est au trauersant.
& ce quarré de NL est $\frac{aa}{zz}xx - \frac{aaom}{pzz}x$
$+ \frac{aam}{pzz}x\sqrt{oo + 4 m p} + \frac{a a o o m m}{2 p p z z} + \frac{a a m}{p z z}$
$- \frac{a a o m m}{2 p p z z}$.

SECOND BOOK

An exception must be made when ox is equal to zero, in which case the latus rectum is $\dfrac{2a^2m^2}{pz^2}$ and the diameter is $2m$. From these data the curve can be determined in accordance with the third problem of the first book of Apollonius.[122]

The demonstrations of the above statements are all very simple, for, forming the product[123] of the quantities given above as latus rectum, diameter, and segment of the diameter NL or OP, by the methods of Theorems 11, 12, and 13 of the first book of Apollonius, the result will contain exactly the terms which express the square of the line CP or CL, which is an ordinate of this diameter.

In this case take IM or $\dfrac{aom}{2pz}$ from NM or from its equal

$$\dfrac{am}{2pz}\sqrt{o^2+4mp}.$$

To the remainder IN add IL or $\dfrac{a}{z}x$, and we have

$$NL = \dfrac{a}{z}x - \dfrac{aom}{2pz} + \dfrac{am}{2pz}\sqrt{o^2+4mp}.$$

Multiplying this by

$$\dfrac{z}{a}\sqrt{o^2+4mp},$$

the latus rectum of the curve, we get

$$x\sqrt{o^2+4mp} - \dfrac{om}{2p}\sqrt{o^2+4mp} + \dfrac{mo^2}{2p} + 2m^2$$

for the rectangle, from which is to be subtracted a rectangle which is to the square of NL as the latus rectum is to the diameter. The square of NL is

$$\dfrac{a^2}{z^2}x^2 - \dfrac{a^2om}{pz^2}x + \dfrac{a^2m}{pz^2}x\sqrt{o^2+4mp} + \dfrac{a^2o^2m^2}{2p^2z^2} + \dfrac{a^2m^3}{pz^2} - \dfrac{a^2om^2}{2p^2z^2}\sqrt{o^2+4mp}.$$

---
[122] See note 113.
[123] "Composant un espace."

75

Divide this by a^2m and multiply the quotient by pz^2, since these terms express the ratio between the diameter and the latus rectum. The result is

$$\frac{p}{m}x^2 - ox + x\sqrt{o^2+4mp} + \frac{o^2m}{2p} - \frac{om}{2p}\sqrt{o^2+4mp} + m^2.$$

This quantity being subtracted from the rectangle previously obtained, we get

$$\overline{CL}^2 = m^2 + ox - \frac{p}{m}x^2.$$

It follows that CL is an ordinate of an ellipse or circle applied to NL, the segment of the axis.

Suppose all the given quantities expressed numerically, as EA=3, AG=5, AB=BR, BS=$\frac{1}{2}$BE, GB=BT, CD=$\frac{3}{2}$CR, CF=2CS, CH=$\frac{2}{3}$CT, the angle ABR=60°; and let CB.CF=CD.CH. All these quanties must be known if the problem is to be entirely determined. Now let AB=x, and CB=y. By the method given above we shall obtain

$$y^2 = 2y - xy + 5x - x^2;$$

$$y = 1 - \frac{1}{2}x + \sqrt{1 + 4x - \frac{3}{4}x^2};$$

whence BK must be equal to 1, and KL must be equal to one-half KI; and since the angle IKL = angle ABR = 60° and angle KIL (which is one-half angle KIB or one-half angle IKL) is 30°, the angle ILK is a right angle. Since IK=AB=x, KL=$\frac{1}{2}x$, IL=$x\sqrt{\frac{3}{4}}$, and the quantity represented by z above is 1, we have $a = \sqrt{\frac{3}{4}}$, $m=1$, $o=4$, $p=\frac{3}{4}$, whence IM=$\sqrt{\frac{16}{3}}$, NM=$\sqrt{\frac{19}{3}}$; and since a^2m (which is $\frac{3}{4}$) is equal to pz^2, and

Livre Second. 333

$-\frac{aaomm}{2pp\zeta\zeta}\sqrt{oo+4mp}$ qu'il faut diuiser par aam & multiplier par $p\zeta\zeta$, a cause que ces termes expliquent la proportion qui est entre le costé trauersant & le droit, & il vient $\frac{p}{m}xx - ox + x\sqrt{oo+4mp} + \frac{oom}{2p}$ $-\frac{om}{2p}\sqrt{oo+4mp} + mm$. ce qu'il faut oster du rectangle precedent, & on trouue $mm + ox - \frac{p}{m}xx$ pour le quarré de C L, qui par consequent est vne ligne appliquée par ordre dans vne Ellipse, ou dans vn cercle, au segment du diametre N L.

Et si on vent expliquer toutes les quantités données par nombres, en faisant par exemple $EA \infty 3$, $AG \infty 5$, $AB \infty BR$, $BS \infty \frac{1}{2}BE$, $GB \infty BT$, $CD \infty \frac{2}{3}CR$, $CF \infty 2CS$, $CH \infty \frac{2}{3}CT$, & que l'angle ABR soit de 60 degrés; & enfin que le rectangle des deux CB, & CF, soit esgal au rectangle des deux autres CD & CH; car il faut auoir toutes ces choses affin que la question soit entierement determinée. & auec cela supposant $AB \infty x$, & $CB \infty y$, on trouue par la façon cy dessus expliquée $yy \infty 2y - xy + 5x - xx$ & $y \infty 1 - \frac{1}{2}x + \sqrt{1 + 4x - \frac{3}{4}xx}$: si bien que B K doit estre 1, & K L doit estre la moitié de K I, & pource que l'angle I K L ou A B R est de 60 degrés, & K I L qui est la moitié de K I B ou I K L, de 30, I L K est droit. Et pource que I K ou A B est nommé x, K L est $\frac{1}{2}x$, & I L est $x\sqrt{\frac{3}{4}}$, & la quantité qui estoit tantost nommée ζ est 1, celle qui estoit a est $\sqrt{\frac{3}{4}}$, celle qui estoit m est 1, celle qui estoit o est 4, & celle qui estoit p est $\frac{3}{4}$, de façon qu'on a $\sqrt{\frac{16}{3}}$

Tt 3 pour

334　　La Geometrie.

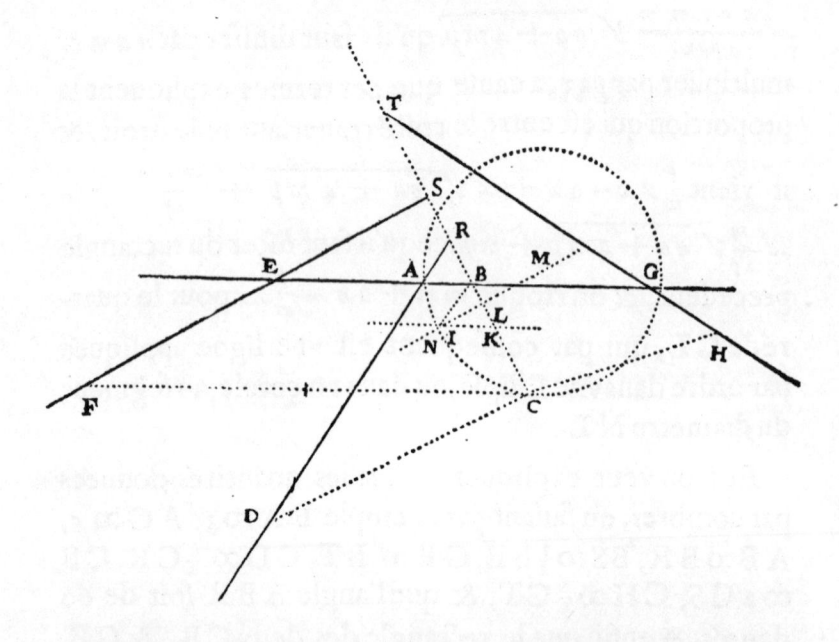

pour I M, & $\sqrt{12\frac{2}{3}}$ pour N M, & pourceque aam qui est $\frac{3}{4}$ est icy esgal à pzz & que l'angle I L C est droit, on trouue que la ligne courbe N C est vn cercle. Et on peut facilement examiner tous les autres cas en mesme sorte.

Quels sont les lieux plans, & solides: & la facon de les trouuer.

　　Au reste a cause que les equations, qui ne montent que iusques au quarré, sont toutes comprises en ce que ie viens d'expliquer; non seulement le problesme des anciens en 3 & 4 lignes est icy entierement acheué; mais aussy tout ce qui appartient à ce qu'ils nommoient la composition des lieux solides; & par consequent aussy a celle des lieux plans, a cause qu'ils sont compris dans les solides. Car ces lieux ne sont autre chose, sinon que lors qu'il est question de trouuer quelque point auquel il

manque

the angle ILC is a right angle, it follows that the curve NC is a circle. A similar treatment of any of the other cases offers no difficulty.

Since all equations of degree not higher than the second are included in the discussion just given, not only is the problem of the ancients relating to three or four lines completely solved, but also the whole problem of what they called the composition of solid loci, and consequently that of plane loci, since they are included under solid loci.[124] For the solution of any one of these problems of loci is nothing more than the finding of a point for whose complete determination one con-

---

[124] Since plane loci are degenerate cases of solid loci. The case in which neither x^2 nor y^2 but only xy occurs, and the case in which a constant term occurs, are omitted by Descartes. The various kinds of solid loci represented by the equation $y = \pm m \pm \frac{n}{z} x \pm \frac{n^2}{x} \pm \sqrt{\pm m^2 \pm ox \pm \frac{p}{m} x}$ may be summarized as follows:
(1) If all the terms of the right member are zero except $\frac{n^2}{x}$, the equation represents an hyperbola referred to its asymptotes. (2) If $\frac{n^2}{x}$ is not present, there are several cases, as follows: (a) If the quantity under the radical sign is zero or a perfect square, the equation represents a straight line; (b) If this quantity is not a perfect square and if $\frac{p}{m} x^2 = 0$, the equation represents a parabola; (c) If it is not a perfect square and if $\frac{p}{m} x^2$ is negative, the equation represents a circle or an ellipse; (d) If $\frac{p}{m} x^2$ is positive, the equation represents a hyperbola. Rabuel, p. 248.

dition is wanting, the other conditions being such that (as in this example) all the points of a single line will satisfy them. If the line is straight or circular, it is said to be a plane locus; but if it is a parabola, a hyperbola, or an ellipse, it is called a solid locus. In every such case an equation can be obtained containing two unknown quantities and entirely analogous to those found above. If the curve upon which the required point lies is of higher degree than the conic sections, it may be called in the same way a supersolid locus,[125] and so on for other cases. If two conditions for the determination of the point are lacking, the locus of the point is a surface, which may be plane, spherical, or more complex. The ancients attempted nothing beyond the composition of solid loci, and it would appear that the sole aim of Apollonius in his treatise on the conic sections was the solution of problems of solid loci.

I have shown, further, that what I have termed the first class of curves contains no others besides the circle, the parabola, the hyperbola, and the ellipse. This is what I undertook to prove.

[125] "Un lieu sursolide."

Livre Second.

manque vne condition pour eſtre entierement determiné, ainſi qu'il arriue en cete exemple, tous les poins d'vne meſme ligne peuuent eſtre pris pour celuy qui eſt demandé. Et ſi cete ligne eſt droite, ou circulaire, on la nomme vn lieu plan. Mais ſi c'eſt vne parabole, ou vne hyperbole, ou vne ellipſe, on la nomme vn lieu ſolide. Et toutefois & quantes que cela eſt, on peut venir a vne Equation qui contient deux quantités inconnuës, & eſt pareille a quelqu'vne de celles que ie viens de reſoudre. Que ſi la ligne qui determine ainſi le point cherché, eſt d'vn degré plus compoſée que les ſections coniques, on la peut nommer, en meſme façon, vn lieu ſurſolide, & ainſi des autres. Et s'il manque deux conditions a la determination de ce point, le lieu ou il ſe trouue eſt vne ſuperficie, laquelle peut eſtre tout de meſme ou plate, ou ſpherique, ou plus compoſée. Mais le plus haut but qu'ayent eu les anciens en cete matiere a eſté de paruenir a la compoſition des lieux ſolides : Et il ſemble que tout ce qu'Apollonius a eſcrit des ſections coniques n'a eſté qu'à deſſein de la chercher.

De plus on voit icy que ce que iay pris pour le premier genre des lignes courbes, n'en peut comprendre aucunes autres que le cercle, la parabole, l'hyperbole, & l'ellipſe. qui eſt tout ce que i'auois entrepris de prouuer.

Que ſi la queſtion des anciens eſt propoſée en cinq lignes, qui ſoient toutes paralleles ; il eſt euident que le point cherché ſera touſiours en vne ligne droite. Mais ſi elle eſt propoſée en cinq lignes, dont il y en ait quatre qui ſoient paralleles, & que la cinquieſme les couppe a angles droits, & meſme que toutes les lignes tirées du point

Quelle eſt la premiere & la plus ſimple de toutes les lignes courbes qui ſeruent en la queſtion des anciens quand elle eſt propoſée en cinq lignes.

336 La Geometrie.

point cherché les rencontrent auſſy a angles droits, & enfin que le parallelepipede compoſé de trois, des lignes ainſi tirées ſur trois de celles qui ſont paralleles, ſoit eſgal au parallelepipede compoſé des deux lignes tirées l'vne ſur la quatrieſme de celles qui ſont paralleles & l'autre ſur celle qui les couppe a angles droits, & d'vne troiſieſ-me ligne donnée. ce qui eſt ce ſemble le plus ſim-ple cas qu'on puiſſe imaginer aprés le precedent ; le point cherché ſera en la ligne courbe, qui eſt deſcrite par le moüuement d'vne parabole en la façon cy deſſus expliquée.

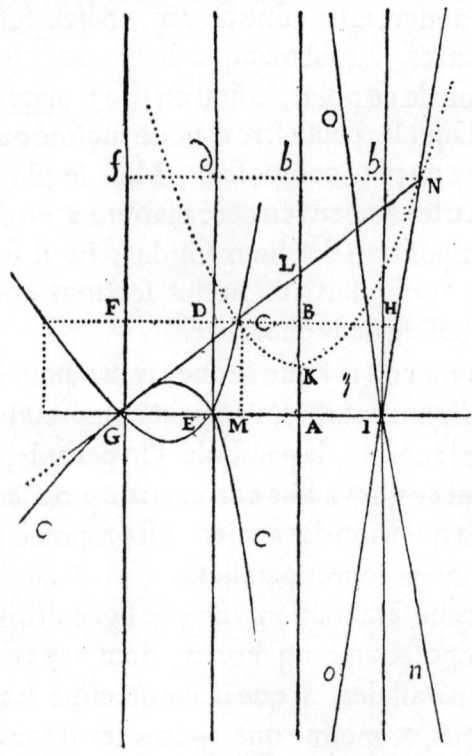

Soient

SECOND BOOK

If the problem of the ancients be proposed concerning five lines, all parallel, the required point will evidently always lie on a straight line. Suppose it be proposed concerning five lines with the following conditions:

(1) Four of these lines parallel and the fifth perpendicular to each of the others;

(2) The lines drawn from the required point to meet the given lines at right angles;

(3) The parallelepiped[126] composed of the three lines drawn to meet three of the parallel lines must be equal to that composed of three lines, namely, the one drawn to meet the fourth parallel, the one drawn to meet the perpendicular, and a certain given line.

This is, with the exception of the preceding one, the simplest possible case. The point required will lie on a curve generated by the motion of a parabola in the following way:

[126] That is, the product of the numerical measures of these lines.

GEOMETRY

Let the required lines be AB, IH, ED, GF, and GA, and let it be required to find the point C, such that if CB, CF, CD, CH, and CM be drawn perpendicular respectively to the given lines, the parallelepiped of the three lines CF, CD, and CH shall be equal to that of the other two, CB and CM, and a third line AI. Let CB=y, CM=x, AI or AE or GE=a; whence if C lies between AB and DE, we have CF=$2a-y$, CD=$a-y$, and CH=$y+a$. Multiplying these three together we get $y^3-2ay^2-a^2y+2a^3$ equal to the product of the other three, namely to axy.

I shall consider next the curve CEG, which I imagine to be described by the intersection of the parabola CKN (which is made to move so that its axis KL always lies along the straight line AB) with the ruler GL (which rotates about the point G in such a way that it constantly lies in the plane of the parabola and passes through the point L). I take KL equal to a and let the principal parameter, that is, the parameter corresponding to the axis of the given parabola, be also equal to a, and let GA=$2a$, CB or MA=y, CM or AB=x. Since the triangles GMC and CBL are similar, GM (or $2a-y$) is to MC (or x) as CB (or y) is to BL, which is therefore equal to $\frac{xy}{2a-y}$. Since KL is a, BK is $a-\frac{xy}{2a-y}$ or $\frac{2a^2-ay-xy}{2a-y}$. Finally, since this same BK is a segment of the axis of the parabola, BK is to BC (its ordinate) as BC is to a (the latus rectum), whence we get $y^3-2ay^2-a^2y+2a^3=axy$, and therefore C is the required point.

LIVRE SECOND. 337

Soient par exemple les lignes cherchées AB, IH, ED, GF, & GA. & qu'on demande le point C, en sorte que tirant CB, CF, CD, CH, & CM a angles droits sur les données, le parallelepipede des trois CF, CD, & CH soit esgal a celuy des 2 autres CB, & CM, & d'vne troisiesme qui soit AI. Ie pose CB $\infty\, y$. CM $\infty\, x$. AI, ou AE, ou GE $\infty\, a$, de façon que le point C estant entre les lignes AB, & DE, iay CF $\infty\, 2a - y$, CD $\infty\, a - y$. & CH $\infty\, y + a$. & multipliant ces trois l'vne par l'autre, iay $y^3 - 2ayy - aay + 2a^3$ esgal au produit des trois autres qui est axy. Aprés cela ie considere la ligne courbe CEG, que i'imagine estre descrite par l'intersection, de la Parabole CKN, qu'on fait mouuoir en telle sorte que son diametre KL est tousiours sur la ligne droite AB, & de la reigle GL qui tourne cependant autour du point G en telle sorte quelle passe tousiours dans le plan de cete Parabole par le point L. Et ie fais KL $\infty\, a$, & le costé droit principal, c'est a dire celuy qui se rapporte a l'aissieu de cete parabole, aussy esgal à a, & GA $\infty\, 2a$, & CB ou MA $\infty\, y$, & CM ou AB $\infty\, x$. Puis a cause des triangles semblables GMC & CBL, GM qui est $2a-y$, est à MC qui est x, comme CB qui est y, est à BL qui est par consequent $\frac{xy}{2a-y}$. Et pourceque LK est a, BK est a $\frac{-xy}{2a-y}$, oubien $\frac{2aa - ay - xy}{2a-y}$. Et enfin pourceque ce mesme BK estant vn segment du diametre de la Parabole, est à BC qui luy est appliquée par ordre, comme celle-cy est au costé droit qui est a, le calcul monstre que

$y^3 - 2ayy - aay + 2a^3$, est esgal à axy. & par conse-

V v   quent

338　　　La Geometrie.

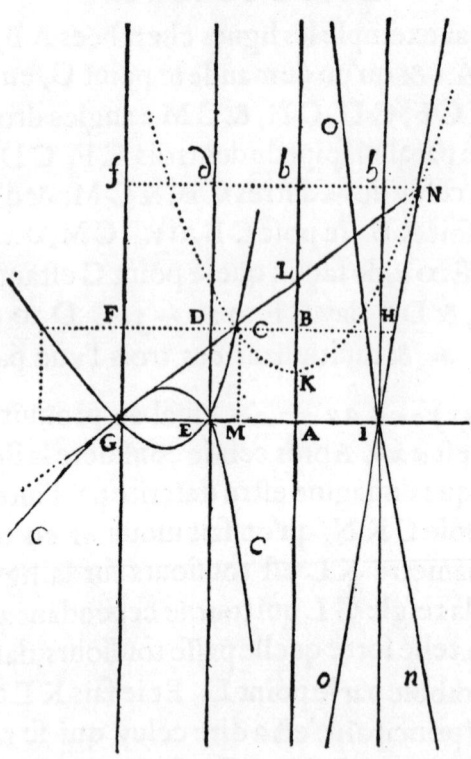

quent que le point C est celuy qui estoit demandé. Et il peut estre pris en tel endroit de la ligne C E G qu'on veuille choisir, ou aussy en son adiointe *c* E G *c* qui se descrit en mesme façon, excepté que le sommet de la Parabole est tourné vers l'autre costé, ou enfin en leurs contreposées N I *o*, *n* I O, qui sont descrites par l'intersection que fait la ligne G L en l'autre costé de la Parabole K N.

Or encore que les paralleles données A B, I H, E D, & G F ne fussent point esgalement distantes, & que G A ne les couppast point a angles droits, ny aussy les lignes tirées

SECOND BOOK

The point C can be taken on any part of the curve CEG or of its adjunct cEGc, which is described in the same way as the former, except that the vertex of the parabola is turned in the opposite direction; or it may lie on their counterparts[127] NI*o* and *n*IO, which are generated by the intersection of the line GL with the other branch of the parabola KN.

Again, suppose that the given parallel lines AB, IH, ED, and GF are not equally distant from one another and are not perpendicular to GA, and that the lines through C are oblique to the given lines. In this case the point C will not always lie on a curve of just the same nature. This may even occur when no two of the given lines are parallel.

[127] "En leurs contreposées."

GEOMETRY

Next, suppose that we have four parallel lines, and a fifth line cutting them, such that the parallelepiped of three lines drawn through the point C (one to the cutting line and two to two of the parallel lines) is equal to the parallelepiped of two lines drawn through C to meet the other two parallels respectively and another given line. In this case the required point lies on a curve of different nature,[128] namely, a curve such that, all the ordinates to its axis being equal to the ordinates of a conic section, the segments of the axis between the vertex and the ordinates[129] bear the same ratio to a certain given line that this line bears to the segments of the axis of the conic section having equal ordinates.[130]

I cannot say that this curve is less simple than the preceding; indeed, I have always thought the former should be considered first, since its description and the determination of its equation are somewhat easier.

I shall not stop to consider in detail the curves corresponding to the other cases, for I have not undertaken to give a complete discussion of the subject; and having explained the method of determining an infinite number of points lying on any curve, I think I have furnished a way to describe them.

It is worthy of note that there is a great difference between this method[131] in which the curve is traced by finding several points upon

[128] The general equation of this curve is $axy - xy^2 + 2a^2x = a^2y - ay^2$. Rabuel, p. 270.

[129] That is, the abscissas of points on the curve.

[130] The thought, expressed in modern phraseology, is as follows: The curve is of such nature that the abscissa of any point on it is a third proportional to the abscissa of a point on a conic section whose ordinate is the same as that of the given point, and a given line. Cf. Rabuel, pp. 270, et seq.

[131] That is, the method of analytic geometry.

88

tirées du point C vers elles, ce point C ne laisseroit pas de se trouuer tousiours en vne ligne courbe, qui seroit de cete mesme nature. Et il s'y peut aussy trouuer quelquefois, encore qu'aucune des lignes données ne soient paralleles. Mais si lorsqu'il y en a 4 ainsi paralleles, & vne cinquiesme qui les trauerse: & que le parallelepipede de trois des lignes tirées du point cherché, l'vne sur cete cinquiesme, & les 2 autres sur 2 de celles qui sont paralleles; soit esgal a celuy, des deux tirées sur les deux autres paralleles, & d'vne autre ligne donnée. Ce point cherché est en vne ligne courbe d'vne autre nature, a sçauoir en vne qui est telle, que toutes les lignes droites appliquées par ordre a son diametre estant esgales a celles d'vne section conique, les segmens de ce diametre, qui sont entre le sommet & ces lignes, ont mesme proportion a vne certaine ligne donnée, que cete ligne donnée a aux segmens du diametre de la section conique, ausquels les pareilles lignes sont appliquées par ordre. Et ie ne sçaurois veritablement dire que cete ligne soit moins simple que la precedente, laquelle iay creu toutefois deuoir prendre pour la premiere, a cause que la description, & le calcul en sont en quelque façon plus faciles.

Pour les lignes qui seruent aux autres cas, ie ne m'aresteray point a les distinguer par especes. car ie n'ay pas entrepris de dire tout ; & ayant expliqué la façon de trouuer vne infinité de poins par ou elles passent, ie pense auoir assés donné le moyen de les descrire.

Mesme il est a propos de remarquer, qu'il y a grande difference entre cete façon de trouuer plusieurs poins

Vv 2   pour

La Geometrie.

Quelles sont les lignes courbes qu'on descrit en trouuant plusieurs de leurs poins, qui peuuent estre receues en Geometrie.

pour tracer vne ligne courbe, & celle dont on se sert pour la spirale, & ses semblables. car par cete derniere on ne trouue pas indifferemment tous les poins de la ligne qu'on cherche, mais seulement ceux qui peuuent estre determinés par quelque mesure plus simple, que celle qui est requise pour la composer, & ainsi a proprement parler on ne trouue pas vn de ses poins. c'est a dire pas vn de ceux qui luy sont tellement propres, qu'ils ne puissent estre trouués que par elle: Au lieu qu'il n'y a aucun point dans les lignes qui seruent a la question proposée, qui ne se puisse rencontrer entre ceux qui se determinent par la façon tantost expliquée. Et pourceque cete façon de tracer vne ligne courbe, en trouuant indifferemment plusieurs de ses poins, ne s'estend qu'a celles qui peuuent aussy estre descrites par vn mouuement regulier & continu, on ne la doit pas entierement reietter de la Geometrie.

Quelles sont aussy celles qu'on descrit auec vne chorde, qui peuuent y estre receues.

Et on n'en doit pas reietter non plus, celle ou on se sert d'vn fil, ou d'vne chorde repliée, pour determiner l'egalité ou la difference de deux ou plusieurs lignes droites qui peuuent estre tirées de chasque point de la courbe qu'on cherche, a certains autres poins, ou sur certaines autres lignes a certains angles. ainsi que nous auons fait en la Dioptrique pour expliquer l'Ellipse & l'Hyperbole. car encore qu'on n'y puisse reçeuoir aucunes lignes qui semblent a des chordes, c'est a dire qui deuienent tantost droites & tantost courbes, a cause que la proportion, qui est entre les droites & les courbes, n'estant pas connuë, & mesme ie croy ne le pouuant estre par les hommes, on ne pourroit rien conclure de là qui fust

it, and that used for the spiral and similar curves.[132] In the latter not any point of the required curve may be found at pleasure, but only such points as can be determined by a process simpler than that required for the composition of the curve. Therefore, strictly speaking, we do not find any one of its points, that is, not any one of those which are so peculiarly points of this curve that they cannot be found except by means of it. On the other hand, there is no point on these curves which supplies a solution for the proposed problem that cannot be determined by the method I have given.

But the fact that this method of tracing a curve by determining a number of its points taken at random applies only to curves that can be generated by a regular and continuous motion does not justify its exclusion from geometry. Nor should we reject the method[133] in which a string or loop of thread is used to determine the equality or difference of two or more straight lines drawn from each point of the required curve to certain other points,[134] or making fixed angles with certain other lines. We have used this method in "La Dioptrique"[135] in the discussion of the ellipse and the hyperbola.

On the other hand, geometry should not include lines that are like strings, in that they are sometimes straight and sometimes curved, since the ratios between straight and curved lines are not known, and I believe cannot be discovered by human minds,[136] and therefore no conclusion based upon such ratios can be accepted as rigorous and exact.

[132] That is, transcendental curves, called by Descartes "mechanical" curves.
[133] Cf. the familiar "mechanical descriptions" of the conic sections.
[134] As for example, the foci, in the description of the ellipse.
[135] This work was published at Leyden in 1637, together with Descartes's *Discours de la Methode*.
[136] This is of course concerned with the problem of the rectification of curves. See Cantor, Vol. II (1), pp. 794 and 807, and especially p. 778. This statement, "ne pouvant être par les hommes" is a very noteworthy one, coming as it does from a philosopher like Descartes. On the philosophical question involved, consult such writers as Bertrand Russell.

Nevertheless, since strings can be used in these constructions only to determine lines whose lengths are known, they need not be wholly excluded.

When the relation between all points of a curve and all points of a straight line is known,[137] in the way I have already explained, it is easy to find the relation between the points of the curve and all other given points and lines; and from these relations to find its diameters, axes, center and other lines[138] or points which have especial significance for this curve, and thence to conceive various ways of describing the curve, and to choose the easiest.

By this method alone it is then possible to find out all that can be determined about the magnitude of their areas,[139] and there is no need for further explanation from me.

[137] Expressed by means of the equation of the curve.
[138] For example, the equations of tangents, normals, etc.
[139] For the history of the quadrature of curves, consult Cantor, Vol. II (1), pp. 758, et seq., Smith, *History*, Vol. II, p. 302.

LIVRE SECOND.

fuſt exact & aſſuré. Toutefois a cauſe qu'on ne ſe ſert de chordes en ces conſtructions, que pour déterminer des lignes droites, dont on connoiſt parfaitement la longeur, cela ne doit point faire qu'on les reiette.

Or de cela ſeul qu'on ſçait le rapport, qu'ont tous les poins d'vne ligne courbe a tous ceux d'vne ligne droite, en la façon que iay expliquée, il eſt ayſé de trouuer auſſy le rapport qu'ils ont a tous les autres poins, & lignes données: & en ſuite de connoiſtre les diametres, les aiſſieux, les centres, & autres lignes, ou poins, a qui chaſque ligne courbe aura quelque rapport plus particulier, ou plus ſimple, qu'aux autres: & ainſi d'imaginer diuers moyens pour les deſcrire, & d'en choiſir les plus faciles. Et meſme on peut auſſy par cela ſeul trouuer quaſi tout ce qui peut eſtre determiné touchant la grandeur de l'eſpace quelles comprenent, ſans qu'il ſoit beſoin que i'en donne plus d'ouuerture. Et enfin pour ce qui eſt de toutes les autres proprietés qu'on peut attribuer aux lignes courbes, elles ne dependent que de la grandeur des angles qu'elles font auec quelques autres lignes. Mais lorſqu'on peut tirer des lignes droites qui les couppent a angles droits, aux poins ou elles ſont rencontrées par celles auec qui elles font les angles qu'on veut meſurer, ou, ce que ie prens icy pour le meſme, qui couppent leurs contingentes; la grandeur de ces angles n'eſt pas plus malayſée a trouuer, que s'ils eſtoient compris entre deux lignes droites. C'eſt pourquoy ie croyray auoir mis icy tout ce qui eſt requis pour les elemens des lignes courbes, lorſque i'auray generalement donné la façon de tirer des lignes droites, qui tombent a angles droits ſur

Que pour trouuer toutes les proprietes des lignes courbes, il ſuffiſt de ſcauoir le rapport qu'ont tous leurs poins a ceux des lignes droites, & la façon de tirer d'autres lignes qui les couppent en tous ces poins a angles droits.

Vv 3   tels

342   LA GEOMETRIE.

tels de leurs poins qu'on voudra choisir. Et i'ose dire que c'est cecy le problesme le plus vtile, & le plus general non seulement que ie sçache, mais mesme que i'aye iamais desiré de sçauoir en Geometrie.

<small>Façon generale pour trouuer des lignes droites, qui couppent les courbes données, ou leurs contingentes, a angles droits.</small>

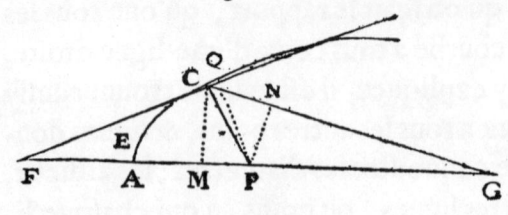

Soit C E la ligne courbe, & qu'il faille tirer vne ligne droite par le point C, qui face auec elle des angles droits. Ie suppose la chose desia faite, & que la ligne cherchée est C P, laquelle ie prolonge iusques au point P, ou elle rencontre la ligne droite G A, que ie suppose estre celle aux poins de laquelle on rapporte tous ceux de la ligne C E : en sorte que faisant M A ou C B $\infty\, y$, & C M, ou B A $\infty\, x$, iay quelque equation, qui explique le rapport, qui est entre x & y. Puis ie fais P C $\infty\, s$, & P A $\infty\, v$, ou P M $\infty\, v - y$, & a cause du triangle rectangle P M C iay ss, qui est le quarré de la baze esgal à $xx + vv - 2vy + yy$, qui sont les quarrés des deux costés. c'est a dire iay $x \infty$ $\sqrt{ss - vv + 2vy - yy}$, oubien $y \infty v + \sqrt{ss - xx}$, & par le moyen de cete equation, i'oste de l'autre equation qui m'explique le rapport qu'ont tous les poins de la courbe C E a ceux de la droite G A, l'vne des deux quantités indeterminées x ou y. ce qui est aysé a faire en mettant partout $\sqrt{ss - vv + 2vy - yy}$ au lieu d'x, & le quarré de cete somme au lieu d'xx, & son cube au lieu d'x^3, & ainsi des autres, si c'est x que ie veuille oster; oubien

Finally, all other properties of curves depend only on the angles which these curves make with other lines. But the angle formed by two intersecting curves can be as easily measured as the angle between two straight lines, provided that a straight line can be drawn making right angles with one of these curves at its point of intersection with the other.[140] This is my reason for believing that I shall have given here a sufficient introduction to the study of curves when I have given a general method of drawing a straight line making right angles with a curve at an arbitrarily chosen point upon it. And I dare say that this is not only the most useful and most general problem in geometry that I know, but even that I have ever desired to know.

Let CE be the given curve, and let it be required to draw through C a straight line making right angles with CE. Suppose the problem solved, and let the required line be CP. Produce CP to meet the straight line GA, to whose points the points of CE are to be related.[141] Then, let MA=CB=y; and CM=BA=x. An equation must be found expressing the relation between x and y.[142] I let PC=s, PA=v, whence PM=$v-y$. Since PMC is a right triangle, we see that s^2, the square of the hypotenuse, is equal to $x^2+v^2-2vy+y^2$, the sum of the squares of the two sides. That is to say, $x=\sqrt{s^2-v^2+2vy-y^2}$ or $y=v+\sqrt{s^2-x^2}$. By means of these last two equations, I can eliminate one of the two quantities x and y from the equation expressing the relation between the points of the curve CE and those of the straight line GA. If x is to be eliminated, this may easily be done by replacing x wherever it occurs by $\sqrt{s^2-v^2+2vy-y^2}$, x^2 by the square of this expression, x^3 by its cube, etc., while if y is to be eliminated, y must be replaced by $v+\sqrt{s^2-x^2}$, and y^2, y^3, . . . by the square of this expres-

[140] That is, the angle between two curves is defined as the angle between the normals to the curve at the point of intersection.

[141] That is, the line GA is taken as one of the coördinate axes.

[142] This will be the equation of the curve. See also the figure on page 97.

SECOND BOOK

sion, its cube, and so on. The result will be an equation in only one unknown quantity, x or y.

For example, if CE is an ellipse, MA the segment of its axis of which CM is an ordinate, r its latus rectum, and q its transverse axis,[143] then by Theorem 13, Book I, of Apollonius,[144] we have $x^2 = ry - \frac{r}{q}y^2$. Eliminating x^2 the resulting equation is

$$s^2 - v^2 + 2vy - y^2 = ry - \frac{r}{q}y^2, \quad \text{or} \quad y^2 + \frac{qry - 2qvy + qv^2 - qs^2}{q - r} = 0.$$

In this case it is better to consider the whole as constituting a single expression than as consisting of two equal parts.[145]

If CE be the curve generated by the motion of a parabola (see pages 47, et seq.) already discussed, and if we represent GA by b, KL by c, and the parameter of the axis KL of the parabola by d, the equation

[143] "Le traversant."

[144] Apollonius, p. 49: "Si conus per axem plano secatur autem alio quoque plano, quod cum utroque latere trianguli per axem posita concurrit, sed neque basi coni parallelum ducitur neque e contrario et si planum, in quo est basis coni, planumque secans concurrunt in recta perpendiculari aut ad basim trianguli per axem positi aut ad eam productam quælibet recta, quæ a sectione coni communi sectioni planorum parallela ducitur ad diametrum sectiones sumpta quadrata æqualis erit spatio adplicato rectæ cuidam, ad quam diametrus sectionis rationem habet, quam habet quadratum rectæ a vertice coni diametro sectionis parallelæ ductæ usque ad basim trianguli ad rectangulum comprehensum rectis ab ea ad latera trianguli abscissis, latitudinem rectam ab ea e diametro ad verticem sectionis abscissam et figura deficiens simili similiterque posita rectangulo a diametro parametroque comprehenso; vocetur autem talis sectio ellipsis." Cf. *Apollonius of Perga*, edited by Sir T. L. Heath, Cambridge, 1896, p. 11.

[145] That is, to transpose all the terms to the left member.

bien si c'est y, en mettant en son lieu $u + \sqrt{ss - xx}$, & le quarré, ou le cube, &c. de cete somme, au lieu d'yy, ou y^3 &c. De façon qu'il reste tousiours aprés cela vne equation, en laquelle il ny a plus qu'vne seule quantité indeterminée, x, ou y.

Comme si C E est vne Ellipse, & que M A soit le segment de son diametre, auquel C M soit appliquée par ordre, & qui ait r pour son costé droit, & q pour le trauersant, on a par le 13 th. du 1 liu. d'Apollonius.

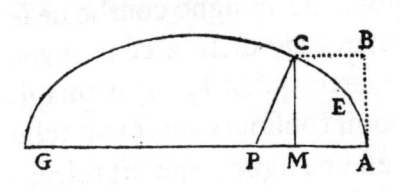

$xx \infty ry - \frac{r}{q} yy$, d'on ostant xx, il reste $ss - vv + 2vy - yy \infty ry - \frac{r}{q} yy$.

oubien,

$yy \frac{\mp qry - 2qvy \mp qvv - qss}{q - r}$ esgal a rien. car il est mieux en cet endroit de considerer ainsi ensemble toute la somme, que d'en faire vne partie esgale a l'autre.

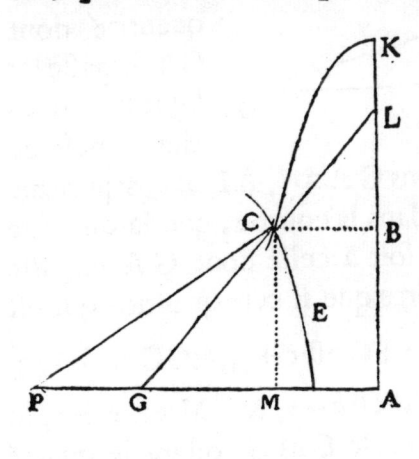

Tout de mesme si C E est la ligne courbe descrite par le mouuement d'vne Parabole en la façon cy dessus expliquée, & qu'on ait posé b pour G A, c pour K L, & d pour le costé droit du diametre K L en la parabole: l'equatió qui explique le rapport qui

qui est entre x & y, est $y - byy - cdy + bcd + dxy \infty 0$.

d'où ostant x, on a $y - byy - cdy + bcd + dy$
$\sqrt{ss - vv + 2vy - yy}$. & remetrant en ordre ces termes par le moyen de la multiplication, il vient

$$y^6 \begin{Bmatrix} -2cd \\ -2by^5 + bb \\ +dd \end{Bmatrix} y^4 \begin{Bmatrix} -2bbcd \\ +4bcd \\ -2ddv \end{Bmatrix} y^3 \begin{Bmatrix} -2bbcd \\ + ccdd \\ -ddss \\ +ddvv \end{Bmatrix} yy - 2bccddy + bbccdd \infty 0.$$

Et ainsi des autres.

Mesme encore que les poins de la ligne courbe ne se rapportassent pas en la façon que iay ditte a ceux d'vne ligne droite, mais en toute autre qu'on sçauroit imaginer, on ne laisse pas de pouuoir tousiours auoir vne telle equation. Comme si C E est vne ligne, qui ait tel rapport aux trois poins F, G, & A, que les lignes droites tirées de chascun de ses poins comme C, iusques au point F, surpassent la ligne F A d'vne quantité, qui ait certaine proportiõ donnée a vne autre quantité dont GA surpasse les lignes tirées des mesmes poins iusques à G. Faisons $GA \infty b$, $AF \infty c$, & prenant à discretion le point C dans la courbe, que la quantité dont CF surpasse FA, soit à celle dont GA surpasse GC, comme d à e, en sorte que si cete quantité qui est indeterminée se nomme z, FC est $c + z$, & GC est $b - \frac{e}{d}z$.
Puis posant $MA \infty y$, GM est $b - y$, & FM est $c + y$, & a cause du triangle rectangle CMG, ostant le quarré de

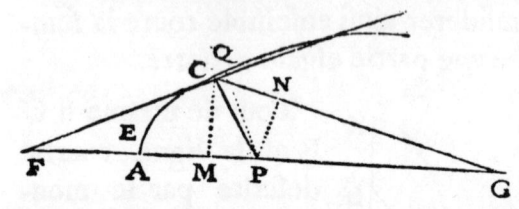

expressing the relation between x and y is $y^3-by^2-cdy+bcd+dxy=0$. Eliminating x, we have

$$y^3-by^2-cdy+bcd+dy\sqrt{s^2-v^2+2vy-y^2}=0.$$

Arranging the terms according to the powers of y by squaring,[146] this becomes

$$y^6-2by^5+(b^2-2cd+d^2)y^4+(4bcd-2d^2v)y^3$$
$$+(c^2d^2-d^2s^2+d^2v^2-2b^2cd)y^2-2bc^2d^2y+b^2c^2d^2=0,$$

and so for the other cases. If the points of the curve are not related to those of a straight line in the way explained, but are related in some other way,[147] such an equation can always be found.

Let CE be a curve which is so related to the points F, G, and A, that a straight line drawn from any point on it, as C, to F exceeds the line FA by a quantity which bears a given ratio to the excess of GA over the line drawn from the point C to G.[148] Let GA=b, AF=c, and taking an arbitrary point C on the curve let the quantity by which CF exceeds FA be to the quantity by which GA exceeds GC as d is to e. Then if we let z represent the undetermined quantity, FC=$c+z$ and GC=$b-\frac{e}{d}z$. Let MA=y, GM=$b-y$, and FM=$c+y$. Since CMG is a right triangle, taking the square of GM from the square of GC we have

---

[146] "En remettant en ordre ces termes par moyen de la multiplication."
[147] "Mais en toute autre qu'on saurait imaginer."
[148] That is the ratio of CF — FA to GA — CG is a constant.

left the square of CM, or $\frac{e^2}{d^2}z^2 - \frac{2be}{d}z + 2by - y^2$. Again, taking the square of FM from the square of FC we have the square of CM expressed in another way, namely: $z^2 + 2cz - 2cy - y^2$. These two expressions being equal they will yield the value of y or MA, which is

$$\frac{d^2z^2 + 2cd^2z - e^2z^2 + 2bdez}{2bd^2 + 2cd^2}.$$

Substituting this value for y in the expression for the square of CM, we have

$$\overline{CM}^2 = \frac{bd^2z^2 + ce^2z^2 + 2bcd^2z - 2bcdez}{bd^2 + cd^2} - y^2.$$

If now we suppose the line PC to meet the curve at right angles at C, and let $PC = s$ and $PA = v$ as before, PM is equal to $v - y$; and since PCM is a right triangle, we have $s^2 - v^2 + 2vy - y^2$ for the square of CM. Substituting for y its value, and equating the values of the square of CM, we have

$$z^2 + \frac{2bcd^2z - 2bcdez - 2cd^2vz - 2bdevz - bd^2s^2 + bd^2v^2 - cd^2s^2 + cd^2v^2}{bd^2 + ce^2 + e^2v - d^2v} = 0$$

for the required equation.

Such an equation having been found[149] it is to be used, not to determine x, y, or z, which are known, since the point C is given, but to find v or s, which determine the required point P. With this in view, observe that if the point P fulfills the required conditions, the circle about P as center and passing through the point C will touch but not cut the curve CE; but if this point P be ever so little nearer to or farther from A than it should be, this circle must cut the curve not only

[149] Three such equations have been found by Descartes, namely those for the ellipse, the parabolic conchoid, and the curve just described.

Livre Second. 345

de G M du quarré de G C, on a le quarré de C M, qui est
$\frac{ee}{dd}zz - \frac{2be}{d}z + 2by - yy$. puis ostant le quarré de F M
du quarré de F C, on a encore le quarré de C M en d'autres termes, a sçauoir $zz + 2cz - 2cy - yy$, & ces termes estant esgaux aux precedens, ils font connoistre y,
ou M A, qui est $\frac{ddzz + 2cddz - eezz + 2bdez}{2bdd + 2cdd}$ & substituant cete somme au lieu d'y dans le quarré de C M, on trouue qu'il s'exprime en ces termes.

$$\frac{bddzz + ceezz + 2bcddz - 2bcdez}{bdd + cdd} - yy.$$

Puis supposant que la ligne droite P C rencontre la courbe a angles droits au point C, & faisant P C ∞ s, & P A ∞ v comme deuant, P M est $v - y$; & a cause du triangle rectangle P C M, on à $ss - vv + 2vy - yy$ pour le quarré de C M, ou derechef ayant au lieu d'y substitué la somme qui luy est esgale, il vient

$$zz \frac{+ 2bcddz - 2bcdez - 2cddvz - 2bdevz - bddss + bddvv -}{bdd + cee \quad ee v - dd v}$$
$- cddss + cddvv$. ∞ o pour l'equation que nous cherchions.

Or aprés qu'on à trouué vne telle equation, au lieu de s'en seruir pour connoistre les quantités x, ou y, ou z, qui sont desia données, puisque le point C est donné, on la doit employer a trouuer v, ou s, qui determinent le point P, qui est demandé. Et a cet effect il faut considerer, que si ce point P est tel qu'on le desire, le cercle dont il sera le centre, & qui passera par le point C, y touchera la ligne courbe C E, sans la coupper: mais que si ce point P, est tant soit peu plus proche, ou plus esloigné du point

X x   A, qu'il

346 LA GEOMETRIE.

A, qu'il ne doit, ce cercle couppera la courbe, non seulement au point C, mais aussy necessairement en quelque autre. Puis il faut aussy considerer, que lorsque ce cercle couppe la ligne courbe C E, l'equation par laquelle on cherche la quantité *x*, ou *y*, ou quelque autre semblable, en supposant P A & P C estre connuës, contient necessairement deux racines, qui sont inesgales. Car par exemple si ce cercle couppe la courbe aux poins C & E, ayant tiré E Q parallele a C M, les noms des quantités indeterminées *x* & *y*, conuiendront aussy bien aux lignes E Q, & Q A, qu'a C M, & M A ; puis P E est esgale a P C, a cause du cercle, si bien que cherchant les lignes E Q & Q A, par P E & P A qu'on suppose comme donneés, on aura la mesme equation, que si on cherchoit C M & M A par P C, P A. d'où il suit euidemment, que la valeur d'*x*, ou d'*y*, ou de telle autre quantité qu'on aura supposee, sera double en cete equation, c'est a dire qu'il y aura deux racines inesgales entre elles; & dont l'vne sera C M, l'autre E Q, si c'est *x* qu'on cherche; oubien l'vne sera M A, & l'autre Q A, si c'est *y*. & ainsi des autres. Il est vray que si le point E ne se trouue pas du mesme costé de la courbe que le point C; il n'y aura que l'vne de ces deux racines qui soit vraye, & l'autre sera renuersée, ou moindre que rien: mais plus ces deux poins, C, & E, sont proches l'vn de l'autre, moins il y a de difference entre ces deux racines;

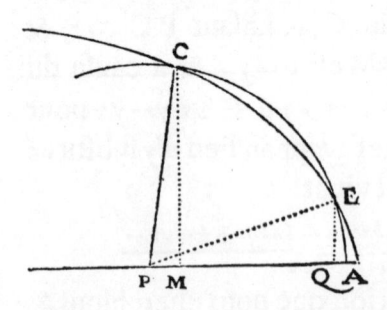

at C but also in another point. Now if this circle cuts CE, the equation involving x and y as unknown quantities (supposing PA and PC known) must have two unequal roots. Suppose, for example, that the circle cuts the curve in the points C and E. Draw EQ parallel to CM. Then x and y may be used to represent EQ and QA respectively in just the same way as they were used to represent CM and MA; since PE is equal to PC (being radii of the same circle), if we seek EQ and QA (supposing PE and PA given) we shall get the same equation that we should obtain by seeking CM and MA (supposing PC and PA given). It follows that the value of x, or y, or any other such quantity, will be two-fold in this equation, that is, the equation will have two unequal roots. If the value of x be required, one of these roots will be CM and the other EQ; while if y be required, one root will be MA and the other QA. It is true that if E is not on the same side of the curve as C, only one of these will be a true root, the other being drawn in the opposite direction, or less than nothing.[150] The nearer together the points C and E are taken however, the less differ-

[150] "Et l'autre sera renversée ou moindre que rien."

ence there is between the roots; and when the points coincide, the roots are exactly equal, that is to say, the circle through C will touch the curve CE at the point C without cutting it.

Furthermore, it is to be observed that when an equation has two equal roots, its left-hand member must be similar in form to the expression obtained by multiplying by itself the difference between the unknown quantity and a known quantity equal to it;[151] and then, if the resulting expression is not of as high a degree as the original equation, multiplying it by another expression which will make it of the same degree. This last step makes the two expressions correspond term by term.

For example, I say that the first equation found in the present discussion,[152] namely

$$y^2 + \frac{qry - 2qvy + qv^2 - qs^2}{q-r},$$

must be of the same form as the expression obtained by making $e=y$ and multiplying $y-e$ by itself, that is, as $y^2 - 2ey + e^2$. We may then compare the two expressions term by term, thus: Since the first term, y^2, is the same in each, the second term,[153] $\frac{qry - 2qvy}{q-r}$, of the first is equal to $-2ey$, the second term of the second; whence, solving for v, or PA, we have $v = e - \frac{r}{q}e + \frac{1}{2}r$; or, since we have assumed e equal to y, $v = y - \frac{r}{q}y + \frac{1}{2}r$. In the same way, we can find s from the third term,

---

[151] That is, the left-hand member will be the square of the binomial $x-a$ when $x=a$.

[152] See page 96. The original has "first equation," not "first member of the equation."

[153] That is, the second term in y.

Livre Second. 347

nes; & enfin elles sont entierement esgales, s'ils sont tous deux ioins en vn; c'est a dire si le cercle, qui passe par C, y touche la courbe C E sans la coupper.

De plus il faut considerer, que lorsqu'il y a deux racines esgales en vne equation, elle a necessairement la mesme forme, que si on multiplie par soy mesme la quantité qu'on y suppose estre inconnuë moins la quantité connue qui luy est esgale, & qu'aprés cela si cete derniere somme n'a pas tant de dimensions que la precedente, on la multiplie par vne autre somme qui en ait autant qu'il luy en manque; affin qu'il puisse y auoir separement equation entre chascun des termes de l'vne, & chascun des termes de l'autre.

Comme par exemple ie dis que la premiere equation trouuée cy dessus, a sçauoir

$yy \dfrac{\pm qry - 2qvy \pm qvv - qss}{q-r}$ doit auoir la mesme forme que celle qui se produist en faisant e esgal a y, & multipliant $y - e$ par soy mesme, d'où il vient $yy - 2ey + ee$, en sorte qu'on peut comparer separement chascun de leurs termes, & dire que puisque le premier qui est yy est tout le mesme en l'vne qu'en l'autre, le second qui est en l'vne $\dfrac{qry - 2qvy}{q-r}$ est esgal au secõd de l'autre qui est $-2ey$, d'où cherchant la quantité v qui est la ligne P A, on à

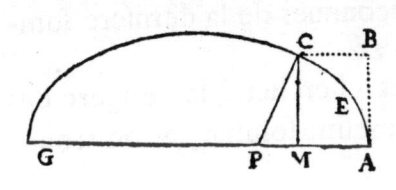

$v \infty e - \dfrac{r}{q}e + \dfrac{1}{2}r$, oubiẽ a cause que nous auons supposé e esgal a y, on a

$v \infty y - \dfrac{r}{q}y + \dfrac{1}{2}r$. Et ainsi

348　LA GEOMETRIE.

ainsi on pourroit trouuer s par le troisiesme terme $ee \infty \frac{qvv - qss}{q-r}$ mais pourceque la quantité v determine assés le point P, qui est le seul que nous cherchions, on n'a pas besoin de passer outre.

Tout de mesme la seconde equation trouuée cy dessus, a sçauoir,

$$y^6 - 2by^5 \begin{Bmatrix} -2cd \\ +bb \\ +dd \end{Bmatrix} y^4 \begin{Bmatrix} +4bcd \\ -2ddv \end{Bmatrix} y^3 \begin{Bmatrix} -2bbcd \\ +ccdd \\ -ddss \\ +ddvv \end{Bmatrix} yy - 2bccddy + bbccdd.$$

doit auoir mesme forme, que la somme qui se produist lorsqu'on multiplie $yy - 2ey + ee$ par

$$y^4 + fy^3 + ggyy + hy + k,\; \text{qui est}$$

$$y^6 \begin{Bmatrix} +f \\ -2e \end{Bmatrix} y^5 \begin{Bmatrix} +gg \\ -2ef \\ +ee \end{Bmatrix} y^4 \begin{Bmatrix} +h \\ -2egg \\ +eef \end{Bmatrix} y^3 \begin{Bmatrix} +k \\ -2eh \\ +egg \end{Bmatrix} yy \begin{Bmatrix} -2ek \\ +eeh \end{Bmatrix} y + eek.$$

de façon que de ces deux equations i'en tire six autres, qui seruent a connoistre les six quantités $f, g, h, k, v,\ \&\ s$: D'où il est fort aysé a entendre, que de quelque genre, que puisse estre la ligne courbe proposée, il vient tousiours par cete façon de proceder autant d'equations, qu'on est obligé de supposer de quantités, qui sont inconnuës. Mais pour demesler par ordre ces equations, & trouuer enfin la quantité v, qui est la seule dont on a besoin, & à l'occasion de laquelle on cherche les autres: Il faut premierement par le second terme chercher f, la premiere des quantités inconnuës de la derniere somme, & on trouue $f \infty 2e - 2b$.

Puis par le dernier il faut chercher k la derniere des quantités inconnuës de la mesme somme, & on trouue $k^4 \infty \frac{bbccdd}{ee}$

Puis

SECOND BOOK

$e^2 = \dfrac{qv^2 - qs^2}{q-r}$; but since v completely determines P, which is all that is required, it is not necessary to go further.[154]

In the same way, the second equation found above,[155] namely,

$$y^6 - 2by^5 + (b^2 - 2cd + d^2)y^4 + (4bcd - 2d^2v)y^3 \\ + (c^2d^2 - 2b^2cd + d^2v^2 - d^2s^2)y^2 - 2bc^2d^2y + b^2c^2d^2,$$

must have the same form as the expression obtained by multiplying

$$y^2 - 2ey + e^2 \text{ by } y^4 + fy^3 + g^2y^2 + h^3y + k^4,$$

that is, as

$$y^6 + (f - 2e)y^5 + (g^2 - 2ef + c^2)y^4 + (h^3 - 2eg^2 + e^2f)y^3 \\ + (k^4 - 2eh^3 + e^2g^2)y^2 + (e^2h^3 - 2ek^4)y + e^2k^4.$$

From these two equations, six others may be obtained, which serve to determine the six quantities $f, g, h, k, v,$ and s. It is easily seen that to whatever class the given curve may belong, this method will always furnish just as many equations as we necessarily have unknown quantities. In order to solve these equations, and ultimately to find v, which is the only value really wanted (the others being used only as means of finding v), we first determine f, the first unknown in the above expression, from the second term. Thus, $f = 2e - 2b$. Then in the last terms we can find k, the last unknown in the same expression, from

---

[154] That is, to construct PC we may lay off $AP = v$ and join P and C. If instead we use the value of e, taking C as center and a radius $CP = e$, we construct an arc cutting AG in P, and join P and C. Rabuel, p. 309. To apply Descartes's method to the circle, for example, it is only necessary to observe that all parameters and diameters are equal, that is, $q = r$; and therefore the equation $v = y - \dfrac{r}{q}y + \dfrac{1}{2}r$ becomes $v = \dfrac{1}{2}q = \dfrac{1}{2}$ diameter. That is, the normal passes through the center and is a radius of the circle. Rabuel, p. 313.

[155] See page 99. As before, Descartes uses "second equation" for "first member of the second equation."

which $k^4 = \dfrac{b^2c^2d^2}{e^2}$. From the third term we get the second quantity

$$g^2 = 3e^2 - 4be - 2cd + b^2 + d^2.$$

From the next to the last term we get h, the next to the last quantity, which is[156]

$$h^3 = \frac{2b^2c^2d^2}{e^3} - \frac{2bc^2d^2}{e^2}.$$

In the same way we should proceed in this order, until the last quantity is found.

Then from the corresponding term (here the fourth) we may find v, and we have

$$v = \frac{2e^3}{d^2} - \frac{3be^2}{d^2} + \frac{b^2e}{d^2} - \frac{2ce}{d} + e + \frac{2bc}{d} + \frac{bc^2}{e^2} - \frac{b^2c^2}{e^3};$$

or putting y for its equal e, we get

$$v = \frac{2y^3}{d^2} - \frac{3by^2}{d^2} + \frac{b^2y}{d^2} - \frac{2cy}{d} + y + \frac{2bc}{d} + \frac{bc^2}{y^2} - \frac{b^2c^2}{y^3},$$

for the length of AP.

[156] Found from.

Livre Second. 349

Puis par le troisiesme terme il faut chercher g la seconde quantité, & on a $gg \infty \; 3ee - 4be - 2cd + bb + dd$. Puis par le penultiesme il faut chercher h la penultiesme quantité, qui est $h^3 \infty \dfrac{2bbccdd}{e^3} - \dfrac{2bccdd}{ee}$. Et ainsi il faudroit continuer suiuant ce mesme ordre iusques a la derniere, s'il y en auoit d'auantage en cete somme; car c'est chose qu'on peut tousiours faire en mesme façon.

Puis par le terme qui suit en ce mesme ordre, qui est icy le quatriesme, il faut chercher la quantité v, & on a

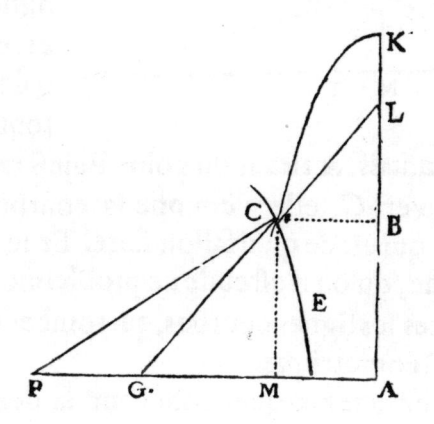

$$v \infty \dfrac{2e^3}{dd} - \dfrac{3bee}{dd} + \dfrac{bbe}{dd} - \dfrac{2ce}{d} + e + \dfrac{2bc}{d} + \dfrac{bcc}{ee} - \dfrac{bbcc}{e^3}.$$

ou mettant y au lieu d'e qui luy est esgal on a

$$v \infty \dfrac{2y^3}{dd} - \dfrac{3byy}{dd} + \dfrac{bby}{dd} - \dfrac{2cy}{d} + y + \dfrac{2bc}{d} + \dfrac{bcc}{yy} - \dfrac{bbcc}{y^3}.$$

pour la ligne A P.

Et ainsi la troisiesme equation, qui est

Xx 3

350 La Geometrie.

$$\frac{+2bcddz--2bcdez--2cddvz--2bdevz--bddss+bddvv}{zz \qquad\qquad\qquad\qquad bdd+cee+eev}$$

$$\frac{--cddss+cddvv}{--ddv}$$ a la mesme forme que

$zz-2fz+ff$, en supposant f esgal a z, si bienque il y a derechef equation entre $-2f$, ou $-2z$, &
$$\frac{+2bcdd--2bcde--2cddv--2bdev}{bdd+cee+eev--ddv}$$ d'où on connoist que
la quantité v est $\frac{bcdd--bcde+bddz+ceez}{cdd+bde--eez+ddz}$

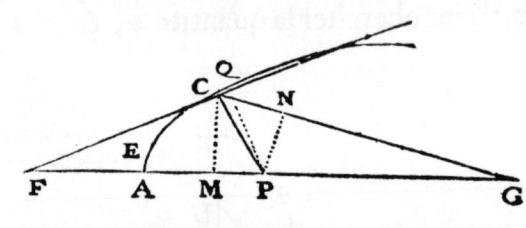

C'est pourquoy composant la ligne A P, de cete somme esgale à v dont toutes les quantités sont connuës, & tirant du point P ainsi trouué, vne ligne droite vers C, elle y couppe la courbe C E a angles droits. qui est ce qu'il falloit faire. Et ie ne voy rien qui empesche, qu'on n'estende ce problesme en mesme façon a toutes les lignes courbes, qui tombent sous quelque calcul Geometrique.

Mesme il est a remarquer touchant la derniere somme, qu'on prent a discretion, pour remplir le nombre des dimensions de l'autre somme, lorsqu'il y en manque, comme nous auons pris tantost
$y^4+fy^3+ggyy+h^3y+k^4$; que les signes $+$ & $-$ y peuuent estre supposés tels, qu'on veut, sans que la ligne v, ou A P, se trouue diuerse pour cela, comme vous pourrés aysement voir par experience. car s'il falloit que ie m'arestasse a demonstrer tous les theoresmes dont ie

fais

SECOND BOOK

Again, the third[157] equation, namely,

$$z^2 + \frac{2bcd^2z - 2bcdez - 2cd^2vz - 2bdevz - bd^2s^2 + bd^2v^2 - cd^2s^2 + cd^2v^2}{bd^2 + ce^2 + e^2v - d^2v},$$

is of the same form as $z^2 - 2fz + f^2$ where $f = z$, so that $-2f$ or $-2z$ must be equal to

$$\frac{2bcd^2 - 2bcde - 2cd^2v - 2bdev}{bd^2 + ce^2 + e^2v - d^2v},$$

whence

$$v = \frac{bcd^2 - bcde + bd^2z + ce^2z}{cd^2 + bde - e^2z + d^2z}.$$

Therefore, if we take AP equal to the above value of v, all the terms of which are known, and join the point P thus determined to C, this line will cut the curve CE at right angles, which was required. I see no reason why this solution should not apply to every curve to which the methods of geometry are applicable.[158]

It should be observed regarding the expression taken arbitrarily to raise the original product to the required degree, as we just now took

$$y^4 + fy^3 + g^2y^2 + h^3y + k^4,$$

that the signs $+$ and $-$ may be chosen at will, without producing different values of v or AP.[159] This is easily found to be the case, but if I should stop to demonstrate every theorem I use, it would require a

---

[157] First member of the third equation.

[158] Let us apply this method to the problem of constructing a normal to a parabola at a given point. As before, $s^2 = x^2 + v^2 - 2vy + y^2$. If we take as the equation of the parabola $x^2 = ry$, and substitute, we have

$$s^2 = ry + v^2 - 2vy + y^2 \quad \text{or} \quad y^2 + (r - 2v)y + v^2 - s^2 = 0.$$

Comparing this with $y^2 - 2ey + e^2 = 0$, we have $r - 2v = -2e$; $v^2 - s^2 = e^2$; $v = \frac{r}{2} + e$. Since $e = y$, $v = \frac{r}{2} + y$. Let AM $= y$, and $v =$ AP; then AM $-$ AP $=$ MP $=$ one-half the parameter. Rabuel, p. 314.

[159] It will be observed that Descartes did not consider a coefficient, as a, in the general sense of a positive or a negative quantity, but that he always wrote the sign intended. In this sentence, however, he suggests some generalization.

much larger volume than I wish to write. I desire rather to tell you in passing that this method, of which you have here an example, of supposing two equations to be of the same form in order to compare them term by term and so to obtain several equations from one, will apply to an infinity of other problems and is not the least important feature of my general method.[160]

I shall not give the constructions for the required tangents and normals in connection with the method just explained, since it is always easy to find them, although it often requires some ingenuity to get short and simple methods of construction.

---

[160] The method may be used to draw a normal to a curve from a given point, to draw a tangent to a curve from a point without, and to discover points of inflexion, maxima, and minima. Compare Descartes's Letters, Cousin, Vol. VI, p. 421. As an illustration, let it be required to find a point of inflexion on the first cubical parabola. Its equation is $y^3 = a^2x$. Assume that D is a point of inflexion, and let $CD = y$, $AC = x$, $PA = s$, and $AE = r$. Since triangle PAE is similar to triangle PCD we have $\frac{y}{x+s} = \frac{r}{s}$, whence $x = \frac{sy - rs}{r}$. Substituting in the equation of the curve, we have $y^3 - \frac{a^2sy}{r} + a^2s = 0$. But if D is a point of inflexion this equation must have three equal roots, since at a point of inflexion there are three coincident points of section. Compare the equation with

$$y^3 - 3ey^2 + 3e^2y - e^3 = 0.$$

Then $3e^2 = 0$ and $e = 0$. But $e = y$, and therefore $y = 0$. Therefore the point of inflexion is (0, 0). Rabuel, p. 321.

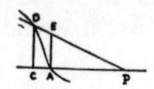

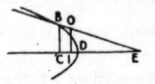

It will be of interest to compare the method of drawing tangents given by Fermat in *Methodus ad disquirendam maximam et minimam*, Toulouse, 1679, which is as follows: It is required to draw a tangent to the parabola BD from a point O without. From the nature of the parabola $\frac{CD}{DI} > \frac{\overline{BC}^2}{\overline{OI}^2}$, since O is without the curve. But by similar triangles $\frac{\overline{BC}^2}{\overline{OI}^2} = \frac{\overline{CE}^2}{\overline{IE}^2}$. Therefore $\frac{CD}{DI} > \frac{\overline{CE}^2}{\overline{IE}^2}$. Let $CE = a$, $CI = e$, and $CD = d$; then $DI = d - e$, and $\frac{d}{d-e} > \frac{a^2}{(a-e)^2}$; whence

$$de^2 - 2ade > -a^2e.$$

Dividing by e, we have $de - 2ad > -a^2$. Now if the line BO becomes tangent to the curve, the point B and O coincide, $de - 2ad = -a^2$, and e vanishes; then $2ad = a^2$ and $a = 2d$ in length. That is $CE = 2CD$.

LIVRE SECOND. 351

fais quelque mention, ie ferois contraint d'efcrire vn volume beaucoup plus gros que ie ne defire. Mais ie veux bien en paffant vous auertir que l'inuention de fuppofer deux equations de mefme forme, pour comparer feparement tous les termes de l'vne a ceux de l'autre, & ainfi en faire naiftre plufieurs d'vne feule, dont vous aués vû icy vn exemple, peut feruir a vne infinité d'autres Problefmes, & n'eft pas l'vne des moindres de la methode dont ie me fers.

Ie n'adioufte point les conftructions, par lefquelles on peut defcrire les contingentes ou les perpendiculaires cherchées, en fuite du calcul que ie viens d'expliquer, a caufe qu'il eft toufiours aifé de les trouuer: Bienque fouuent on ait befoin d'vn peu d'adreffe, pour les rendre courtes & fimples.

Comme par exemple, fi D C eft la premiere conchoide des anciens, dont A foit le pole, & B H la regle: en forte que toutes les lignes droites qui regardent vers A, & font comprifes entre la courbe C D, & la droite B H, comme D B & C E, foient efgales: Et qu'on veuille trouuer la ligne C G qui la couppe au point C a angles droits. On pourroit en cherchant, dans la ligne B H, le point par où cete ligne C G doit paffer, felon la methode icy expli-

Exemple de la conftruction de ce problefme, en la conchoide.

352 LA GEOMETRIE.

expliquée, s'engager dans vn calcul autant ou plus long qu'aucun des precedens: Et toutefois la construction, qui deuroit aprés en estre deduite, est fort simple. Car il ne faut que prendre C F en la ligne droite C A, & la faire esgale à C H qui est perpendiculaire sur H B: puis du point F tirer F G, parallele à B A, & esgale à E A: au moyen de quoy on a le point G, par lequel doit passer C G la ligne cherchée.

Explication de 4 nouueaux genres d'Oüales, qui feruent a l'Optique.

Au reste affin que vous sçachiées que la consideration des lignes courbes icy proposée n'est pas sans vsage, & qu'elles ont diuerses proprietés, qui ne cedent en rien a celles des sections coniques, ie veux encore adiouster icy l'explication de certaines Oüales, que vous verrés estre tres vtiles pour la Theorie de la Catoptrique, & de la Dioptrique. Voycy la façon dont ie les descris.

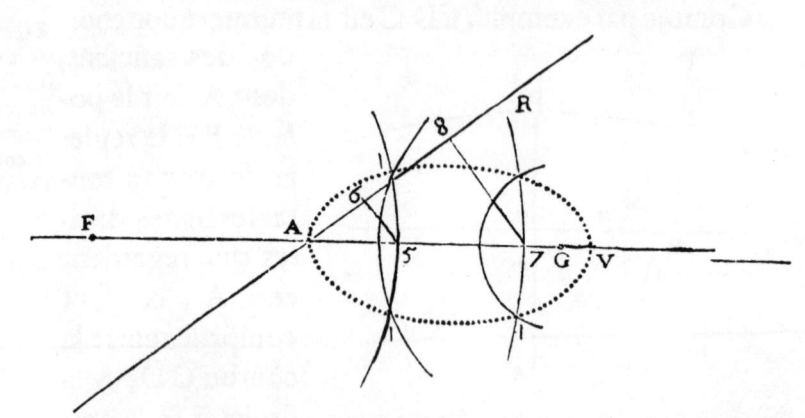

Premierement ayant tiré les lignes droites F A, & A R, qui s'entrecouppent au point A, sans qu'il importe a quels angles, ie prens en l'vne le point F a discretion, c'est a dire plus ou moins esloigné du point A selon que

ie

SECOND BOOK

Given, for example, CD, the first conchoid of the ancients (see page 113). Let A be its pole and BH the ruler, so that the segments of all straight lines, as CE and DB, converging toward A and included between the curve CD and the straight line BH are equal. Let it be required to find a line CG normal to the curve at the point C. In trying to find the point on BH through which CG must pass (according to the method just explained), we would involve ourselves in a calculation as long as, or longer than any of those just given, and yet the resulting construction would be very simple. For we need only take CF on CA equal to CH, the perpendicular to BH; then through F draw FG parallel to BA and equal to EA, thus determining the point G, through which the required line CG must pass.

To show that a consideration of these curves is not without its use, and that they have diverse properties of no less importance than those of the conic sections I shall add a discussion of certain ovals which you will find very useful in the theory of catoptrics and dioptrics. They

may be described in the following way: Drawing the two straight lines FA and AR (p. 114) intersecting at A under any angle, I choose arbitrarily a point F on one of them (more or less distant from A according as the oval is to be large or small). With F as center I describe a circle cutting FA at a point a little beyond A, as at the point 5. I then draw the straight line 56[161] cutting AR at 6, so that A6 is less than A5, and so that A6 is to A5 in any given ratio, as, for example, that which measures the refraction,[162] if the oval is to be used for dioptrics. This being done, I take an arbitrary point G in the line FA on the same side as the point 5, so that AF is to GA in any given ratio. Next, along the line A6 I lay off RA equal to GA, and with G as center and a radius equal to R6 I describe a circle. This circle will cut the first one in two points 1, 1,[163] through which the first of the required ovals must pass.

Next, with F as center I describe a circle which cuts FA as little nearer to or farther from A than the point 5, as, for example, at the point 7. I then draw 78 parallel to 56 and with G as center and a radius equal to R8 I describe another circle. This circle will cut the one through 7 in the points 1, 1[164] which are points of the same oval. We can thus find as many points as may be desired, by drawing lines parallel to 78 and describing circles with F and G as centers.

[161] The confusion resulting from the use of Arabic figures to designate points is here apparent.
[162] That is, the ratio corresponding to the index of refraction.
[163] "Au point 1."
[164] "Au point 1."

LIVRE SECOND. 353

ie veux faire ces Oualesplus ou moins grandes, & de ce point F comme centre ie defcris vn cercle, qui paſſe quelque peu au delà du point A, comme par le point 5, puis de ce point 5 ie tire la ligne droite 5 6, qui couppe l'autre au point 6, en ſorte qu' A 6 ſoit moindre qu' A 5, felon telle proportion donnée qu'on veut, a ſçauoir ſelon celle qui meſure les Refractions ſi on s'en veut feruir pour la Dioptrique. Aprés cela ie prens auſſy le point G, en la ligne F A, du coſté où eſt le point 5, a diſcretion, c'eſt a dire en faiſant que les lignes A F & G A ont entre elles telle proportion donnée qu'on veut. Puis ie fais R A eſgale à G A en la ligne A 6. & du centre G deſcriuant vn cercle, dont le rayon ſoit eſgal à R 6, il couppe l'autre cercle de part & d'autre au point 1, qui eſt l'vn de ceux par où doit paſſer la premiere des Oualescherchées. Puis derechef du centre F ie deſcris vn cercle, qui paſſe vn peu au deça, ou au delà du point 5, comme par le point 7, & ayant tiré la ligne droite 7 8 parallele a 5 6, du centre G ie deſcris vn autre cercle, dont le rayon eſt eſgal a la ligne R 8. & ce cercle couppe celuy qui paſſe par le point 7 au point 1, qui eſt encore l'vn de ceux de la meſme Ouale. Et ainſi on en peut trouuer autant d'autres qu'on voudra, en tirant derechef d'autres lignes paralleles à 7 8, & d'autres cercles des centres F, & G.

Pour la ſeconde Ouale il n'y a point de difference, ſinon qu'au lieu d' A R il faut de l'autre coſté du point A prendre A S eſgal à A G, & que le rayon du cercle deſcrit du centre G, pour coupper celuy qui eſt deſcrit du centre F & qui paſſe par le point 5, ſoit eſgal a la

Yy ligne

354   La Geometrie.

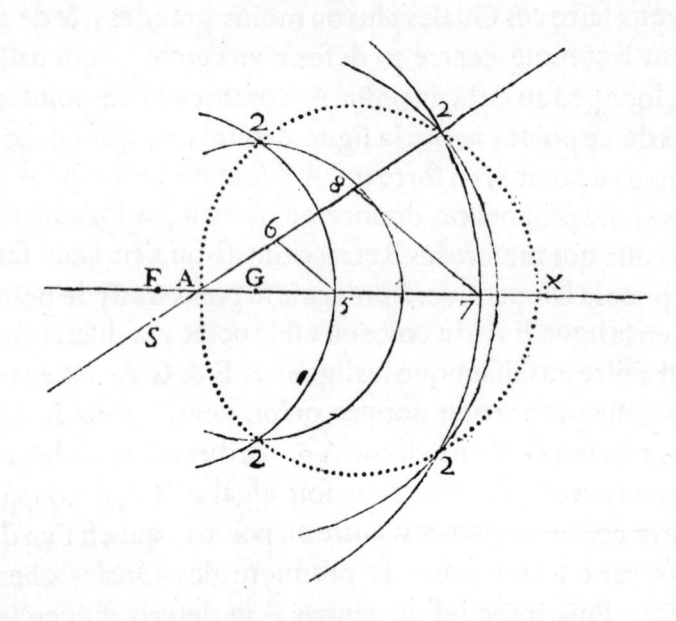

ligne S 6; ou qu'il soit esgal à S 8, si c'est pour coupper
celuy qui passe par le point 7. & ainsi des autres.   au
moyen dequoy ces cercles s'entrecouppent aux poins
marqués 2, 2, qui sont ceux de cete seconde Ouale
A 2 X.

Pour la troisiesme, & la quatriesme, au lieu de la ligne
A G il faut prendre A H de l'autre costé du point A, à
sçauoir du mesme qu'est le point F. Et il y a icy de plus
a obseruer que cete ligne A H doit estre plus grande que
A F: laquelle peut mesme estre nulle, en sorte que le
point F se rencontre où est le point A, en la description
de toutes ces oüales. Aprés cela les lignes A R, & A S
estant esgales à A H, pour descrire la troisiesme ouale
A 3 Y, ie fais vn cercle du centre H, dont le rayon est
esgal

SECOND BOOK

In the construction of the second oval the only difference is that instead of AR we must take AS on the other side of A, equal to AG, and that the radius of the circle about G cutting the circle about F and passing through 5 must be equal to the line S6; or if it is to cut the circle through 7 it must be equal to S8, and so on. In this way the circles intersect in the points 2, 2, which are points of this second oval A2X.

To construct the third and fourth ovals (see page 121), instead of AG I take AH on the other side of A, that is, on the same side as F. It should be observed that this line AH must be greater than AF, which in any of these ovals may even be zero, in which case F and A coincide. Then, taking AR and AS each equal to AH, to describe the third oval,

GEOMETRY

A3Y, I draw a circle about H as center with a radius equal to S6 and cutting in the point 3 the circle about F passing through 5, and another with a radius equal to S8 cutting the circle through 7 in the point also marked 3, and so on.

Finally, for the fourth oval, I draw circles about H as center with radii equal to R6, R8, and so on, and cutting the other circles in the points marked 4.[165]

[165] In all four ovals AF and AR or AF and AS intersect at A under any angle. F may coincide with A, and otherwise its distance from A determines the size of the oval. The ratio A5 : A6 is determined by the index of refraction of the material used. In the first two ovals, if A does not coincide with F it lies between F and G, and the ratio AF : AG is arbitrary. In the last two, if F does not coincide with A it lies between A and H, and the ratio AF : AH is arbitrary. In the first oval AR = AG and the points R, 6, 8 are on the same side of A. In the second oval AS = AG and S is on the opposite side of A from 6, 8. In the third oval AS = AH and S is on the opposite side of A from 6, 8. In the fourth oval AR = AH and R, 6, 8 are on the same side of A. Rabuel, p. 342.

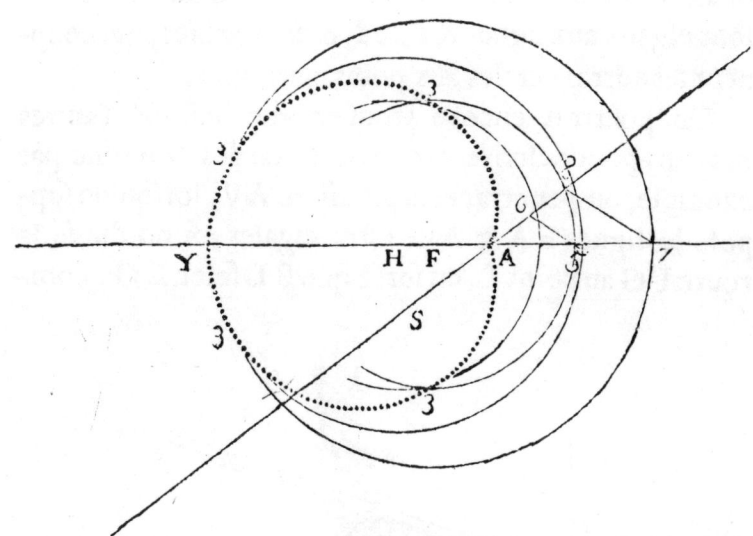

Livre Second. 355

esgal à S 6, qui couppe au point 3 celuy du centre F, qui passe par le point 5; & vn autre dont le rayon est esgal a S 8, qui couppe celuy qui passe par le point 7, au point aussy marqué 3; & ainsi des autres. Enfin pour la derniere

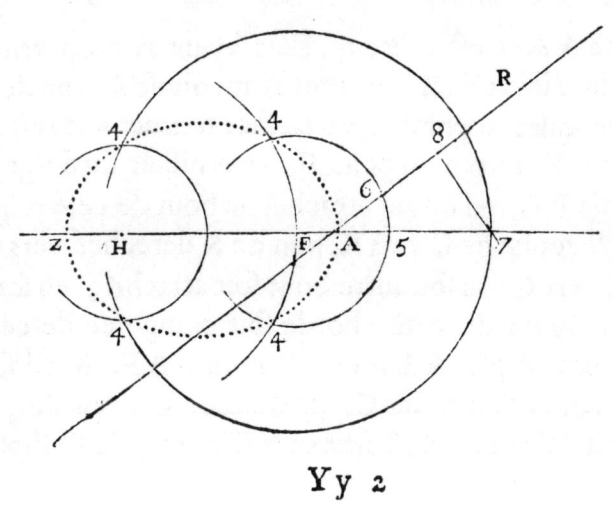

ouale

356 LA GEOMETRIE.

ouale ie fais des cercles du centre H , dont les rayons sont esgaux aux lignes R 6, R 8, & semblables, qui couppent les autres cercles aux poins marqués 4.

On pourroit encore trouuer vne infinité d'autres moyens pour descrire ces mesmes ouales. comme par exemple, on peut tracer la premiere A V, lorsqu'on suppose les lignes F A & A G estre esgales, si on diuise la toute F G au point L, en sorte que F L soit a L G, com-

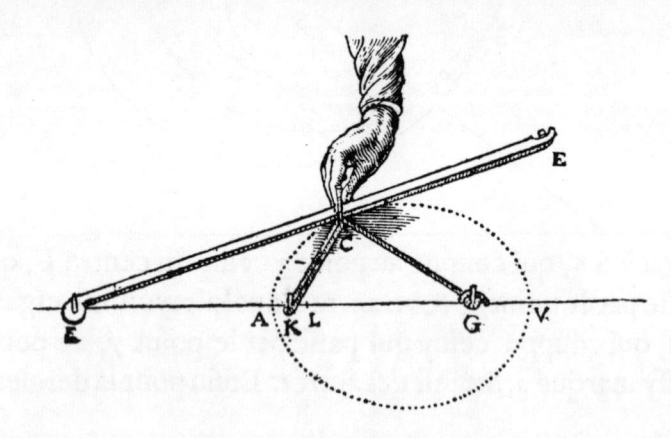

me A 5 à A 6. c'est à dire qu'elles ayent la proportion, qui mesure les refractions. Puis ayant diuisé A L en deux parties esgales au point K, qu'on face tourner vne reigle, comme F E, autour du point F, en pressant du doigt C, la chorde E C, qui estant attachée au bout de cete reigle vers E, se replie de C vers K, puis de K derechef vers C, & de C vers G, ou son autre bout soit attaché , en sorte que la longeur de cete chorde soit composée de celle des lignes G A plus A L plus F E moins A F. & ce sera le mouuement du point C, qui descrira cete ouale , a l'imitation de ce qui a esté dit en la Dioptriq; de l'Ellipse,

&

There are many other ways of describing these same ovals. For example, the first one, AV (provided we assume FA and AG equal) might be traced as follows: Divide the line FG at L so that FL : LG=A5 : A6, that is, in the ratio corresponding to the index of refraction. Then bisecting AL at K, turn a ruler FE about the point F, pressing with the finger at C the cord EC, which, being attached at E to the end of the ruler, passes from C to K and then back to C and from C to G, where its other end is fastened. Thus the entire length of the cord is composed of GA+AL+FE−AF, and the point C will describe the first oval in a way similar to that in which the

ellipse and hyperbola are described in *La Dioptrique*.[166] But I cannot give any further attention to this subject.

Athough these ovals seem to be of almost the same nature, they nevertheless belong to four different classes, each containing an infinity of sub-classes, each of which in turn contains as many different kinds as does the class of ellipses or of hyperbolas; the sub-classes depending upon the value of the ratio of A5 to A6. Then, as the ratio of AF to AG, or of AF to AH changes, the ovals of each sub-class change in kind, and the length of AG or AH determines the size of the oval.[167]

If A5 is equal to A6, the ovals of the first and third classes become straight lines; while among those of the second class we have all possible hyperbolas, and among those of the fourth all possible ellipses.[168]

In the case of each oval it is necessary further to consider two portions having different properties. In the first oval the portion toward A (see page 114) causes rays passing through the air from F to converge towards G upon meeting the convex surface 1A1 of a lens whose index of refraction, according to dioptrics, determines such ratios as that of A5 to A6, by means of which the oval is described.

[166] See the notes on pages 10, 55, 112.

[167] Compare the changes in the ellipse and hyperbola as the ratio of the length of the transverse axis to the distance between the foci changes.

[168] These theorems may be proved as follows: (1) Given the first oval, with $A5 = A6$; then $RA = GA$; $FP = F5$; $GP = R6 = AR - R6 = GA - A5 = G5$. Therefore $FP + GP = F5 + G5$. That is, the point P lies on the straight line FG. (2) Given the second oval, with $A5 = A6$; then $F2 = F5 = FA + A5$; $G2 = S6 = SA + A6 = SA + A5$; $G2 - F2 = SA - FA = GA - FA = C$. Therefore 2 lies on a hyperbola whose foci are F and G, and whose transverse axis is $GA - FA$. The proof for the third oval is analogous to (1) and that for the fourth to (2).

It may be noted that the first oval is the same curve as that described on page 98. For $FP = F5$, whence $FP - AF = A5$, and $AR = AG$; $GP = R6$; $AG - GP = A6$. If then $A5 : A6 = d : e$ we have, as before,

$$FP - AF : AG - GP = d : e.$$

Livre Second.

& de l'Hyperbole. mais ie ne veux point m'arefter plus long tems fur ce fuiet.

Or encore que toutes ces ouales femblent eftre quafi de mefme nature, elles font neanmoins de 4 diuers genres, chafcun defquels contient fous foy vne infinité d'autres genres, qui derechef contienent chafcun autant de diuerfes efpeces, que fait le genre des Ellipfes, ou celuy des Hyperboles. Car felon que la proportion, qui eft entre les lignes A 5, A 6, ou femblables, eft differente ; le genre fubalterne de ces ouales eft different. Puis felon que la proportion, qui eft entre les lignes A F, & A G, ou A H, eft changée, les ouales de chafque genre fubalterne changent d'efpece. Et felon qu' A G, ou A H eft plus ou moins grande, elles font diuerfes en grandeur. Et fi les lignes A 5 & A 6 font efgales, au lieu des ouales du premier genre ou du troifiefme, on ne defcrit que des lignes droites; mais au lieu de celles du fecond on a toutes les Hyperboles poffibles; & au lieu de celles du dernier toutes les Ellipfes.

Outre cela en chafcune de ces ouales il faut confiderer deux parties, qui ont diuerfes proprietés ; a fçauoir en la premiere, la partie qui eft vers A, fait que les rayons, qui eftant dans l'air vienent du point F, fe retournent tous vers le point G, lorfqu'ils rencontrent la fuperficie conuexe d'vn verre, dont la fuperficie eft 1 A 1, & dans lequel les refractions fe font telles, que fuiuant ce qui a efté dit en la Dioptrique, elles peuuent toutes eftre mefurées par la proportion, qui eft entre les lignes A 5 & A 6, ou femblables, par l'ayde defquelles on a defcrit cete ouale.

Les proprietés de ces ouales touchant les reflexions, & les refractions.

Y y 3

Mais

358   La Geometrie.

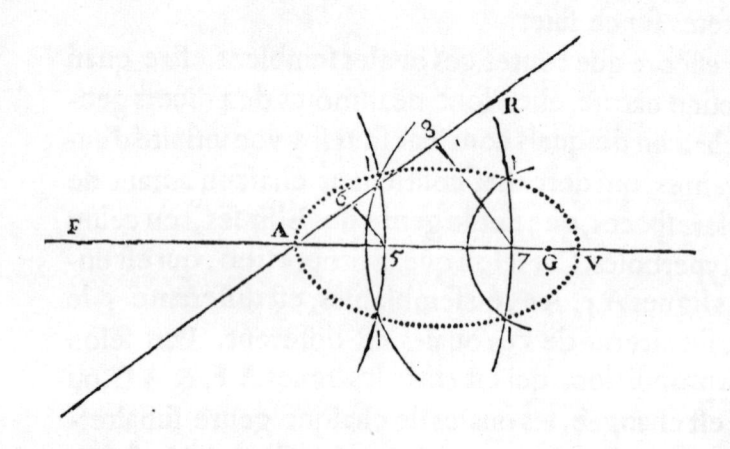

Mais la partie, qui est vers V, fait que les rayons qui vienent du point G se refleschiroient tous vers F, s'ils y rencontroient la superficie concaue d'vn miroir, dont la figure fust 1 V 1, & qui fust de telle matiere qu'il diminuast la force de ces rayons, selon la proportion qui est entre les lignes A 5 & A 6 : Car de ce qui a esté demonstré en la Dioptrique, il est euident que cela posé, les angles de la reflexion seroient inesgaus, aussy bien que sont ceux de la refraction, & pourroient estre mesurés en mesme sorte.

En la seconde ouale la partie 2 A 2 sert encore pour les reflexions dont on suppose les angles estre inesgaux. car estant en la superficie d'vn miroir composé de mesme matiere que le precedent, elle feroit tellement refleschir tous les rayons, qui viendroient du point G, qu'ils sembleroient après estre refleschis venir du point F. Et il est a remarquer, qu'ayant fait la ligne A G beaucoup
plus

But the portion toward V causes all rays coming from G to converge toward F when they strike the concave surface of a mirror of the shape of 1V1 and of such material that it diminishes the velocity of these rays in the ratio of A5 to A6, for it is proved in dioptrics that in this case the angles of reflection will be unequal as well as the angles of refraction, and can be measured in the same way.

Now consider the second oval. Here, too, the portion 2A2 (see page 118) serves for reflections of which the angles may be assumed unequal. For if the surface of a mirror of the same material as in the case of the first oval be of this form, it will reflect all rays from G, making them seem to come from F. Observe, too, that if the line AG

is considerably greater than AF, such a mirror will be convex in the center (toward A) and concave at each end; for such a curve would be heart-shaped rather than oval. The other part, X2, is useful for refracting lenses; rays which pass through the air toward F are refracted by a lens whose surface has this form.

The third oval is of use only for refraction, and causes rays traveling through the air toward F (page 121) to move through the glass toward H, after they have passed through the surface whose form is A3Y3, which is convex throughout except toward A, where it is slightly concave, so that this curve is also heart-shaped. The difference between the two parts of this oval is that the one part is nearer F and farther from H, while the other is nearer H and farther from F.

Similarly, the last of these ovals is useful only in the case of reflection. Its effect is to make all rays coming from H (see the second figure on page 121) and meeting the concave surface of a mirror of the same material as those previously discussed, and of the form A4Z4, converge towards F after reflection.

The points F, G and H may be called the "burning points" [169] of these ovals, to correspond to those of the ellipse and hyperbola, and they are so named in dioptrics.

I have not mentioned several other kinds of reflection and refraction that are effected[170] by these ovals; for being merely reverse or opposite effects they are easily deduced.

[169] That is, the foci, from the Latin *focus*, "hearth." The word *focus* was first used in the geometric sense by Kepler, *Ad Vitellionem Paralipomena,* Frankfort, 1604. Chap. 4, Sect. 4.

[170] "Reglées."

Livre Second. 359

plus grande que A F, ce miroir feroit conuexe au milieu, vers A, & concaue aux extremitez: car telle eſt la figure de cete ligne, qui en cela repreſente plutoſt vn coeur qu'vne ouale.

Mais ſon autre partie X 2 ſert pour les refractions, & fait que les rayons, qui eſtant dans l'air tendent vers F, ſe detournent vers G, en trauerſant la ſuperficie d'vn verre, qui en ait la figure.

La troiſieſme ouale ſert toute aux refractions, & fait que les rayons, qui eſtant dans l'air tendent vers F, ſe vont rendre vers H dans le verre, aprés qu'ils ont trauerſé ſa ſuperficie, dont la figure eſt A 3 Y 3, qui eſt conuexe par tout, excepté vers A où elle eſt vn peu concaue, en ſorte qu'elle a la figure d'vn coeur auſſy bien que la precedente. Et la difference qui eſt entre les deux parties de cete ouale, conſiſte en ce que le point F eſt plus proche de l'vne, que n'eſt le point H; & qu'il eſt plus eſloigné de l'autre, que ce meſme point H.

En meſme façon la derniere ouale ſert toute aux reflexions, & fait que ſi les rayons, qui vienent du point H, rencontroient la ſuperficie concaue d'vn miroir de meſme matiere que les precedens, & dont la figure fuſt A 4 Z 4, ils ſe refleſchiroient tous vers F.

De façon qu'on peut nommer les poins F, & G, ou H les poins bruſlans de ces ouales, a l'exemple de ceux des Ellipſes, & des Hyperboles, qui ont eſté ainſi nommés en la Dioptrique.

I'omets quantité d'autres refractions, & reflexions, qui ſont reiglées par ces meſmes ouales : car n'eſtant que les conuerſes, ou les contraires de celles cy, elles en
peuuent

360   **La Geometrie.**

Demoustration des proprietés de ces ouales touchant les reflexions & refractions.

peuuent facilement estre deduites. Mais il ne faut pas que i'omette la demonstration de ce que i'ay dit. & a cet effect, prenons par exemple le point C a discretion en la premiere partie de la premiere de ces ouales ; puis tirons la ligne droite CP, qui couppe la courbe au point C à angles droits, ce qui est facile par le problesme precedent ; Car prenant b pour AG, c pour AF, $c + z$ pour FC ; & supposant que la proportion qui est entre d & e, que ie prendray icy tousiours pour celle qui mesure les refractions du verre proposé, designe aussi celle qui est entre les lignes A 5, & A 6, ou semblables, qui ont serui pour descrire cete ouale, ce qui donne $b - \frac{e}{d}z$ pour GC: on trouue que la ligne A P est

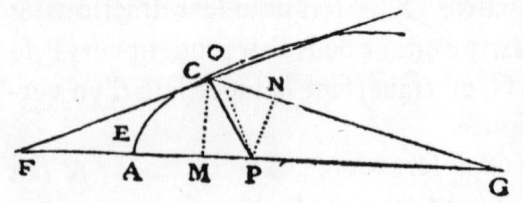

$$\frac{bcdd - bcde + bddz + ceez}{bde + cdd + ddz - eez}$$ ainsi qu'il a esté monstré cy dessus.

De plus du point P ayant tiré P Q a angles droits sur la droite F C, & P N aussi a angles droits sur G C, considerons que si P Q est à P N, comme d est à e, c'est à dire, comme les lignes qui mesurent les refractions du verre conuexe A C, le rayon qui vient du point F au point C, doit tellement s'y courber en entrant dans ce verre, qu'il s'aille rendre aprés vers G: ainsi qu'il est tres euident de ce qui a esté dit en la Dioptrique. Puis enfin voyons par le calcul, s'il est vray, que P Q soit à P N, comme d est à e. Les triangles rectangles P Q F, & C M F sont semblables ;

SECOND BOOK

I must not, however, fail to prove the statements already made. For this purpose, take any point C on the first part of the first oval, and draw the straight line CP normal to the curve at C. This can be done by the method given above,[171] as follows:

Let AG=b, AF=c, FC=$c+z$. Suppose the ratio of d to e, which I always take here to measure the refractive power of the lens under consideration, to represent the ratio of A5 to A6 or similar lines used to describe the oval. Then

$$GC = b - \frac{e}{d}z,$$

whence

$$AP = \frac{bcd^2 - bcde + bd^2z + ce^2z}{bde + cd^2 + d^2z - e^2z}.$$

From P draw PQ perpendicular to FC, and PN perpendicular to GC.[172] Now if PQ : PN=d : e, that is, if PQ : PN is equal to the same ratio as that between the lines which measure the refraction of the convex glass AC, then a ray passing from F to C must be refracted toward G upon entering the glass. This follows at once from dioptrics.

[171] See page 115.
[172] Here PQ is the sine of the angle of incidence and PN is the sine of the angle of refraction. The ray FC is reflected along CG.

GEOMETRY

Now let us determine by calculation if it be true that PQ : PN $=d:e$. The right triangles PQF and CMF are similar, whence it follows that CF : CM $=$ FP : PQ, and $\dfrac{\text{FP}\cdot\text{CM}}{\text{CF}} =$ PQ. Again, the right triangles PNG and CMG are similar, and therefore $\dfrac{\text{GP}\cdot\text{CM}}{\text{CG}} =$ PN. Now since the multiplication or division of two terms of a ratio by the same number does not alter the ratio, if $\dfrac{\text{FP}\cdot\text{CM}}{\text{CF}} : \dfrac{\text{GP}\cdot\text{CM}}{\text{CG}} = d:e$, then, dividing each term of the first ratio by CM and multiplying each by both CF and CG, we have FP . CG : GP . CF $=d:e$. Now by construction,

$$FP = c + \frac{bcd^2 - bcde + bd^2z + ce^2z}{cd^2 + bde - e^2z + d^2z},$$

or

$$FP = \frac{bcd^2 + c^2d^2 + bd^2z + cd^2z}{cd^2 + bde - e^2z + d^2z},$$

and

$$CG = b - \frac{e}{d}z.$$

Then

$$FP \cdot CG = \frac{b^2cd^2 + bc^2d^2 + b^2d^2z + bcd^2z - bcdez - c^2dez - bdez^2 - cdez^2}{cd^2 + bde - e^2z + d^2z}.$$

Then

$$GP = b - \frac{bcd^2 - bcde + bd^2z + ce^2z}{cd^2 + bde - e^2z + d^2z};$$

or

$$GP = \frac{b^2de + bcde - be^2z - ce^2z}{cd^2 + bde - e^2z + d^2z};$$

and CF $=c+z$. So that

$$GP \cdot CF = \frac{b^2cde + bc^2de + b^2dez + bcdez - bce^2z - c^2e^2z - be^2z^2 - ce^2z^2}{cd^2 + bde - e^2z + d^2z}.$$

Livre Second. 361

blables; d'où il suit que CF est à CM, comme FP est a PQ; & par consequent que FP, estant multipliée par CM, & diuisée par CF, est esgale a PQ. Tout de mesme les triangles rectangles PNG, & CMG sont semblables; d'où il suit que GP, multipliée par CM, & diuisée par CG, est esgale a PN. Puis a cause que les multiplications, ou diuisions, qui se font de deux quantités par vne mesme, ne changent point la proportion qui est entre elles; si FP multipliée par CM, & diuisée par CF, est à GP multipliée aussy par CM & diuisée par CG; comme d est à e, en diuisant l'vne & l'autre de ces deux sommes par CM, puis les multipliant toutes deux par CF, & derechef par CG, il reste FP multipliée par CG, qui doit estre à GP multipliée par CF, comme d est à e.

Or par la construction FP est $c\ \dfrac{\maltese\, bcdd - bcde \maltese\, bddz \maltese\, ceez}{bde \maltese\, cdd \maltese\, ddz - eez}$

oubien FP $\infty\ \dfrac{bcdd \maltese\, ccdd \maltese\, bddz \maltese\, cddz}{bde \maltese\, cdd \maltese\, ddz - eez}$. & CG est

$b - \dfrac{e}{d}z$. si bien que multipliant FP par CG il vient

$$\dfrac{bbcdd \maltese\, bccdd \maltese\, bbddz \maltese\, bcddz - bcdez - ccdez - bdezz - cdezz}{bde \maltese\, cdd \maltese\, ddz - eez}.$$

Puis GP est $b\ \dfrac{- bcdd \maltese\, bcde - bddz - ceez}{bde \maltese\, cdd \maltese\, ddz - eez}$. oubien

GP $\infty\ \dfrac{bbde \maltese\, bcde - beez - ceez}{bde \maltese\, cdd \maltese\, ddz - eez}$. & CF est $c + z$;

si bien que multipliant GP par CF, il vient

$$\dfrac{bbcde \maltese\, bccde - bceez - cceez \maltese\, bbdez \maltese\, bcdez - beezz - ceezz}{bde \maltese\, cdd \maltese\, ddz - eez}.$$

Et pource que la premiere de ces sommes diuisée par d, est la mesme que la seconde diuisée par e, il est manifeste, que FP multipliée par CG est a GP multipliée par CF;

Zz   c'est

c'eſt a dire que P Q eſt à P N, comme d eſt à e, qui eſt tout ce qu'il falloit demonſtrer.

Et ſçachés, que cete meſme demonſtration s'eſtend a tout cequi a eſté dit des autres refractions ou reflexions, qui ſe font dans les ouales propoſées; ſans qu'il y faille changer aucune choſe, que les ſignes $+$ & $-$ du calcul. c'eſt pourquoy chaſcun les peut ayſement examiner de ſoymeſme, ſans qu'il ſoit beſoin que ie m'y areſte.

Mais il faut maintenent, que ie ſatisface a ce que iay omis en la Dioptrique, lorſqu'aprés auoir remarqué, qu'il peut y auoir des verres de pluſieurs diuerſes figures, qui facent auſſy bien l'vn que l'autre, que les rayons venans d'vn meſme point de l'obiet, s'aſſemblent tous en vn autre point aprés les auoir trauerſés. & qu'entre ces verres, ceux qui ſont fort conuexes d'un coſté, & concaues de l'autre, ont plus de force pour bruſler, que ceux qui ſont eſgalement conuexes des deux coſtés. au lieu que tout au contraire ces derniers ſont les meilleurs pour les lunetes. ie me ſuis contenté d'expliquer ceux, que i'ay crû eſtre les meilleurs pour la prattique, en ſuppoſant la difficulté que les artiſans peuuent auoir a les tailler. C'eſt pourquoy, affin qu'il ne reſte rien a ſouhaiter touchant la theorie de cete ſcience, ie doy expliquer encore icy la figure des verres, qui ayant l'vne de leurs ſuperficies autant conuexe, ou concaue, qu'on voudra, ne laiſſent pas de faire que tous les rayons, qui vienent vers eux d'vn meſme point, ou paralleles, s'aſſemblent aprés en vn meſme point; & celle des verres qui font le ſemblable, eſtant eſgalement conuexes des deux coſtés, oubien la conue-

SECOND BOOK

The first of these products divided by d is equal to the second divided by e, whence it follows that $PQ : PN = FP . CG : GP . CF = d : e$, which was to be proved. This proof may be made to hold for the reflecting and refracting properties of any one of these ovals, by proper changes of the signs plus and minus; and as each can be investigated by the reader, there is no need for further discussion here.[173]

It now becomes necessary for me to supplement the statements made in my Dioptrique[174] to the effect that lenses of various forms serve equally well to cause rays coming from the same point and passing through them to converge to another point; and that among such lenses those which are convex on one side and concave on the other are more powerful burning-glasses than those which are convex on both sides; while, on the other hand, the latter make the better telescopes.[175] I shall describe and explain only those which I believe to have the greatest practical value, taking into consideration the difficulties of cutting. To complete the theory of the subject, I shall now have to describe

---

[173] To obtain the equation of the first oval we may proceed as follows: Let $AF = c$; $AG = b$; $FC = c+z$; $GC = b - \frac{e}{d}z$. Let $CM = x$, $AM = y$. $FM = c+y$; $GM = b-y$. Draw PC normal to the curve at any point C. Let $AP = v$. Then $\overline{CF}^2 = \overline{CM}^2 + \overline{FM}^2$. Also, $c^2 + 2cz + z^2 = x^2 + c^2 + 2cy + y^2$, whence

$$z = -c + \sqrt{x^2 + c^2 + 2cy + y^2}.$$

Also, $\overline{CG}^2 = \overline{CM}^2 + \overline{GM}^2$, whence

$$b^2 - 2\frac{be}{d}z + \frac{e^2}{d^2}z^2 = x^2 + b^2 - 2by + y^2.$$

Substituting in this equation the value of z obtained above, squaring, and simplifying, we obtain:

$$\left[(d^2 - e^2)x^2 + (d^2 - e^2)y^2 - 2(e^2c + bd^2)y - 2ec(ec - bd) \right]^2 = 4e^2(bd + ec)^2(x^2 + c^2 + 2cy + y^2). \text{ Rabuel, p. 348.}$$

[174] Descartes: *La Dioptrique*, published with *Discours de la Methode*, Leyden, 1637. See also Cousin, vol. III, p. 401.

[175] "Lunetes." The laws of reflection were familiar to the geometers of the Platonic school, and burning-glasses, in the form of spherical glass shells filled with water, or balls of rock crystal are discussed by Pliny, Hist. Nat. xxxvi, 67 (25) and xxxvii, 10. Ptolemy, in his treatise on Optics, discussed reflection, refraction, and plane and concave mirrors.

again the form of lens which has one side of any desired degree of convexity or concavity, and which makes all the rays that are parallel or that come from a single point converge after passing through it; and also the form of lens having the same effect but being equally convex on both sides, or such that the convexity of one of its surfaces bears a given ratio to that of the other.

In the first place, let G, Y, C, and F be given points, such that rays coming from G or parallel to GA converge at F after passing through a concave lens. Let Y be the center of the inner surface of this lens and C its edge, and let the chord CMC be given, and also the altitude of the arc CYC. First we must determine which of these ovals can be used for a lens that will cause rays passing through it in the direction of H (a point as yet undetermined) to converge toward F after leaving it.

There is no change in the direction of rays by means of reflection or refraction which cannot be effected by at least one of these ovals; and it is easily seen that this particular result can be obtained by using either part of the third oval, marked 3A3 or 3Y3 (see page 121), or the part of the second oval marked 2X2 (see page 118). Since the same method applied to each of these, we may in each case take Y

LIVRE SECOND. 363

conuexité de l'vne de leurs superficies ayant la proportion donnée à celle de l'autre.

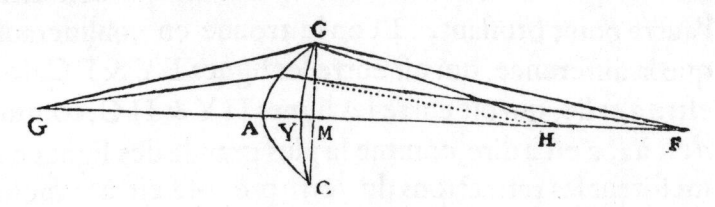

Posons pour le premier cas, que les poins G, Y, C, & F estant donnés, les rayons qui vienent du point G, oubien qui sont paralleles à G A se doiuent assembler au point F, aprés auoir trauersé vn verre si concaue, qu'Y estant le milieu de sa superficie interieure, l'extremité en soit au point C, en sorte que la chorde C M C, & la fleche Y M de l'arc C Y C, sont données. La question va là, que premierement il faut considerer, de laquelle des ouales expliquées, la superficie du verre Y C, doit auoir la figure, pour faire que tous les rayons, qui estant dedans tendent vers vn mesme point, comme vers H, qui n'est pas encore connu, s'aillent rendre vers vn autre, a sçauoir vers F, aprés en estre sortis. Car il n'y a aucun effect touchant le rapport des rayons changé par reflexion, ou refraction d'vn point a vn autre, qui ne puisse estre causé par quelqu'vne de ces ouales. & on voit aysement que cetuycy le peut estre par la partie de la troisiesme Ouale, qui a tantost esté marquée 3 A 3, ou par celle de la mesme, qui a esté marquée 3 Y 3, ou enfin par la partie de la seconde qui a esté marquée 2 X 2. Et pourceque ces trois tombent icy sous mesme calcul, on doit tant pour l'vne, que pour l'autre prendre Y pour

Commēt on peut faire vn verre autant conuexe ou concaue, en l'vne de ses superficies, qu'on voudra, qui rassemble a vn point donné, tous les rayons qui vienent d'vn autre point donné.

Zz 2 leur

LA GEOMETRIE.

leur sommet, C pour l'vn des poins de leur circonference, & F pour l'vn de leurs poins bruslans; aprés quoy il ne reste plus a chercher que le point H, qui doit estre l'autre point bruslant. Et on le trouue en considerant, que la difference, qui est entre les lignes F Y & F C, doit estre a celle, qui est entre les lignes H Y & H C, comme *d* est à *e*, c'est a dire, comme la plus grande des lignes qui mesurent les refractions du verre proposé est à la moindre; ainsi qu'on peut voir manifestement de la description de ces oualles. Et pourceque les lignes F Y & F C sont données, leur difference l'est aussy, & en suite celle qui est entre H Y & H C; pourceque la proportion qui est entre ces deux differences est donnée. Et de plus a cause que Y M est donnée, la difference qui est entre M H, & H C, l'est aussy; & enfin pourceque C M est donnée, il ne reste plus qu'à trouuer M H le costé du triangle

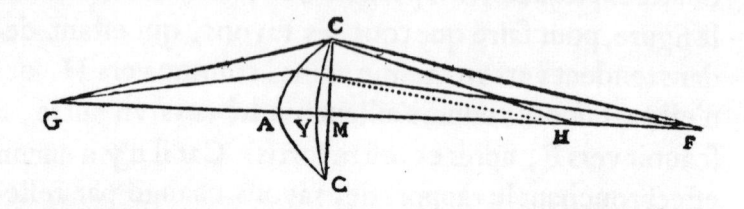

rectangle C M H, dont on a l'autre costé C M, & on a aussy la difference qui est entre C H la baze, & M H le costé demandé. d'où il est aysé de le trouuer. car si on prent *k* pour l'excés de C H sur M H, & *n* pour la longeur de la ligne C M, on aura $\frac{nn}{2k} - \frac{1}{2} k$ pour M H. Et aprés auoir ainsi le point H, s'il se trouue plus loin du point Y, que

(see pages 137 and 138), as the vertex, C as a point on the curve,[176] and F as one of the foci. It then remains to determine H, the other focus. This may be found by considering that the difference between FY and FC is to the difference between HY and HC as d is to e; that is, as the longer of the lines measuring the refractive power of the lens is to the shorter, as is evident from the manner of describing the ovals.

Since the lines FY and FC are given we know their difference; and then, since the ratio of the two differences is known, we know the difference between HY and HC.

Again, since YM is known, we know the difference between MH and HC, and therefore CM. It remains to find MH, the side of the right triangle CMH. The other side of this triangle, CM, is known, and also the difference between the hypotenuse, CH and the required side, MH. We can therefore easily determine MH as follows:

Let $k = \text{CH} - \text{MH}$ and $n = \text{CM}$; then $\dfrac{n^2}{2k} - \dfrac{1}{2}k = \text{MH}$, which determines the position of the point H.

[176] "Circonference."

If HY is greater than HF, the curve CY must be the first part of the third class of oval, which has already been designated by 3A3.

But suppose that HY is less than FY. This includes two cases: In the first, HY exceeds HF by such an amount that the ratio of their difference to the whole line FY is greater than the ratio of e, the smaller of the two lines that represent the refractive power, to d, the larger; that is, if HF$=c$, and HY$=c+h$, then dh is greater than $2ce+eh$. In this case CY must be the second part 3Y3 of the same oval of the third class.

In the second case dh is less than or equal to $2ce+eh$, and CY is the second part 2X2 of the oval of the second class.

Finally, if the points H and F coincide, FY $=$ FC and the curve YC is a circle.

It is also necessary to determine CAC, the other surface of the lens. If we suppose the rays falling on it to be parallel, this will be an ellipse having H as one of its foci, and the form is easily determined. If, however, we suppose the rays to come from the point G, the lens must have the form of the first part of an oval of the first class, the two foci of which are G and H and which passes through the point C. The point A is seen to be its vertex from the fact that the excess of GC over GA is to the excess of HA over HC as d is to e. For if k represents the difference between CH and HM, and x represents AM, then $x-k$ will represent the difference between AH and CH; and if g represents the difference between GC and GM, which are given, $g+x$

Livre Second.

que n'en eſt le point F, la ligne C Y doit eſtre la premiere partie de l'ouale du troiſieſme genre, qui a tantoſt eſté nommée 3 A 3: Mais ſi H Y eſt moindre que F Y, oubien elle ſurpaſſe H F de tant, que leur difference eſt plus grande a raiſon de la toute F Y, que n'eſt e la moindre des lignes qui meſurent les refractions comparée auec d la plus grande, c'eſt a dire que faiſant H F ∞ c, & H Y ∞ $c + h$, dh eſt plus grande que $2ce + eh$, & lors C Y doit eſtre la ſeconde partie de la meſme ouale du troiſieſme genre, qui a tantoſt eſté nomée 3 Y 3; Oubien dh eſt eſgale, ou moindre que $2ce + eh$: & lors C Y doit eſtre la ſeconde partie de l'ouale du ſecond genre qui a cy deſſus eſté nommée 2 X 2. Et enfin ſi le point H eſt le meſme que le point F, ce qui n'arriue que lorſque F Y & F C ſont eſgales cete ligne Y C eſt vn cercle.

Aprés cela il faut chercher C A C l'autre ſuperficie de ce verre, qui doit eſtre vne Ellipſe, dont H ſoit le point bruſlant; ſi on ſuppoſe que les rayons qui tombent deſſus ſoiët paralleles; & lors il eſt ayſé de la trouuer. Mais ſi on ſuppoſe qu'ils vienët du point G, ce doit eſtre la premiere partie d'vne ouale du premier genre, dont les deux poins bruſlans ſoiët G & H, & qui paſſe par le point C: d'où on trouue le point A pour le ſommet de cete ouale, en conſiderãt, que G C doit eſtre plus grãde que G A, d'vne quantité, qui ſoit a celle dont H A ſurpaſſe H C, comme d à e. car ayant pris k pour la difference, qui eſt entre C H, & H M, ſi on ſuppoſe x pour A M, on aura $x - k$, pour la difference qui eſt entre A H, & C H; puis ſi on prent g pour celle, qui eſt entre G C, & G M, qui ſont données, on aura $g + x$ pour celle, qui eſt entre G C, & G A; &

Zz 3 pour-

Commēt on peut faire vn verre, qui ait le mefme effect que le precedēt, & que la conuexité del'vne de ſes ſuperficies ait la proportion donnée auec celle del'autre.

pourceque cete derniere $g + x$ eſt à l'autre $x - k$, comme d eſt à e, on a $ge + ex \infty dx - dk$, oubien $\frac{ge \mp dk}{d - e}$ pour la ligne x, ou A M, par laquelle on determine le point A qui eſtoit cherché.

Poſons maintenant pour l'autre cas, qu'on ne donne que les poins G C, & F, auec la proportion qui eſt entre les lignes A M, & Y M, & qu'il faille trouuer la figure du verre A C Y, qui face que tous les rayons, qui vienent du point G s'aſſemblent au point F.

On peut derechef icy ſe ſeruir de deux ouales dont l'vne, A C, ait G & H pour ſes poins bruſlans; & l'autre,

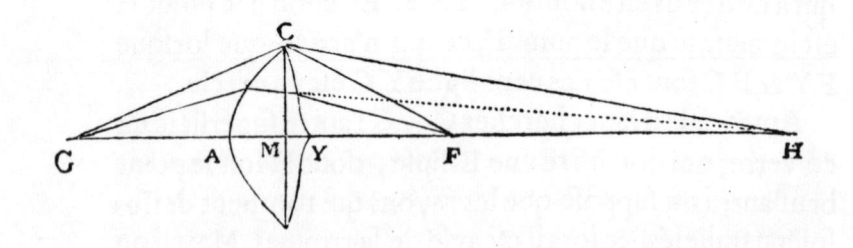

C Y, ait F & H pour les ſiens. Et pour les trouuer, premierement ſuppoſant le point H qui eſt commun a toutes deux eſtre connu, ie cherche A M par les trois poins G, C, H, en la façon tout maintenent expliquée; a ſçauoir preuant k pour la difference, qui eſt entre C H, & H M; & g pour celle qui eſt entre G C, & G M : & A C eſtant la premiere partie de l'Ouale du premier genre, iay $\frac{ge \mp dk}{d - e}$ pour A M : puis ie cherche auſſy M Y par les trois poins F, C, H, en ſorte que C Y ſoit la premiere partie d'vne ouale du troiſieſme genre; & prenant y pour M Y,

&

will represent the difference between GC and GA; and since $g+x : x-k = d : e$, we have $ge+ex = dx-dk$, or $AM = x = \frac{ge+dk}{d-e}$, which enables us to determine the required point A.

Again, suppose that only the points G, C, and F are given, together with the ratio of AM to YM; and let it be required to determine the form of the lens ACY which causes all the rays coming from the point G to converge to F.

In this case, we can use two ovals, AC and CY; with foci G and H, and F and H respectively. To determine these, let us suppose first that H, the focus common to both, is known. Then AM is determined by the three points G, C, and H in the way just now explained; that is if k represents the difference between CH and HM, and g the difference between GC and GM, and if AC be the first part of the oval of the first class, we have $AM = \frac{ge+dk}{d-e}$.

We may then find MY by means of the three points F, C, and H. If CY is the first part of an oval of the third class and we take y for MY and f for the difference between CF and FM, we have the dif-

ference between CF and FY equal to $f+y$; then let the difference between CH and HM equal k, and the difference between CH and HY equal $k+y$. Now $k+y : f+y = e : d$, since the oval is of the third class, whence $MY = \dfrac{fe-dk}{d-e}$. Therefore, $AM+MY=AY=\dfrac{ge+fe}{d-e}$, whence it follows that on whichever side the point H may lie, the ratio of the line AY to the excess of GC+CF over GF is always equal to the ratio of e, the smaller of the two lines representing the refractive power of the glass, to $d-e$, the difference of these two lines, which gives a very interesting theorem.[17]

The line AY being found, it must be divided in the proper ratio into AM and MY, and since M is known the points A and Y, and finally the point H, may be found by the preceding problem. We must first find whether the line AM thus found is greater than, equal to, or less than $\dfrac{ge}{d-e}$. If it is greater, AC must be the first part of one of the third class, as they have been considered here. If it is smaller, CY must be the first part of an oval of the first class and AC the first part

[17] "Qui est un assez beau théorème."

LIVRE SECOND. 367

& f pour la difference, qui est entre C F, & F M, i'ay
$f + y$, pour celle qui est entre C F, & F Y: puis ayant desia k pour celle qui est entre C H, & H M, iay $k + y$ pour celle qui est entre C H, & H Y, que ie scay deuoir estre
à $f + y$ comme e est à d, a cause de l'Ouale du troisiesme genre, d'où ie trouue que y ou M Y est $\frac{fe - dk}{d - e}$ puis ioignant ensemble les deux quantités trouuées pour A M, & M Y, ie trouue $\frac{ge + fe}{d - e}$ pour la toute A Y ; D'où il suit que de quelque costé que soit supposé le point H, cete ligne A Y est tousiours composée d'vne quantité, qui est a celle dont les deux ensemble G C, & C F surpassent la toute G F, Comme e, la moindre des deux lignes qui seruent a mesurer les refractions du verre proposé, est à $d - e$, la difference qui est entre ces deux lignes; ce qui est vn assés beau theoresme. Or ayant ainsi la toute A Y, il la faut couper selon la proportion que doiuent auoir ses parties A M & M Y; au moyen de quoy pource qu'on a desia le point M, on trouue aussy les poins A & Y ; & en suite le point H, par le problesme precedent. Mais auparauant il faut regarder, si la ligne A M ainsi trouuée est plus grande que $\frac{ge}{d - e}$ ou plus petite, ou esgale. Car si elle est plus grande, on aprent de là que la courbe A C doit estre la premiere partie d'vne ouale du premier genre; & C Y la premiere d'vne du troisiesme, ainsi qu'elles ont esté icy supposées: au lieu que si elle est plus petite, cela monstre que c'est C Y, qui doit estre la premiere partie d'vne ouale du premier genre; & que A C doit estre la premiere d'vne du troisiesme : Enfin si A M est esgale à $\frac{ge}{d - e}$

368　　La Geometrie.

$\frac{ge}{d--e}$ les deux courbes A C & C Y doiuent estre deux hyperboles.

On pourroit estendre ces deux problesmes a vne infinité d'autres cas, que ie ne m'areste pas a deduire, à cause qu'ils n'ont eu aucun vsage en la Dioptrique.

On pourroit aussy passer outre, & dire, lorsque l'vne des superficies du verre est donnée, pourueû qu'elle ne soit que toute plate, ou composée de sections coniques, ou de cercles; comment on doit faire son autre superficie, affin qu'il transmette tous les rayons d'vn point donné, a vn autre point aussy donné. car ce n'est rien de plus difficile que ce que ie viens d'expliquer ; ou plutost c'est chose beaucoup plus facile, à cause que le chemin en est ouuert. Mais i'ayme mieux, que d'autres le cherchent, affinque s'ils ont encore vn peu de peine à le trouuer, cela leur face d'autant plus estimer l'inuention des choses qui sont icy demonstrées.

Commēt on peut appliquer ce qui a esté dit icy des lignes courbes descrites sur vne superficie plate, à celles qui se descriuēt dãs vn espace qui a trois dimensions.　　Au reste ie n'ay parlé en tout cecy, que des lignes courbes, qu'on peut descrire sur vne superficie plate ; mais il est aysé de rapporter ce que i'en ay dit, à toutes celles qu'on sçauroit imaginer estre formées, par le mouuement regulier des poins de quelque cors, dans vn espace qui a trois dimensions. A sçauoir en tirant deux perpendiculaires, de chascun des poins de la ligne courbe qu'on veut considerer, sur deux plans qui s'entrecouppent a angles droits, l'vne sur l'vn, & l'autre sur l'autre. car les extremités de ces perpendiculaires descriuent deux autres lignes courbes, vne sur chascun de ces plans, desquelles on peut, en la façon cy dessus expliquée, determiner tous

les

of one of the third class. Finally, if AM is equal to $\frac{ge}{d-e}$, the curves AC and CY must both be hyperbolas.

These two problems can be extended to an infinity of other cases which I will not stop to deduce, since they have no practical value in dioptrics.

I might go farther and show how, if one surface of a lens is given and is neither entirely plane nor composed of conic sections or circles, the other surface can be so determined as to transmit all the rays from a given point to another point, also given. This is no more difficult than the problems I have just explained; indeed, it is much easier since the way is now open; I prefer, however, to leave this for others to work out, to the end that they may appreciate the more highly the discovery of those things here demonstrated, through having themselves to meet some difficulties.

In all this discussion I have considered only curves that can be described upon a plane surface, but my remarks can easily be made to apply to all those curves which can be conceived of as generated by the regular movement of the points of a body in three-dimensional space.[178] This can be done by dropping perpendiculars from each point of the curve under consideration upon two planes intersecting at right angles, for the ends of these perpendiculars will describe two other curves, one in each of the two planes, all points of which may be determined in the way already explained, and all of which may be related to those of a straight line common to the two planes; and by means of these the points of the three-dimensional curve will be entirely determined.

[178] This is the hint which Descartes gives of the possibility of the extension of his theory to solid geometry. This extension was effected largely by Parent (1666-1716), Clairaut (1713-1765), and Van Schooten (d. 1661).

GEOMETRY

We can even draw a straight line at right angles to this curve at a given point, simply by drawing a straight line in each plane normal to the curve lying in that plane at the foot of the perpendicular drawn from the given point of the three-dimensional curve to that plane and then drawing two other planes, each passing through one of the straight lines and perpendicular to the plane containing it; the intersection of these two planes will be the required normal.

And so I think I have omitted nothing essential to an understanding of curved lines.

Livre Second.

les poins, & les rapporter a ceux de la ligne droite , qui eſt commune a ces deux plans, au moyen dequoy ceux de la courbe, qui a trois dimenſions, ſont entierement determinés. Meſme ſi on veut tirer vne ligne droite, qui couppe cete courbe au point donné a angles droits · il faut ſeulement tirer deux autres lignes droites dans les deux plans, vne en chaſcun, qui couppent a angles droits les deux lignes courbes, qui y ſont, aux deux poins, où tombent les perpendiculaires qui vienent de ce point donné. car ayant eſleué deux autres plans , vn ſur chaſcune de ces lignes droites, qui couppe a angles droits le plan où elle eſt, on aura l'interſection de ces deux plans pour la ligne droite cherchée. Et ainſi ie penſe n'auoir rien omis des elemens, qui ſont neceſſaires pour la connoiſſance des lignes courbes.

BOOK THIRD

Geometry

BOOK III

ON THE CONSTRUCTION OF SOLID AND SUPERSOLID PROBLEMS

WHILE it is true that every curve which can be described by a continuous motion should be recognized in geometry, this does not mean that we should use at random the first one that we meet in the construction of a given problem. We should always choose with

LA
GEOMETRIE
LIVRE TROISIESME.

De la construction des Problesmes, qui sont Solides, ou plusque Solides.

ENCORE que toutes les lignes courbes, qui peuuent estre descrites par quelque mouuement regulier, doiuent estre receuës en la Geometrie, ce n'est pas a dire qu'il soit permis de se seruir indifferemment de la premiere qui se rencontre, pour la construction de chasque pro-

De quelles lignes courbes on peut se seruir, en la construction de chasq; problesme.

Aaa

370 　　　　La Geometrie.

problefme: mais il faut auoir foin de choifir toufiours la plus fimple, par laquelle il foit poffible de le refoudre. Et mefme il eft a remarquer, que par les plus fimples on ne doit pas feulement entendre celles, qui peuuent le plus ayfement eftre defcrites, ny celles qui rendent la conftruction, ou la demonftration du Problefme propofé plus facile, mais principalement celles, qui font du plus fimple genre, qui puiffe feruir a determiner la quantité qui eft cherchée.

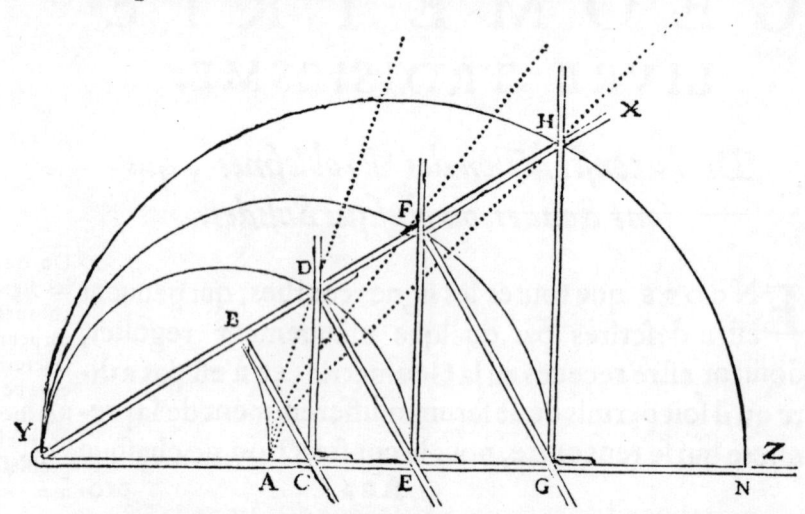

Exemple touchant l'inuentiõ de plufieurs moyẽnes proprotionelles.

Comme par exemple ie ne croy pas, qu'il y ait aucune façon plus facile, pour trouuer autant de moyennes proportionnelles, qu'on veut, ny dont la demonftration foit plus euidente, que d'y employer les lignes courbes, qui fe defcriuent par l'inftrument XYZ cy deffus expliqué. Car voulant trouuer deux moyennes proportionnelles entre YA & YE, il ne faut que defcrire vn cercle, dont le diametre foit YE; & pource que ce cercle couppe

care the simplest curve that can be used in the solution of a problem, but it should be noted that the simplest means not merely the one most easily described, nor the one that leads to the easiest demonstration or construction of the problem, but rather the one of the simplest class that can be used to determine the required quantity.

For example, there is, I believe, no easier method of finding any number of mean proportionals,[179] nor one whose demonstration is clearer, than the one which employs the curves described by the instrument XYZ, previously explained.[180] Thus, if two mean proportionals between YA and YE be required, it is only necessary to describe

[179] For the history of this problem, see Heath, *History,* Vol. I, p. 244, et seq.
[180] See page 46.

a circle upon YE as diameter cutting the curve AD in D, and YD is then one of the required mean proportionals. The demonstration becomes obvious as soon as the instrument is applied to YD, since YA (or YB) is to YC as YC is to YD as YD is to YE.

Similarly, to find four mean proportionals between YA and YG, or six between YA and YN, it is only necessary to draw the circle YFG, which determines by its intersection with AF the line YF, one of the four mean proportionals; or the circle YHN, which determines by its intersection with AH the line YH, one of the six mean proportionals, and so on.

But the curve AD is of the second class, while it is possible to find two mean proportionals by the use of the conic sections, which are curves of the first class.[181] Again, four or six mean proportionals can be found by curves of lower classes than AF and AH respectively. It would therefore be a geometric error to use these curves. On the other hand, it would be a blunder to try vainly to construct a problem by means of a class of lines simpler than its nature allows.[182]

Before giving the rules for the avoidance of both these errors, some general statements must be made concerning the nature of equations. An equation consists of several terms, some known and some unknown, some of which are together equal to the rest; or rather, all of which taken together are equal to nothing; for this is often the best form to consider.[183]

[181] If we let x and y represent the two mean proportionals between a and b we have $a : x = x : y = y : b$, whence $x^2 = ay$; $y^2 = bx$, and $xy = ab$. Therefore x and y may be found by determining the intersections of two parabolas or of a parabola and a hyperbola.

[182] Cf. Pappus, Book IV, Prop. 31, Vol. I, p. 273. See also Guisnée, *Application de l'Algèbre a la Géométrie,* Paris, 1733, p. 28, and L'Hospital, *Traité Analytique des Sections Coniques,* Paris, 1707, p. 400.

[183] The advantage of this arrangement had been recognized by several writers before Descartes.

Livre Troisiesme.

pe la courbe A D au point D, Y D est l'vne des moyennes proportionnelles cherchées. Dont la demonstration se voit a l'œil par la seule application de cet instrument sur la ligne Y D. car comme Y A, ou Y B, qui luy est esgale est a Y C; ainsi Y C est a Y D; & Y D a Y E.

Toutdemesme pour trouuer quatre moyennes proportionelles entre Y A & Y G; ou pour en trouuer six entre Y A & Y N, il ne faut que tracer le cercle Y F G, qui couppant A F au point F, determine la ligne droite Y F, qui est l'vne de ces quatre proportionnelles ; ou Y H N, qui couppant A H au point H, determine Y H l'vne des six, & ainsi des autres.

Mais pourceque la ligne courbe A D est du second genre, & qu'on peut trouuer deux moyenes proportionelles par les sections coniques, qui sont du premier ; & aussy pourcequ'on peut trouuer quatre ou six moyenes proportionelles, par des lignes qui ne sont pas de genres si composés, que sont A F, & A H, ce seroit vne faute en Geometrie que de les y employer. Et c'est vne faute aussy d'autre costé de se trauailler inutilement a vouloir construire quelque problesme par vn genre de lignes plus simple, que sa nature ne permet.

Or affin que ie puisse icy donner quelques reigles, pour euiter l'vne & l'autre de ces deux fautes, il faut que ie die quelque chose en general de la nature des Equations; c'est a dire des sommes composées de plusieurs termes partie connus, & partie inconnus, dont les vns sont esgaux aux autres, ou plutost qui considerés tous ensemble sont esgaux a rien. car ce sera souuent le meilleur de les considerer en cete sorte.

De la nature des Equatiōs.

Aaa 2 Scachés

372   LA GEOMETRIE.

Combien il peut y auoir de racines en chafq; Equatió.

Scachés donc qu'en chafque Equation, autant que la quantité inconnuë a de dimenfions, autant peut il y auoir de diuerfes racines, c'eft a dire de valeurs de cete quantité. car par exemple fi on fuppofe x efgale a 2; oubien $x - 2$ efgal a rien ; & derechef $x \infty 3$; oubien $x - 3 \infty 0$; en multipliant ces deux equations $x - 2 \infty 0$, & $x - 3 \infty 0$, l'vne par l'autre, on aura $xx - 5x + 6 \infty 0$, oubien $xx \infty 5x - 6$, qui eft vne Equation en laquelle la quantité x vaut 2 & tout enfemble vaut 3. Que fi derechef on fait $x - 4 \infty 0$, & qu'on multiplie cete fomme par $xx - 5x + 6 \infty 0$, on aura $x^3 - 9xx + 26x - 24 \infty 0$, qui eft vne autre Equation en laquelle x ayant trois dimenfions a auffy trois valeurs, qui font 2, 3, & 4.

Quelles font les fauffes racines.

Mais fouuent il arriue, que quelques vnes de ces racines font fauffes, ou moindres que rien. comme fi on fuppofe que x defigne auffy le defaut d'vne quantité, qui foit 5, on a $x + 5 \infty 0$, qui eftant multipliée par $x^3 - 9xx + 26x - 24 \infty 0$ fait

$$x^4 - 4x^3 - 19xx + 106x - 120 \infty 0$$

pour vne equation en laquelle il y a quatre racines, a fçauoir trois vrayes qui font 2, 3, 4, & vne fauffe qui eft 5.

Cóment on peut diminuer le nombre des dimenfions d'vne Equation lorfqu'on connoift quelqu'vne de fes racines.

Et on voit euidemment de cecy, que la fomme d'vne equation, qui contient plufieurs racines, peut toufiours eftre diuifée par vn binóme compofé de la quantité inconnuë, moins la valeur de l'vne des vrayes racines, laquelle que ce foit; ou plus la valeur de l'vne des fauffés. Au moyen de quoy on diminue d'autant fes dimenfions.

Et reciproquement que fi la fomme d'vne equation
ne

THIRD BOOK

Every equation can have[184] as many distinct roots (values of the unknown quantity) as the number of dimensions of the unknown quantity in the equation.[185] Suppose, for example, $x=2$ or $x-2=0$, and again, $x=3$, or $x-3=0$. Multiplying together the two equations $x-2=0$ and $x-3=0$, we have $x^2-5x+6=0$, or $x^2=5x-6$. This is an equation in which x has the value 2 and at the same time[186] x has the value 3. If we next make $x-4=0$ and multiply this by $x^2-5x+6=0$, we have $x^3-9x^2+26x-24=0$ another equation, in which x, having three dimensions, has also three values, namely, 2, 3, and 4.

It often happens, however, that some of the roots are false[187] or less than nothing. Thus, if we suppose x to represent the defect[188] of a quantity 5, we have $x+5=0$ which, multiplied by $x^3-9x^2+26x-24=0$, yields $x^4-4x^3-19x^2+106x-120=0$, an equation having four roots, namely three true roots, 2, 3, and 4, and one false root, 5.[189]

It is evident from the above that the sum[190] of an equation having several roots is always divisible by a binomial consisting of the unknown quantity diminished by the value of one of the true roots, or plus the value of one of the false roots. In this way,[191] the degree of an equation can be lowered.

On the other hand, if the sum of the terms of an equation[192] is not divisible by a binomial consisting of the unknown quantity plus or

[184] It is worthy of note that Descartes writes "can have" ("peut-il y avoir"), not "must have," since he is considering only real positive roots.

[185] That is, as the number denoting the degree of the equation.

[186] "Tout ensemble,"—not quite the modern idea.

[187] "Racines fausses," a term formerly used for "negative roots." Fibonacci, for example, does not admit negative quantities as roots of an equation. *Scritti de Leonardo Pisano*, published by Boncompagni, Rome, 1857. Cardan recognizes them, but calls them "æstimationes falsæ" or "fictæ," and attaches no special significance to them. See Cardan, *Ars Magna*, Nurnberg, 1545, p. 2. Stifel called them "Numeri absurdi," as also in Rudolff's Coss, 1545.

[188] "Le défaut." If $x=-5$, -5 is the "defect" of 5, that is, the remainder when 5 is subtracted from zero.

[189] That is, three positive roots, 2, 3, and 4, and one negative root, -5.

[190] "Somme," the left member when the right member is zero; that is, what we represent by $f(x)$ in the equation $f(x)=0$.

[191] That is, by performing the division.

[192] "Si la somme d'un équation."

minus some other quantity, then this latter quantity is not a root of the equation. Thus the[193] above equation $x^4-4x^3-19x^2+106x-120=0$ is divisible by $x-2$, $x-3$, $x-4$ and $x+5$,[194] but is not divisible by x plus or minus any other quantity. Therefore the equation can have only the four roots, 2, 3, 4, and 5.[195] We can determine also the number of true and false roots that any equation can have, as follows:[196] An equation can have as many true roots as it contains changes of sign, from + to − or from − to +; and as many false roots as the number of times two + signs or two − signs are found in succession.

Thus, in the last equation, since $+x^4$ is followed by $-4x^3$, giving a change of sign from + to −, and $-19x^2$ is followed by $+106x$ and $+106x$ by -120, giving two more changes, we know there are three true roots; and since $-4x^3$ is followed by $-19x^2$ there is one false root.

It is also easy to transform an equation so that all the roots that were false shall become true roots, and all those that were true shall become false. This is done by changing the signs of the second, fourth,

---

[193] First member of the equation. Descartes always speaks of dividing the equation.

[194] Incorrectly given as $x-5$ in some editions.

[195] Where 5 would now be written − 5. Descartes neither states nor explicitly assumes the fundamental theorem of algebra, namely, that every equation has at least one root.

[196] This is the well known "Descartes's Rule of Signs." It was known however, before his time, for Harriot had given it in his *Artis analyticae praxis*, London, 1631. Cantor says Descartes may have learned it from Cardan's writings, but was the first to state it as a general rule. See Cantor, Vol. II(1) pp. 496 and 725.

ne peut eſtre diuiſée par vn binôme compoſé de la quan- tité inconnue $+$ ou $-$ quelque autre quantité, cela teſ- moigne que cete autre quantité n'eſt la valeur d'aucune de ſes racines. Comme cete derniere

$$x^4 - 4x^3 - 19xx + 106x - 120 \infty 0$$

peut bien eſtre diuiſée, par $x-2$, & par $x-3$, & par $x-4$, & par $x+5$; mais non point par $x+$ ou $-$ aucune autre quantité. ce qui monſtre qu'elle ne peut auoir que les quatre racines 2, 3, 4, & 5.

Cóment on peut examiner ſi quelque quantité donnée eſt la valeur d'vne racine.

On connoiſt auſſy de cecy combien il peut y auoir de vrayes racines, & combien de fauſſes en chaſque Equation. A ſçauoir il y en peut auoir autant de vrayes, que les ſignes $+$ & $-$ s'y trouuent de fois eſtre changés ; & autant de fauſſes qu'il s'y trouue de fois deux ſignes $+$, ou deux ſignes $-$ qui s'entreſuiuent. Comme en la derniere, a cauſe qu'aprés $+x^4$ il y a $-4x^3$, qui eſt vn changement du ſigne $+$ en $-$, & aprés $-19xx$ il y a $+106x$, & aprés $+106x$ il y a -120 qui ſont encore deux autres changemens, on connoiſt qu'il y a trois vrayes racines; & vne fauſſe, a cauſe que les deux ſignes $-$, de $4x^3$, & $19xx$, s'entreſuiuent.

Combien il peut y auoir de vrayes racines en chaſque Equatió.

De plus il eſt ayſé de faire en vne meſme Equation, que toutes les racines qui eſtoient fauſſes deuienent vrayes, & par meſme moyen que toutes celles qui eſtoiẽt vrayes deuienent fauſſes : a ſçauoir en changeant tous les ſignes $+$ ou $-$ qui ſont en la ſeconde, en la quatrieſme, en la ſixieſme, ou autres places qui ſe deſignent par les nombres pairs, ſans changer ceux de la premiere, de la troiſieſme, de la cinquieſme & ſemblables qui ſe deſignent par les nombres impairs.

Cóment on fait que les fauſſes racines d'vne Equation deuienẽt vrayes, & les vrayes fauſſes.

Aaa 3

impairs. Comme si au lieu de

$+x^4 - 4x^3 - 19xx + 106x - 120 \infty 0$

on escrit

$+x^4 + 4x^3 - 19xx - 106x - 120 \infty 0$

on a vne Equation en laquelle il n'y a qu'vne vraye racine, qui est 5, & trois fausses qui sont 2, 3, & 4.

<small>Cõment on peut augmenter ou diminuer les racines d'vne Equation, sans les connoistre.</small> Que si sans connoistre la valeur des racines d'vne Equation, on la veut augmenter, ou diminuer de quelque quantité connuë, il ne faut qu'au lieu du terme inconnu en supposer vn autre, qui soit plus ou moins grand de cete mesme quantité, & le substituer par tout en la place du premier.

Comme si on veut augmenter de 3 la racine de cete Equation

$x^4 + 4x^3 - 19xx - 106x - 120 \infty 0$

il faut prendre y au lieu d'x, & penser que cete quantité y est plus grande qu'x de 3, en sorte que $y - 3$ est esgal a x, & au lieu d'xx, il faut mettre le quarré d'$y - 3$ qui est $yy - 6y + 9$ & au lieu d'x^3 il faut mettre son cube qui est $y^3 - 9yy + 27y - 27$, & enfin au lieu d'x^4 il faut mettre son quarré de quarré qui est $y^4 - 12y^3 + 54yy - 108y + 81$. Et ainsi descriuant la somme precedente en substituant par tout y au lieu d'x on a

$$y^4 - 12y^3 + 54yy - 108y + 81$$
$$+ 4y^3 - 36yy + 108y - 108$$
$$- 19yy + 114y - 171$$
$$- 106y + 318$$
$$- 120$$

$$y^4 - 8y^3 - 1yy \quad + 8y \quad \infty 0$$

oubien

sixth, and all even terms, leaving unchanged the signs of the first, third, fifth, and other odd terms. Thus, if instead of

$$+x^4-4x^3-19x^2+106x-120=0$$

we write

$$+x^4+4x^3-19x^2-106x-120=0$$

we get an equation having one true root, 5, and three false roots, 2, 3, and 4.[197]

If the roots of an equation are unknown and it be desired to increase or diminish each of these roots by some known number, we must substitute for the unknown quantity throughout the equation, another quantity greater or less by the given number. Thus, if it be desired to increase by 3 the value of each root of the equation

$$x^4+4x^3-19x^2-106x-120=0$$

put y in the place of x, and let y exceed x by 3, so that $y-3=x$. Then for x^2 put the square of $y-3$, or y^2-6y+9; for x^3 put its cube, $y^3-9y^2+27y-27$; and for x^4 put its fourth power,[198] or

$$y^4-12y^3+54y^2-108y+81.$$

Substituting these values in the above equation, and combining, we have

$$\begin{aligned} y^4 &- 12y^3 + 54y^2 - 108y + 81 \\ &+ 4y^3 - 36y^2 + 108y - 108 \\ & \quad\quad\;\; - 19y^2 + 114y - 171 \\ & \quad\quad\quad\quad\quad\;\; - 106y + 318 \\ & \quad\quad\quad\quad\quad\quad\quad\quad - 120 \\ \hline y^4 &- 8y^3 - y^2 + 8y \quad\quad\quad = 0,^{[199]} \end{aligned}$$

or
$$y^3-8y^2-y+8=0,$$

[197] In absolute value.

[198] "Son quarré de quarré," that is, its fourth power.

[199] Descartes wrote this $y^4-8y^3-y^2+8y$ * ∞ 0, indicating by a star the absence of a term in a complete polynomial.

GEOMETRY

whose true root is now 8 instead of 5, since it has been increased by 3. If, on the other hand, it is desired to diminish by 3 the roots of the same equation, we must put $y+3 = x$ and $y^2+6y+9 = x^2$, and so on. so that instead of $x^4 + 4x^3 - 19x^2 - 106x - 120 = 0$, we have

$$\begin{array}{r} y^4 + 12y^3 + 54y^2 + 108y + 81 \\ +\ 4y^3 + 36y^2 + 108y + 108 \\ -\ 19y^2 - 114y - 171 \\ -\ 106y - 318 \\ -\ 120 \\ \hline y^4 + 16y^3 + 71y^2 -\ 4y - 420 = 0. \end{array}$$

It should be observed that increasing the true roots of an equation diminishes[200] the false roots by the same amount; and on the contrary diminishing the true roots increases the false roots; while diminishing either a true or a false root by a quantity equal to it makes the root zero; and diminishing it by a quantity greater than the root renders a true root false or a false root true.[201] Thus by increasing the true root 5 by 3, we diminish each of the false roots, so that the root previously 4 is now only 1, the root previously 3 is zero, and the root previously 2 is now a true root, equal to 1, since $-2+3 = +1$. This explains why the equation $y^3-8y^2-y+8=0$ has only three roots,

[200] In absolute value.
[201] For example, the false root 5 diminished by 7 means $-(5-7)= +2$.

164

Livre Troisiesme. 375

oubien $y^3 -- 8yy -- 1y + 8 \infty 0$.

où la vraye racine qui estoit 5 est maintenant 8, a cause du nombre trois qui luy est aiousté.

Que si on veut au contraire diminuer de trois la racine de cete mesme Equation, il faut faire $y + 3 \infty x$ & $yy + 6y + 9 \infty xx$. & ainsi des autres de façon qu'au lieu de

$x^4 + 4x^3 -- 19xx -- 106x -- 120 \infty 0$

on met

$$\begin{array}{r} y_4 + 12y^3 + 54yy + 108y + 81 \\ + 4y^3 + 36\ yy + 108y + 108 \\ -- 19yy -- 114y -- 171 \\ -- 106y -- 318 \\ -- 120 \\ \hline \end{array}$$

$y^4 + 16y^3 + 71yy -- \quad 4y -- 420 \infty 0$.

Et il est a remarquer qu'en augmentant les vrayes racines d'vne Equation, on diminue les fausses de la mesme quantité; ou au contraire en diminuant les vrayes, on augmente les fausses. Et que si on diminue soit les vnes soit les autres, d'vne quantité qui leur soit esgale, elles deuienent nulles, & que si c'est d'vne quantité qui les surpasse, de vrayes elles deuienent fausses, ou de fausses vrayes. Comme icy en augmentant de 3 la vraye racine qui estoit 5, on a diminué de 3 chascune des fausses, en sorte que celle qui estoit 4 n'est plus qu'1, & celle qui estoit 3 est nulle, & celle qui estoit 2 est deuenue vraye & est 1, a cause que -- 2 + 3 fait + 1. c'est pourquoy en cete Equation $y^3 -- 8yy -- 1y + 8 \infty 0$ il ny a plus que 3 racines, entre lesquelles il y en a deux qui sont vrayes,

Qu'en augmentant les vrayes racines on diminue les fausses, & au contraire.

1. &

376   LA GEOMETRIE.

1, & 8, & vne fauſſe qui eſt auſſy 1. & en cete autre

$$y^4 + 16y^3 + 71yy - 4y - 420 \infty 0$$

il n'y en a qu'vne vraye qui eſt 2, a cauſe que $+5 - 3$ fait $+2$, & trois fauſſes qui ſont 5, 6, & 7.

Cóment on peut oſter le ſecond terme d'vne E-quation.

Or par cete façon de changer la valeur des racines ſans les connoiſtre, on peut faire deux choſes, qui auront cy aprés quelque vſage: la premiere eſt qu'on peut touſiours oſter le ſecond terme de l'Equation qu'on examine, a ſçauoir en diminuant les vrayes racines, de la quantité connuë de ce ſecond terme diuiſée par le nombre des dimenſions du premier, ſi l'vn de ces deux termes eſtant marqué du ſigne $+$, l'autre eſt marqué du ſigne $-$; oubien en l'augmentant de la meſme quantité, s'ils ont tous deux le ſigne $+$, ou tous deux le ſigne $-$. Comme pour oſter le ſecond terme de la derniere Equatiõ qui eſt

$$y^4 + 16y^3 + 71yy - 4y - 420 \infty 0$$

ayant diuiſé 16 par 4, a cauſe des 4 dimenſions du terme y^4, il vient derechef 4, c'eſt pourquoy ie fais $z - 4 \infty y$, & i'eſcris

$$z^4 - 16z^3 + 96zz - 256z + 256$$
$$+ 16z^3 - 192zz + 768z - 1024$$
$$+ 71zz - 568z + 1136$$
$$- 4z + 16$$
$$- 420$$

$$\overline{z^4 \quad * \quad - 25zz - 60 \quad z - 36 \infty 0.}$$

ou la vraye racine qui eſtoit 2, eſt 6, a cauſe qu'elle eſt augmentée de 4; & les fauſſes qui eſtoient 5, 6, & 7, ne ſont plus que 1, 2, & 3, a cauſe qu'elles ſont diminuées chaſcune de 4.

Tout

two of them, 1 and 8, being true roots, and the third, also 1, being false; while the other equation $y^4-16y^3+71y^2-4y-420=0$ has only one true root, 2, since $+5-3=+2$, and three false roots, 5, 6, and 7.

Now this method of transforming the roots of an equation without determining their values yields two results which will prove useful: First, we can always remove the second term of an equation by diminishing its true roots by the known quantity of the second term divided by the number of dimensions of the first term, if these two terms have opposite signs; or, if they have like signs, by increasing the roots by the same quantity.[202] Thus, to remove the second term of the equation $y^4+16y^3+71y^2-4y-420=0$ I divide 16 by 4 (the exponent of y in y^4), the quotient being 4. I then make $z-4=y$ and write

$$
\begin{array}{r}
z^4 - 16z^3 + 96z^2 - 256z + 256 \\
+ 16z^3 - 192z^2 + 768z - 1024 \\
+ 71z^2 - 568z + 1136 \\
- 4z + 16 \\
- 420 \\
\hline
z^4 \qquad - 25z^2 - 60z - 36 = 0.
\end{array}
$$

The true root of this equation which was 2 is now 6, since it has been increased by 4, and the false roots, 5, 6, and 7, are only 1, 2, and 3,

[202] That is, by diminishing the roots by a quantity equal to the coefficient of the second term divided by the exponent of the highest power of x, with the opposite sign.

since each has been diminished by 4. Similarly, to remove the second terms of $x^4-2ax^3+(2a^2-c^2)x^2-2a^3x+a^4=0$; since $2a \div 4 = \frac{1}{2}a$ we must put $z+\frac{1}{2}a=x$ and write

$$\begin{aligned}
z^4 + 2az^3 + \tfrac{3}{2}a^2z^2 + \tfrac{1}{2}a^3z + \tfrac{1}{16}a^4 & \\
- 2az^3 - 3a^2z^2 - \tfrac{3}{2}a^3z - \tfrac{1}{4}a^4 & \\
+ 2a^2z^2 + 2a^3z + \tfrac{1}{2}a^4 & \\
- c^2z^2 - ac^2z - \tfrac{1}{4}a^2c^2 & \\
- 2a^3z - a^4 & \\
+ a^4 & \\
\hline
z^4 + \left(\tfrac{1}{2}a^2-c^2\right)z^2 - (a^3+ac^2)z + \tfrac{5}{16}a^4 - \tfrac{1}{4}a^2c^2 = 0. &
\end{aligned}$$

Having found the value of z, that of x is found by adding $\frac{1}{2}a$. Second, by increasing the roots by a quantity greater than any of the false roots[203] we make all the roots true. When this is done, there will be no two consecutive + or − terms; and further, the known quantity of the third term will be greater than the square of half that of the second term. This can be done even when the false roots are unknown, since approximate values can always be obtained for them and the roots can then be increased by a quantity as large as or larger than is required. Thus, given,

[203] In absolute value.

LIVRE TROISIESME. 377

Tout de mesme si on veut oster le second terme de
$$x^4 - 2ax^3 \genfrac{}{}{0pt}{}{+\,2aa}{-\,cc} xx - 2a^3x + a^4 \infty\, 0,$$
pourceque divisant $2a$ par 4 il vient $\frac{1}{2}a$; il faut faire $z + \frac{1}{2}a \infty x$. & escrire

$$\begin{array}{l} z^4 + 2az^3 + \frac{3}{2}aazz + \frac{1}{2}a^3z + \frac{1}{16}a^4 \\ - 2az^3 - 3aazz - \frac{3}{2}a^3z - \frac{1}{4}a^4 \\ + 2aazz + 2a^3 + \frac{1}{2}a^4 \\ - cc - acc - \frac{1}{4}aacc \\ - 2a^3 - a^4 \\ + a^4 \end{array}$$

$$\overline{z^4 \quad * \quad + \frac{1}{2}aazz - a^3z + \frac{5}{16}a^4 \quad \infty\, 0}$$
$$ - cc - acc - \frac{1}{4}aacc$$

& si on trouue aprés la valeur de z, en luy adioustant $\frac{1}{2}a$ on aura celle de x.

La seconde chose, qui aura cy aprés quelque vsage, est, qu'on peut tousiours en augmentant la valeur des vrayes racines, d'vne quantité qui soit plus grande que n'est celle d'aucune des fausses, faire qu'elles deuienent toutes vrayes, en sorte qu'il n'y ait point deux signes +, ou deux signes – qui s'entresuiuent, & outre cela que la quantité connuë du troisiesme terme soit plus grande, que le quarré de la moitié de celle du second. Car encore que cela se face, lorsque ces fausses racines sont inconnuës, il est aysé neanmoins de iuger a peu pré. de leur grandeur, & de prendre vne quantité, qui les surpasse d'autant, ou de plus, qu'il n'est requis a cet effect. Comme si on a

Cóment on peut faire que toutes les fausses racines d'vne Equation deuienēt vrayes, sans que les vrayes deuienēt fausses.

Bbb x^6

378　La Geometrie.

$x^6 \mathbin{\text{✚}} nx^5 - 6nnx^4 \mathbin{\text{✚}} 36n^3x^3 - 216n^4x^2 \mathbin{\text{✚}} 1296n^5x - 7776n^6 \infty 0.$

en faifant $y - 6n \infty x$, on trouuera

$$\begin{array}{l}
y^6 - 36ny^5 \mathbin{\text{✚}} 540nny^4 - 4320n^3y^3 \mathbin{\text{✚}} 19440n^4yy - 46656n^5y \mathbin{\text{✚}} 46656n^6 \\
 \mathbin{\text{✚}} n - 30nn \mathbin{\text{✚}} 360n^3 - 2160n^4 \mathbin{\text{✚}} 6480n^5 - 7776n^6 \\
  - 6nn \mathbin{\text{✚}} 144n^3 - 1296n^4 \mathbin{\text{✚}} 5184n^5 - 7776n^6 \\
  \mathbin{\text{✚}} 36n^3 - 648n^4 \mathbin{\text{✚}} 3888n^5 - 7776n^6 \\
  - 216n^4 \mathbin{\text{✚}} 2592n^5 - 7776n^6 \\
  \mathbin{\text{✚}} 1296n^5 - 7776n^6
\end{array}$$

$y^6 - 35ny^5 \mathbin{\text{✚}} 504nny^4 - 3780n^3y^3 \mathbin{\text{✚}} 15120n^4y^2 - 27216n^5y \; \infty \; 0.$

Ou il est manifeste, que $504nn$, qui est la quantité connuë du troisiesme terme est plus grande, que le quarré de $\frac{35}{2}n$, qui est la moitié de celle du second. Et il n'y a point de cas, pour lequel la quantité, dont on augmente les vrayes racines, ait besoin a cet effect, d'estre plus grande, a proportion de celles qui sont données, que pour cetuy cy.

Cōment on fait que toutes les places d'vne Equation soient remplies.

Mais a cause que le dernier terme s'y trouue nul, si on ne desire pas que cela soit, il faut encore augmenter tant soit peu la valeur des racines ; Et ce ne sçauroit estre de si peu, que ce ne soit assés pour cet effect. Non plus que lorsqu'on veut accroistre le nombre des dimensions de quelque Equation, & faire que toutes les places de ses termes soient remplies. Comme si au lieu de $x^5 * * * * - b \infty 0$, on veut auoir vne Equation, en laquelle la quantité inconnue ait six dimensions, & dont aucun des termes ne soit nul, il faut premierement pour

$x^5 \; * \; * \; * \; * - b \infty 0$ escrire
$x^6 \; * \; * \; * \; * - bx \; * \infty 0$

puis ayant fait $y - a \infty x$, on aura

$y^6 - 6ay^5 \mathbin{\text{✚}} 15aay^4 - 20a^3y^3 \mathbin{\text{✚}} 15a^4yy - 6a^5y \mathbin{\text{✚}} a^6$
$- by \mathbin{\text{✚}} ab \; \infty \; 0$

Qu'il est manifeste que tant petite que la quantité a soit
supposée

THIRD BOOK

$$x^6 + nx^5 - 6n^2x^4 + 36n^3x^3 - 216n^4x^2 + 1296n^5x - 7776n^6 = 0,$$

make $y - 6n = x$ and we have,

$$\begin{aligned}
&\left.\begin{array}{r}y^6 - 36n \\ + n\end{array}\right\} \left.\begin{array}{r}y^5 + 540n^2 \\ - 30n^2 \\ - 6n^2\end{array}\right\} \left.\begin{array}{r}y^4 - 4320n^3 \\ + 360n^3 \\ + 144n^3 \\ + 36n^3\end{array}\right\} \left.\begin{array}{r}y^3 + 19440n^4 \\ - 2160n^4 \\ - 1296n^4 \\ - 648n^4 \\ - 216n^4\end{array}\right\} \left.\begin{array}{r}y^2 - 46656n^5 \\ + 6480n^5 \\ + 5184n^5 \\ + 3888n^5 \\ + 2592n^5 \\ + 1296n^5\end{array}\right\} \left.\begin{array}{r}y + 46656n^6 \\ - 7776n^6 \\ - 7776n^6 \\ - 7776n^6 \\ - 7776n^6 \\ - 7776n^6 \\ - 7776n^6\end{array}\right. \\
&\overline{y^6 - 35ny^5 + 504n^2y^4 - 3780n^3y^3 + 15120n^4y^2 - 27216n^5y = 0.}
\end{aligned}$$

Now it is evident that $504n^2$, the known quantity[204] of the third term, is larger than $\left(\frac{35}{2}n\right)^2$; that is, than the square of half that of the second term; and there is no case for which the true roots need be increased by a quantity larger in proportion to those given than for this one.

If it is undesirable to have the last term zero, as in this case, the roots must be increased just a little more, yet not too little, for the purpose. Similarly if it is desired to raise the degree of an equation, and also to have all its terms present, as if instead of $x^5 - b = 0$, we wish an equation of the sixth degree with no term zero, first, for $x^5 - b = 0$ write $x^6 - bx = 0$, and letting $y - a = x$ we have

$$y^6 - 6ay^5 + 15a^2y^4 - 20a^3y^3 + 15a^4y^2 - (6a^5 + b)y + a^6 + ab = 0.$$

It is evident that, however small the quantity a, every term of this equation must be present.

[204] I. e., the coefficient.

We can also multiply or divide all the roots of an equation by a given quantity, without first determining their values. To do this, suppose the unknown quantity when multiplied or divided by the given number to be equal to a second unknown quantity. Then multiply or divide the known quantity of the second term by the given quantity, that in the third term by the square of the given quantity, that in the fourth term by its cube, and so on, to the end.

This device is useful in changing fractional terms of an equation to whole numbers, and often[205] in rationalizing the terms. Thus, given $x^3 - \sqrt{3}\, x^2 + \frac{26}{27} x - \frac{8}{27\sqrt{3}} = 0$, let there be required another equation in which all the terms are expressed in rational numbers. Let $y = \sqrt{3}$ and multiply the second term by $\sqrt{3}$, the third by 3, and the last by $3\sqrt{3}$. The resulting equation is $y^3 - 3y^2 + \frac{26}{9} y - \frac{8}{9} = 0$. Next let it be required to replace this equation by another in which the known quantities are expressed only by whole numbers. Let $z = 3y$. Multiplying 3 by 3, $\frac{26}{9}$ by 9, and $\frac{8}{9}$ by 27, we have

$$z^3 - 9z^2 + 26z - 24 = 0.$$

The roots of this equation are 2, 3, and 4; and hence the roots of the

[205] But not always. Compare the case mentioned on page 175.

suppofee toutes les places de l'Equation ne laiſſent pas d'eſtre remplies.

De plus on peut, ſans connoiſtre la valeur des vrayes racines d'vne Equation, les multiplier, ou diuiſer toutes, par telle quantité connuë qu'on veut. Ce qui ſe fait en ſuppoſant que la quantité inconnuë eſtant multipliée, ou diuiſée, par celle qui doit multiplier, ou diuiſer les racines, eſt eſgale a quelque autre. Puis multipliant, ou diuiſant la quantité connuë du ſecond terme, par cete meſme qui doit multiplier, ou diuiſer les racines ; & par ſon quarré, celle du troiſieſme ; & par ſon cube, celle du quatrieſme ; & ainſi iuſques au dernier. Ce qui peut ſeruir pour reduire a des nombres entiers & rationaux, les fractions, ou ſouuent auſſy les nombres ſours, qui ſe trouuent dans les termes des Equations. Comme ſi on a

$x^3 - \sqrt{3}\,xx + \frac{26}{27}x - \frac{8}{27\sqrt{3}} \infty 0$,

Commēt on peut multiplier ou diuiſer les racines ſans les connoiſtre.

Cōment on reduiſt les nombres rompus d'vne Equation a des entiers.

& qu'on veuille en auoir vne autre en ſa place, dont tous les termes s'expriment par des nombres rationaux; il faut ſuppoſer $y \infty x\sqrt{3}$, & multiplier par $\sqrt{3}$ la quantité connuë du ſecond terme, qui eſt auſſy $\sqrt{3}$, & par ſon quarré qui eſt 3 celle du troiſieſme qui eſt $\frac{26}{27}$, & par ſon cube qui eſt $3\sqrt{3}$ celle du dernier, qui eſt $\frac{8}{27\sqrt{3}}$, ce qui fait

$y^3 - 3yy + \frac{26}{9}y - \frac{8}{9} \infty 0$

Puis ſi on en veut auoir encore vne autre en la place de celle cy, dont les quantites connuës ne s'expriment que par des nombres entiers; il faut ſuppoſer $z \infty 3y$, & multipliant 3 par 3, $\frac{26}{9}$ par 9, & $\frac{8}{9}$ par 27 on trouue

$z^3 - 9zz + 26z - 24 \infty 0$, où les racines eſtant 2, 3, & 4, on connoiſt de là que celles de l'autre d'auparauant eſtoient

estoient $\frac{2}{3}$, 1, & $\frac{4}{3}$, & que celles de la premiere estoient $\frac{2}{9}\sqrt{3}$, $\frac{1}{3}\sqrt{3}$, & $\frac{4}{9}\sqrt{3}$.

Cóment on rend la quantité connuë de l'vn des termes d'vne Equation esgale a telle autre qu'on veut.

Cete operation peut aussy seruir pour rendre la quantité connuë de quelqu'un des termes de l'Equatiõ esgale a quelque autre donnée, comme si ayant
$$x^3 \ast -bbx+c^3 \infty 0.$$
On veut auoir en sa place vne autre Equation, en laquelle la quantité connuë, du terme qui occupe la troisiesme place, a sçauoir celle qui est icy bb, soit $3aa$, il faut supposer $y \infty x \sqrt{\frac{3aa}{bb}}$; puis escrire $y^3 \ast -3aay+\frac{3a^3c^3}{b^3}\sqrt{3} \infty 0$.

Que les racines, tant vrayes que fausses peuuent estre reelles ou imaginaires.

Au reste tant les vrayes racines que les fausses ne sont pas tousiours reelles; mais quelquefois seulement imaginaires; c'est a dire qu'on peut bien tousiours en imaginer autant que iay dit en chasque Equation; mais qu'il n'y a quelquefois aucune quantité, qui corresponde a celles qu'on imagine. comme encore qu'on en puisse imaginer trois en celle cy, $x^3 -6xx+13x-10 \infty 0$, il n'y en a toutefois qu'vne reelle, qui est 2, & pour les deux autres, quoy qu'on les augmente, ou diminue, ou multiplie en la façon que ie viens d'expliquer, on ne sçauroit les rendre autres qu'imaginaires.

La reduction des Equatiõs cubiques lorsque le problesme est plan.

Or quand pour trouuer la construction de quelque problesme, on vient a vne Equation, en laquelle la quantité inconnuë a trois dimensions; premierement si les quantités connuës, qui y sont, contienent quelques nombres rompus, il les faut reduire a d'autres entiers, par la multiplication tantost expliquée ; Et s'ils en contienent de sours, il faut aussy les reduire a d'autres rationaux, autant qu'il sera possible, tant par cete mesme multiplication,

THIRD BOOK

preceding equation are $\frac{2}{3}$, 1 and $\frac{4}{3}$, and those of the first equation are

$$\frac{2}{9}\sqrt{3}, \frac{1}{3}\sqrt{3}, \text{ and } \frac{4}{9}\sqrt{3}.$$

This method can also be used to make the known quantity of any term equal to a given quantity. Thus, given the equation

$$x^3 - b^2 x + c^3 = 0,$$

let it be required to write an equation in which the coefficient of the third term,[206] namely b^2, shall be replaced by $3a^2$. Let

$$y = x\sqrt{\frac{3a^2}{b^2}}$$

and we have

$$y^3 - 3a^2 y + \frac{3a^3 c^3}{b^3}\sqrt{3} = 0.$$

Neither the true nor the false roots are always real; sometimes they are imaginary;[207] that is, while we can always conceive of as many roots for each equation as I have already assigned,[208] yet there is not always a definite quantity corresponding to each root so conceived of. Thus, while we may conceive of the equation $x^3 - 6x^2 + 13x - 10 = 0$ as having three roots, yet there is only one real root, 2, while the other two, however we may increase, diminish, or multiply them in accordance with the rules just laid down, remain always imaginary.

When the construction of a problem involves the solution of an equation in which the unknown quantity has three dimensions,[209] the following steps must be taken:

First, if the equation contains some fractional coefficients,[210] change them to whole numbers by the method explained above;[211] if it con-

---
[206] Descartes wrote this equation $x \quad * \quad - bbx + c^3 \infty 0$, the star showing, as explained on page 163, that a term is missing. Hence, he speaks of $-b^2 x$ as the third term.
[207] "Mais quelquefois seulement imaginaires." This is a rather interesting classification, signifying that we may have positive and negative roots that are imaginary. The use of the word "imaginary" in this sense begins here.
[208] This seems to indicate that Descartes realized the fact that an equation of the nth degree has exactly n roots. Cf. Cantor, Vol. II(1), p. 724.
[209] That is, a cubic equation.
[210] "Nombres rompues," the "numeri fracti" of the medieval Latin writers and "numeri rotti" of the Italians. The expression "broken numbers" was often used by early English writers.
[211] That is, transform the equation into one having integral coefficients.

GEOMETRY

tains surds, change them as far as possible into rational numbers, either by multiplication or by one of several other methods easy enough to find. Second, by examining in order all the factors of the last term, determine whether the left member of the equation is divisible[212] by a binomial consisting of the unknown quantity plus or minus any one of these factors. If it is, the problem is plane, that is, it can be constructed by means of the ruler and compasses; for either the known quantity of the binomial is the required root[213] or else, having divided the left member of the equation by the binomial, the quotient is of the second degree, and from this quotient the root can be found as explained in the first book.[214]

Given, for example, $y^6-8y^4-124y^2-64 = 0$.[215] The last term, 64, is divisible by 1, 2, 4, 8, 16, 32, and 64; therefore we must find whether the left member is divisible by y^2-1, y^2+1, y^2-2, y^2+2, y^2-4, and so on. We shall find that it is divisible by y^2-16 as follows:

$$\begin{array}{r}+y^6 - 8y^4 - 124y^2 - 64 = 0\\ -y^6 - 8y^4 - 4y^2 \\ \hline 0 - 16y^4 - 128y^2 \\ -16 - 16 \\ \hline + y^4 + 8y^2 + 4 = 0\end{array} - 16$$

Beginning with the last term, I divide -64 by -16 which gives $+4$; write this in the quotient; multiply $+4$ by $+y^2$ which gives $+4y^2$ and

[212] "Qui divise toute la somme."
[213] That is, the root that satisfies the conditions of the problem.
[214] See page 13.
[215] Descartes considers this equation as a function of y^2.

LIVRE TROISISEME. 381

tiplication, que par diuers autres moyens, qui sont assés faciles a trouuer. Puis examinant par ordre toutes les quantités, qui peuuent diuiser sans fraction le dernier terme, il faut voir, si quelqu'vne d'elles, iointe auec la quantité inconnuë par le signe $+$ ou $-$, peut composer vn binome, qui diuise toute la somme; & si cela est le Problesme est plan, c'est a dire il peut estre construit auec la reigle & de compas; Car oubien la quantité connuë de ce binosme est la racine cherchée; oubien l'Equation estant diuisée par luy, se reduist a deux dimensions, en sorte qu'on en peut trouuer aprés la racine, par ce qui a esté dit au premier liure.

Par exemple si on a

$$y^6 - 8y^4 - 124y^2 - 64 \infty 0.$$

le dernier terme, qui est 64, peut estre diuisé sans fraction par 1, 2, 4, 8, 16, 32, & 64; C'est pourquoy il faut examiner par ordre si cete Equation ne peut point estre diuisée par quelqu'vn des binomes, $yy - 1$ ou $yy + 1, yy - 2$ ou $yy + 2, yy - 4$ &c. & on trouue qu'elle peut l'estre par $yy - 16$, en cete sorte.

$$
\begin{array}{c}
+\ y^6 - 8y^4 - 124yy - 64 \infty 0 \\
- y^6 - 8y^4 - 4yy \\ \hline
0 - 16y^4 - 128yy \\
16 16 \\ \hline
+ y^4 + 8yy + 4 \infty 0.
\end{array}
$$

Ie commence par le dernièr terme, & diuise -64 par -16, ce qui fait $+4$, que i'escris dans le quotient, puis ie multiplie $+4$ par $+yy$, ce qui fait $+4yy$; c'est pourquoy i'escris $-4yy$ en la somme, qu'il faut diuiser. car il y faut

La façon de diuiser vne Equation par vn binome qui contiét sa racine.

Bbb 3

faut toufiours efcrire le figne $+$ ou $-$ tout contraire a celuy que produift la multiplication. & ioignant $-124yy$ auec $-4yy$, iay $-128yy$, que ie diuife derechef par -16, & iay $+8yy$, pour mettre dans le quotient & en le multipliant par yy, iay $-8y^4$, pour ioindre auec le terme qu'il faut diuifer, qui eft auffy $-8y^4$, & ces deux enfemble font $-16y^4$, que ie diuife par -16, ce qui fait $+1y^4$ pour fe quotient, & $-1y_6$ pour ioindre auec $+1y^6$, ce qui fait o, & monftre que la diuifion eft acheuée. Mais s'il eftoit refté quelque quantité, oubien qu'on n'euft pû diuifer fans fraction quelqu'vn des termes precedens, on euft par la reconnu, quelle ne pouuoit eftre faite.

Tout de mefme fi on a $y^6 \genfrac{}{}{0pt}{}{+aa}{-2cc} y^4 \genfrac{}{}{0pt}{}{-a^4}{+c^4} yy \genfrac{}{}{0pt}{}{-a^6}{-2a^4cc} \infty 0.$
le dernier terme fe peut diuifer fans fraction par $a, aa, aa+cc, a^3+acc$, & femblables. Mais il n'y en a que deux qu'on ait befoin de confiderer, à fçauoir aa & $aa+cc$; car les autres donnant plus ou moins de dimenfions dans le quotient, qu'il n'y en a en la quantité connuë du penultiefme terme, empefcheroient que la diuifion ne s'y pûft faire. Et notés, que ie ne conte icy les dimenfions d'y^6, que pour trois, a caufe qu'il ny a point d'y^5, ny d'y^3, ny d'y en toute la fomme. Or en examinant le binóme $yy-aa-cc \infty 0$, on trouue que la diuifion fe peut faire par luy en cete forte.

$$+y^6 \genfrac{}{}{0pt}{}{+aa}{-2cc} y^4 \genfrac{}{}{0pt}{}{-a^4}{+c^4} yy \genfrac{}{}{0pt}{}{-a^6}{-2a^4cc} \infty 0,$$
$$\underline{-y^6 \genfrac{}{}{0pt}{}{-2aa}{+cc} \quad \genfrac{}{}{0pt}{}{-a^4}{-aacc} \genfrac{}{}{0pt}{}{-aa-cc}{-aa-cc}}$$
$$+y^4 \genfrac{}{}{0pt}{}{+2aa}{-cc} yy \genfrac{}{}{0pt}{}{+a^4}{+aacc} \infty 0. \qquad \text{Ce-}$$

write in the dividend (for the opposite sign from that obtained by the multiplication must always be used). Adding $-124y^2$ and $-4y^2$ I have $-128y^2$. Dividing this by -16 I have $+8y^2$ in the quotient, and multiplying by y^2 I have $-8y^4$ to be added to the corresponding term, $-8y^4$, in the dividend. This gives $-16y^4$ which divided by -16 yields $+y^4$ in the quotient and $-y^6$ to be added to $+y^6$ which gives zero, and shows that the division is finished.

If, however, there is a remainder, or if any modified term is not exactly divisible by 16, then it is clear that the binomial is not a divisor.[216]

Similarly, given

$$\left. \begin{array}{l} y^6 + \left. \begin{array}{l} a^2 \\ -2c^2 \end{array} \right\} y^4 \left. \begin{array}{l} -a^4 \\ +c^4 \end{array} \right\} y^2 \left. \begin{array}{l} -a^6 \\ -2a^4c^2 \\ -a^2c^4 \end{array} \right\} = 0, \end{array} \right.$$

the last term is divisible by a, a^2, a^2+c^2, a^3+ac^2, and so on, but only two of these need be considered, namely a^2 and a^2+c^2. The others give a term in the quotient of lower or higher degree than the known quantity of the next to the last term, and thus render the division impossible.[217] Note that I am here considering y^6 as of the third degree, since there are no terms in y^5, y^3, or y. Trying the binomial

$$y^2 - a^2 - c^2 = 0$$

we find that the division can be performed as follows:

$$\left. \begin{array}{l} +y^6 + \left. \begin{array}{l} a^2 \\ -y^6 - 2c^2 \end{array} \right\} y^4 \left. \begin{array}{l} -a^4 \\ +c^4 \end{array} \right\} y^2 \left. \begin{array}{l} -a^6 \\ -2a^4c^2 \end{array} \right\} \\ \overline{} \\ 0 - 2a^2 \left. \begin{array}{l} \\ +c^2 \end{array} \right\} y^4 \left. \begin{array}{l} -a^4 \\ -a^2c^2 \end{array} \right\} y^2 \left. \begin{array}{l} -a^2c^4 \\ -a^2-c^2 \end{array} \right\} \\ \overline{-a^2-c^2 \quad -a^2-c^2} \\ +y^4 \qquad + 2a^2 \left. \begin{array}{l} \\ -c^2 \end{array} \right\} y^2 + \left. \begin{array}{l} a^4 \\ +a^2c^2 \end{array} \right\} = 0, \end{array} \right. = 0$$

---

[216] This is evidently a modified form of our modern "synthetic division," the basis of our "Remainder Theorem," and of Horner's Method of solving numerical equations, a method known to the Chinese in the thirteenth century. See Cantor, Vol. II(1), pp. 279 and 287. See also Smith and Mikami, *History of Japanese Mathematics*, Chicago, 1914; Smith, I, 273.

[217] This is not a general rule.

GEOMETRY

This shows that a^2+c^2 is the required root, which can easily be proved by multiplication.

But when no binomial divisor of the proposed equation can be found, it is certain that the problem depending upon it is solid,[218] and it is then as great a mistake to try to construct it by using only circles and straight lines as it is to use the conic sections to construct a problem requiring only circles; for any evidence of ignorance may be termed a mistake.

Again, given an equation in which the unknown quantity has four dimensions.[219] After removing any surds or fractions, see if a binomial having one term a factor of the last term of the expression will divide the left member. If such a binomial can be found, either the known quantity of the binomial is the required root, or,[220] after the division is performed, the resulting equation, which is of only three dimensions, must be treated in the same way. If no such binomial can be found, we must increase or diminish the roots so as to remove the second term, in the way already explained, and then reduce it to another of the third degree, in the following manner: Instead of

$$x^4 \pm px^2 \pm qx \pm r = 0$$

write

$$y^6 \pm 2py^4 + (p^2 \pm 4r)y^2 - q^2 = 0.\text{[221]}$$

[218] That is, that it involves a conic or some higher curve.

[219] A biquadratic equation.

[220] "Either, or," as in the original. It is like saying that the root of $x^2-a^2=0$ is either $x=a$ or $x=-a$.

[221] Descartes wrote substantially "Instead of

$$+ x^4 *.pxx.qx.r \infty 0$$

write

$$+ y^6.2py^4 + (pp.4r)yy - qq \infty 0."$$

The symbolism is characteristic of Descartes.

LIVRE TROISIESME. 383

Ce qui monstre que la racine cherchée est $aa+cc$. Et la preuue en est aysée a faire par la multiplication.

Mais lorsqu'on ne trouue aucun binóme, qui puisse ainsi diuiser toute la somme de l'Equation proposee, il est certain que le Problesme qui en depend est solide. Et ce n'est pas vne moindre faute aprés cela, de tascher a le construire sans y employer que des cercles & des lignes droites, que ce seroit d'employer des sections coniques a construire ceux ausquels on n'a besoin que de cercles. car enfin tout ce qui tesmoigne quelque ignorance s'appele faute. Quels problesmes sont solides, lorsque l'Equation est cubique.

Que si on a vne Equation dont la quantité inconnuë ait quatre dimensions, il faut en mesme façon, aprés en auoir osté les nombres sours, & rompus, s'il y en a, voir si on pourra trouuer quelque binóme, qui diuise toute la somme, en le composant de l'vne des quantités, qui diuisent sans fraction le dernier terme. Et si on en trouue vn, oubien la quantité connuë de ce binóme est la racine cherchée; ou du moins aprés cete diuision, il ne reste en l'Equation, que trois dimensions, en suite dequoy il faut derechef l'examiner en la mesme sorte. Mais lorsqu'il ne se trouue point de tel binóme, il faut en augmentant, ou diminuant la valeur de la racine, oster le second terme de la somme, en la façon tantost expliquée. Et aprés la reduire a vne autre, qui ne contiene que trois dimensions. Ce qui se fait en cete sorte. La reduction des Equations qui ont quatre dimesions, lorsque le problesme est plan. Et quels sont ceux qui sont solides.

Au lieu de $+x^4 \quad{}^* .pxx .qx . r \infty 0$,

il faut escrire $+y^6 . 2py^4 \genfrac{}{}{0pt}{}{+pp}{-4r}yy -- qq \infty 0$.

Et pour les signes $+$ ou $--$ que iay omis, s'il y a

eu

384   La Geometrie.

eu $+p$ en la precedente Equation, il faut mettre en cellecy $+2p$, ou s'il y a eu $-p$, il faut mettre $-2p$. & au contraire s'il y a eu $+r$, il faut mettre $-4r$, ou s'il y a eu $-r$, il faut mettre $+4r$. & foit qu'il y ait eu $+q$, ou $-q$, il faut toufiours mettre $-qq$, & $+pp$. au moins fi on fuppofe que x^4, & y^6 font marqués du fignes $+$, car ce feroit tout le contraire fi on y fuppofoit le figne $-$.

Par exemple fi on a $+x^4 * -4xx - 8x + 35 \infty 0$ il faut efcrire en fon lieu $y^6 - 8y^4 - 124yy - 64 \infty 0$. car la quantité que iay, nommée p eftant -4, il faut mettre $-8y^4$ pour $2py^4$. & celle, que iay nommée r eftant 35, il faut mettre $\genfrac{}{}{0pt}{}{+16}{-140}yy$, c'eft a dire $-124yy$, au lieu de $\genfrac{}{}{0pt}{}{+pp}{-4r}yy$. & enfin q eftant 8, il faut mettre -64, pour $-qq$.
Tout de mefme au lieu de $+x^4 * -17xx - 20x - 6 \infty 0$. il faut efcrire $\qquad +y^6 - 34y^4 + 313yy - 400 \infty 0$.
Car 34 eft double de 17, & 313 en eft le quarré ioint au quadruple de 6, & 400 eft le quarré de 20.

Tout de mefme auffy au lieu de

$$+z^4 \genfrac{}{}{0pt}{}{+\frac{1}{2}aa}{-cc}zz \genfrac{}{}{0pt}{}{-a^3}{-acc}z \genfrac{}{}{0pt}{}{+\frac{5}{16}a^4}{-\frac{1}{4}aacc} \infty 0,$$

Il faut efcrire

$$y^6 \genfrac{}{}{0pt}{}{+aa}{-2cc} y \genfrac{}{}{0pt}{}{-a^4}{+c^4} yy \genfrac{}{}{0pt}{}{-a^6}{-2a^4cc}{-aac^4} \infty 0.$$

Car p eft $+\frac{1}{2}aa - cc$, & pp, eft $\frac{1}{4}a^4 - aacc + c^4$, & $4r$ eft $-\frac{5}{4}a^4 + aacc$, & enfin $-qq$ eft $-a^6 - 2a^4cc - aac^4$.

Aprés que l'Equation eft ainfi reduite a trois dimenfions, il faut chercher la valeur d'yy par la methode defia expliquée; Et fi celle ne peut eftre trouuée, on n'a point befoin

For the ambiguous[222] sign put $+2p$ in the second expression if $+p$ occurs in the first; but if $-p$ occurs in the first, write $-2p$ in the second; and on the contrary, put $-4r$ if $+r$, and $+4r$ if $-r$ occurs; but whether the first expression contains $+q$ or $-q$ we always write $-q^2$ and $+p^2$ in the second, provided that x^4 and y^6 have the sign $+$; otherwise, we write $+q^2$ and $-p^2$. For example, given

$$x^4 - 4x^2 - 8x + 35 = 0$$

replace it by

$$y^6 - 8y^4 - 124y^2 - 64 = 0.$$

For since $p = -4$, we replace $2py^4$ by $-8y^4$; and since $r = 35$, we replace $(p^2 - 4r)y^2$ by $(16-140)y^2$ or $-124y^2$; and since $q = 8$, we replace $-q^2$ by -64.

Similarly, instead of

$$x^4 - 17x^2 - 20x - 6 = 0$$

we must write

$$y^6 - 34y^4 + 313y^2 - 400 = 0,$$

for 34 is twice 17, and 313 is the square of 17 increased by four times 6, and 400 is the square of 20.

In the same way, instead of

$$+z^4 + \left(\frac{1}{2}a^2 - c^2\right)z^2 - (a^3 + ac^2)z - \frac{5}{16}a^4 - \frac{1}{4}a^2c^2 = 0,$$

we must write

$$y^6 + (a^2 - 2c^2)y^4 + (c^4 - a^4)y^2 - a^6 - 2a^4c^2 - a^2c^4 = 0;$$

for

$$p = \frac{1}{2}a^2 - c^2,\ p^2 = \frac{1}{4}a^4 - a^2c^2 + c^4,\ 4r = -\frac{5}{4}a^4 + a^2c^2.$$

And, finally,

$$-q^2 = -a^6 - 2a^4c^2 - a^2c^4.$$

When the equation has been reduced to three dimensions, the value of y^2 is found by the method already explained. If this cannot be

[222] Descartes wrote "pour les signes $+$ ou $-$ que j'ai omis."

GEOMETRY

done it is useless to pursue the question further, for it follows inevitably that the problem is solid. If, however, the value of y^2 can be found, we can by means of it separate the preceding equation into two others, each of the second degree, whose roots will be the same as those of the original equation. Instead of $+ x^4 \pm px^2 \pm qx \pm r = 0$, write the two equations

$$+ x^2 - yx + \frac{1}{2}y^2 \pm \frac{1}{2}p \pm \frac{q}{2y} = 0$$

and

$$+ x^2 + yx + \frac{1}{2}y^2 \pm \frac{1}{2}p \pm \frac{q}{2y} = 0.$$

For the ambiguous signs write $+\frac{1}{2}p$ in each new equation, when p has a positive sign, and $-\frac{1}{2}p$ when p has a negative sign, but write $+\frac{q}{2y}$ when we have $-yx$, and $-\frac{q}{2y}$ when we have $+yx$, provided q has a positive sign, and the opposite when q has a negative sign. It is then easy to determine all the roots of the proposed equation, and consequently to construct the problem of which it contains the solution, by the exclusive use of circles and straight lines. For example, writing $y^6 - 34y^4 + 313y^2 - 400 = 0$ instead of $x^4 - 17x^2 - 20x - 6 = 0$ we find that $y^2 = 16$; then, instead of the original equation

$$+ x^4 - 17x^2 - 20x - 6 = 0$$

write the two equations $+ x^2 - 4x - 3 = 0$ and $+ x^2 + 4x + 2 = 0$. For, $y = 4$, $\frac{1}{2}y^2 = 8$, $p = 17$, $q = 20$, and therefore

$$+ \frac{1}{2}y^2 - \frac{1}{2}p - \frac{q}{2y} = -3$$

and

$$+ \frac{1}{2}y^2 - \frac{1}{2}p + \frac{q}{2y} = +2.$$

LIVRE TROISIESME. 385

besoin de passer outre; car il suit de là infalliblement, que le problesme est solide. Mais si on la trouue, on peut diuiser par son moyen la precedente Equation en deux autres, en chascune desquelles la quantité inconnuë n'aura que deux dimensions, & dont les racines seront les mesmes que les siennes. A sçauoir, au lieu de

$$+x^4 \ast .pxx.qx.r \infty 0,$$

il faut escrire ces deux autres

$$+xx-yx+\tfrac{1}{2}yy.\tfrac{1}{2}p.\tfrac{q}{2y} \infty 0, \&$$

$$+xx+yx+\tfrac{1}{2}yy.\tfrac{1}{2}p.\tfrac{q}{2y} \infty 0.$$

Et pour les signes + & -- que i'ay omis, s'il y a + p en l'Equation precedente, il faut mettre + $\tfrac{1}{2}p$ en chascune de celles cy; & -- $\tfrac{1}{2}p$, s'il y a en l'autre -- p. Mais il faut mettre + $\tfrac{q}{2y}$, en celle où il y a -- yx; & -- $\tfrac{q}{2y}$, en celle où il y a + yx, lorsqu'il y a + q en la premiere. Et au contraire s'il y a -- q, il faut mettre -- $\tfrac{q}{2y}$, en celle où il y a -- yx; & + $\tfrac{q}{2y}$, en celle où il y a + yx. Ensuite dequoy il est aysé de connoistre toutes les racines de l'Equation proposée, & par consequent de construire le problesme, dont elle contient la solution, sans y employer que des cercles, & des lignes droites.

Par exemple a cause que faisant

$$y^6-34y^4+313yy-400 \infty 0, \text{ pour}$$

$$x^4 \ast -17xx-20x-6 \infty 0,$$ on trouue que yy est 16, on doit au lieu de cete Equation

$$+x^4 \ast -17xx-20x-20x-6 \infty 0,$$ escrire ces deux

Ccc autres

386   La Geometrie.

autres $+xx-4x-3 \infty 0$. Et $+xx+4x+2\infty 0$.
car y est 4, $\frac{1}{2}yy$ est 8, p est 17, & q est 20, de façon que
$+\frac{1}{2}yy-\frac{1}{2}p-\frac{q}{2y}$ fait -3, & $+\frac{1}{2}yy-\frac{1}{2}p+\frac{q}{2y}$ fait $+2$. Et
tirant les racines de ces deux Equations, on trouue toutes les mesmes, que si on les tiroit de celle où est x^4, à sçauoir on en trouue vne vraye, qui est $\sqrt{7}+2$, & trois fausses, qui sont $\sqrt{7}-2$, $2+\sqrt{2}$, & $2-\sqrt{2}$.
Ainsi ayant $x^4-4xx-8x+35\infty 0$, pource que la racine de $y^6-8y^4-124yy+64\infty 0$, est derechef 16, il faut escrire
$xx-4x+5\infty 0$, & $xx+4x+7\infty 0$.

Car icy $+\frac{1}{2}yy-\frac{1}{2}p-\frac{q}{2y}$ fait 5, & $+\frac{1}{2}yy-\frac{1}{2}p+\frac{q}{2y}$ fait 7. Et pourcequ'on ne trouue aucune racine, ny vraye, ny fausse, en ces deux dernieres Equations, on connoist de là que les quatre de l'Equation dont elles procedent sont imaginaires; & que le Problesme, pour lequel on l'a trouuée, est plan de sa nature; mais qu'il ne sçauroit en aucune façon estre construit, a cause que les quantités données ne peuuent se ioindre.

    Tout de mesme ayant
$$z^4 * \begin{matrix}+\frac{1}{2}aa \\ -cc\end{matrix} \bigg\} zz \begin{matrix}-a^3 \\ -acc\end{matrix} \bigg\} z \begin{matrix}+\frac{5}{16}a^4 \\ -\frac{1}{4}aacc\end{matrix} \infty 0,$$
pourcequ'on trouue $aa+cc$ pour yy, il faut escrire
$zz-\sqrt{aa+cc}\,z+\frac{3}{4}aa-\frac{1}{2}a\sqrt{aa+cc}\infty 0$, &
$zz+\sqrt{aa+cc}\,z+\frac{3}{4}aa+\frac{1}{2}a\sqrt{aa+cc}\infty 0$.

Car y est $\sqrt{aa+cc}$, & $+\frac{1}{2}yy+\frac{1}{2}p$ est $\frac{3}{4}aa$, & $\frac{q}{2y}$ est $\frac{1}{2}a\sqrt{aa+cc}$. D'où on connoist que la valeur de z est

THIRD BOOK·

Obtaining the roots of these two equations, we get the same results as if we had obtained the roots of the equation containing x^4, namely, one true root, $\sqrt{7}+2$, and three false ones, $\sqrt{7}-2, 2+\sqrt{2}$, and $2-\sqrt{2}$. Again, given $x^4-4x^2-8x+35=0$, we have $y^6-8y^4-124y^2-64=0$, and since the root of the latter equation is 16, we must write $x^2-4x+5=0$ and $x^2+4x+7=0$. For in this case,

$$+\frac{1}{2}y^2-\frac{1}{2}p-\frac{q}{2y}=5$$

and

$$+\frac{1}{2}y^2-\frac{1}{2}p+\frac{q}{2y}=7.$$

Now these two equations have no roots either true or false,[223] whence we know that the four roots of the original equation are imaginary; and that the problem whose solution depends upon this equation is plane, but that its construction is impossible, because the given quantities cannot be united.[224]

Similarly, given

$$z^4+\left(\frac{1}{2}a^2-c^2\right)z^2-(a^3+ac^2)z+\frac{5}{16}a^4-\frac{1}{4}a^2c^2=0,$$

since we have found $y^2=a^2+c^2$, we must write

$$z^2-\sqrt{a^2+c^2}\,z+\frac{3}{4}a^2-\frac{1}{2}a\sqrt{a^2+c^2}=0$$

and

$$z^2+\sqrt{a^2+c^2}\,z+\frac{3}{4}a^2+\frac{1}{2}a\sqrt{a^2+c^2}=0.$$

---

[223] That is, all its roots are imaginary.
[224] That is, the given quantities cannot be taken together in the same problem.

For $y = \sqrt{a^2+c^2}$ and $+\frac{1}{2}y^2 + \frac{1}{2}p = \frac{3}{4}a^2$, and $\frac{q}{2y} = \frac{1}{2}a\sqrt{a^2+c^2}$, then we have

$$z = \frac{1}{2}\sqrt{a^2+c^2} + \sqrt{-\frac{1}{2}a^2 + \frac{1}{4}c^2 + \frac{1}{2}a\sqrt{a^2+c^2}}$$

or

$$z = \frac{1}{2}\sqrt{a^2+c^2} - \sqrt{-\frac{1}{2}a^2 + \frac{1}{4}c^2 + \frac{1}{2}a\sqrt{a^2+c^2}}.$$

Now we already have $z + \frac{1}{2}a = x$, and therefore x, the quantity in the search for which we have performed all these operations, is

$$+\frac{1}{2}a + \sqrt{\frac{1}{4}a^2 + \frac{1}{4}c^2} - \sqrt{\frac{1}{4}c^2 - \frac{1}{2}a^2 + \frac{1}{2}a\sqrt{a^2+c^2}}.$$

To emphasize the value of this rule, I shall apply it to a problem. Given the square AD and the line BN, to prolong the side AC to E, so that EF, laid off from E on EB, shall be equal to NB.

Pappus showed that if BD is produced to G, so that DG = DN, and a circle is described on BG as diameter, the required point E will be the intersection of the straight line AC (produced) with the circumference of this circle.[225]

Those not familiar with this construction would not be likely to discover it, and if they applied the method suggested here they would never think of taking DG for the unknown quantity rather than CF or FD, since either of these would much more easily lead to an equa-

---

[225] Pappus Lib. VII, Prop. 72, Vol. II, p. 783. The following is in substance the proof given by Pappus. He first gives an elaborate proof of the following lemma: Given a square ABCD, and E a point in AC produced, EG perpendicular to BE at E, meeting BD produced in G, and F the point of intersection of BE and CD. Then $\overline{CD}^2 + \overline{FE}^2 = \overline{DG}^2$. Then he proceeds as follows: By the construction given in the problem, $\overline{DN}^2 = \overline{BD}^2 + \overline{BN}^2$. By the lemma, $\overline{DG}^2 = \overline{CD}^2 + \overline{FE}^2$. By construction, BD = CD and DG = DN. Therefore, FE = BN.

LIVRE TROISIESME. 387

est $\frac{1}{2}\sqrt{aa+cc} + \sqrt{-\frac{1}{2}aa + \frac{1}{4}cc + \frac{1}{2}a\sqrt{aa+cc}}$,
oubien $\frac{1}{2}\sqrt{aa+cc} - \sqrt{-\frac{1}{2}aa + \frac{1}{4}cc + \frac{1}{2}a\sqrt{aa+cc}}$.
Et pourceque nous auions fait cy dessus $z + \frac{1}{2}a \infty x$, nous apprenons que la quantité x, pour la connoissance de laquelle nous auons fait toutes ces operations, est

$+\frac{1}{2}a + \sqrt{\frac{1}{4}aa + \frac{1}{4}cc} - \sqrt{\frac{1}{4}cc - \frac{1}{2}aa + \frac{1}{2}a\sqrt{aa+cc}}$.

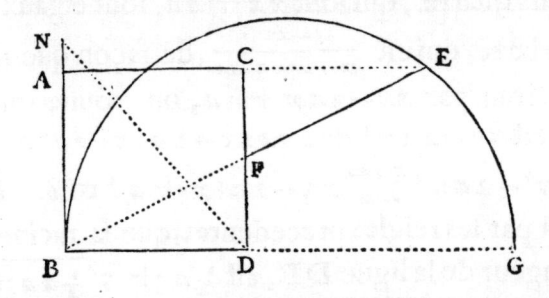

Mais affin qu'on puisse mieux connoistre l'vtilité de cete reigle il faut que ie l'applique a quelq; Problesme. Si le quarré A D, & la ligne B N estant donnés, il faut prolonger le costé A C iusques a E, en sorte qu'E F, tirée d'E vers B, soit esgale a N B. On apprent de Pappus, qu'ayant premierement prolongé B D iusques à G, en sorte que D G soit esgale à D N, & ayant descrit vn cercle dont le diametre soit B G, si on prolonge la ligne droite A C, elle rencontrera la circonference de ce cercle au point E, qu'on demandoit. Mais pour ceux qui ne sçauroiet point cete côstruction elle seroit assés difficile à rencôtrer, & en la cherchât par la methode icy proposée, ils ne s'auiseroiët iamais de prédre D G pour la quâtité inconnuë, mais plutost C F, ou F D, a cause que ce

Exemple de l'vsage de ces reductions.

Ccc 2   sont

font elles qui conduifent le plus ayfement a l'Equatiõ: & lors ils en trouueroiët vne qui ne feroit pas facile a demefler, fans la reigle que ie viens d'expliquer. Car pofant a pour B D ou C D, & c pour E F, & x pour D F, on a C F $\infty\, a - x$, & cõme C F ou $a - x$, eft à F E ou c, ainfi F D ou x, eft a B F, qui par confequent eft $\frac{cx}{a-x}$. Puis a caufe du triangle rectangle B D F, dont les coftés font l'vn x & l'autre a, leurs quarrés, qui font $xx + aa$, font efgaux a celuy de la baze, qui eft $\frac{ccxx}{xx - 2ax + aa}$, de façon que multipliant le tout par $xx - 2ax + aa$, on trouue que l'Equation eft $x^4 - 2ax^3 + 2aaxx - 2a^3x + a^4 \infty\, ccxx$, oubien $x^4 - 2ax^3 {+2aa \atop -cc} xx - 2a^3 x + a^4 \infty\, 0$. Et on connoift par les reigles precedentes, que fa racine, qui eft la longeur de la ligne D F, eft $\frac{1}{2} a + \sqrt{\frac{1}{4} aa + \frac{1}{4} cc}$ $- \sqrt{\frac{1}{4} cc - \frac{1}{2} aa + \frac{1}{2} a \sqrt{aa + cc}}$.

Que fi on pofoit B F, ou C E, ou B E pour la quantité inconnuë, on viendroit derechef à vne Equation, en laquelle il y auroit 4 dimenfions, mais qui feroit plus ayfée a démefler, & on y viendroit affés ayfement; au lieu que fi c'eftoit D G qu'on fuppofaft, on viendroit beaucoup plus difficilement a l'Equation, mais auffy elle feroit tres fimple. Ce que ie mets icy pour vous auertir, que lorfque le Problefme propofé n'eft point folide, fi en le cherchant par vn chemin on vient a vne Equation fort compofee, on peut ordinairement venir a vne plus fimple, en le cherchant par vn autre.

Ie pourrois encore aioufter diuerfes reigles pour démefler les Equations, qui vont au Cube, ou au Quarre

de

tion. They would thus get an equation which could not easily be solved without the rule which I have just explained.

For, putting a for BD or CD, c for EF and x for DF, we have $CF = a-x$, and, since CF is to FE as FD is to BF, we have

$$a-x : c = x : BF,$$

whence $BF = \dfrac{cx}{a-x}$. Now, in the right triangle BDF whose sides are x and a, x^2+a^2, the sum of their squares, is equal to the square of the hypotenuse, which is $\dfrac{c^2x^2}{x^2-2ax+a^2}$ Multiplying both sides by

we get the equation,
$$x^2-2ax+a^2$$
$$x^4-2ax^3+2a^2x^2-2a^3x+a^4 = c^2x^2,$$
or
$$x^4-2ax^3+(2a^2-c^2)x^2-2a^3x+a^4 = 0,$$

and by the preceding rule we know that its root, which is the length of the line DF, is

$$\frac{1}{2}a + \sqrt{\frac{1}{4}a^2 + \frac{1}{4}c^2} - \sqrt{\frac{1}{4}c^2 - \frac{1}{2}a^2 + \frac{1}{2}a\sqrt{a^2+c^2}}.$$

If, on the other hand, we consider BF, CE, or BE as the unknown quantity, we obtain an equation of the fourth degree, but much easier to solve, and quite simply obtained.[226]

Again, if DG were used, the equation would be much more difficult to obtain, but its solution would be very simple. I state this simply to warn you that, when the proposed problem is not solid, if one method of attack yields a very complicated equation a much simpler one can usually be found by some other method.

[226] Taking BF as the unknown quantity, the resulting equation is
$$x^4 + 2cx^3 + (c^2 - 2a^2)x^2 - 2a^2cx - a^2c^2 = 0.$$
Rabuel, p. 487.

I might add several different rules for the solution of cubic and biquadratic equations but they would be superfluous, since the construction of any plane problem can be found by means of those already given.

I could also add rules for equations of the fifth, sixth, and higher degrees, but I prefer to consider them all together and to state the following general rule:

First, try to put the given equation into the form of an equation of the same degree obtained by multiplying together two others, each of a lower degree. If, after all possible ways of doing this have been tried, none has been sucessful, then it is certain that the given equation cannot be reduced to a simpler one; and, consequently, if it is of the third or fourth degree, the problem depending upon it is solid; if of the fifth or sixth, the problem is one degree more complex, and so on. I have also omitted here the demonstration of most of my statements, because they seem to me so easy that if you take the trouble to examine them systematically the demonstrations will present themselves to you and it will be of much more value to you to learn them in that way than by reading them.

LIVRE TROISIESME. 389

de quarré, mais elles seroient superflues; car lorsque les Problesmes sont plans, on en peut tousiours trouuer la construction par celles cy.

Ie pourrois aussy en adiouster d'autres pour les Equations qui montent iusques au sursolide, ou au Quarré de cube, ou au delà, mais i'ayme mieux les comprendre toutes en vne, & dire en general, que lorsqu'on a tasché de les reduire a mesme forme, que celles d'autant de dimensions, qui vienent de la multiplication de deux autres qui en ont moins, & qu'ayant dénombré tous les moyens, par lesquels cete multiplication est possible, la chose n'a pû succeder par aucun, on doit s'assurer qu'elles ne sçauroient estre reduites a de plus simples. En sorte que si la quantité inconnuë a 3 on 4 dimensions, le Problesme pour lequel on la cherche est solide; & si elle en a 5, on 6, il est d'vn degré plus composé; & ainsi des autres. *Regle generale pour reduire les Equatiõs qui passent le quarré de quarré.*

Au reste i'ay omis icy les demonstrations de la plus part de ce que iay dit a cause qu'elles m'ont semblé si faciles, que pourvû que vous preniés la peine d'examiner methodiquement si iay failly, elles se presenteront a vous d'elles mesme: & il sera plus vtile de les apprendre en cete façon, qu'en les lisant.

Or quand on est assuré, que le Problesme proposé est solide, soit que l'Equation par laquelle on le cherche monte au quarré de quarré, soit qu'elle ne monte que iusques au cube, on peut tousiours en trouver la racine par l'vne des trois sections coniques, laquelle que ce soit ou mesme par quelque partie de l'vne d'elles, tant petite qu'elle puisse estre; en ne se seruãt au reste que de lignes droites, & de cercles. Mais ie me contenteray icy de donner *Facon generale pour construire tous les problesmes solides, reduits a vne Equatiõ de trois ou quatre dimensions.*

Ccc 3

390 LA GEOMETRIE.

donner vne reigle generale pour les trouuer toutes par le moyen d'vne Parabole, a cause qu'elle est en quelque façon la plus simple.

Premierement il faut oster le second terme de l'Equation proposée, s'il n'est desia nul, & ainsi la reduire à telle forme, $z^3 \infty *. apz.aaq$, si la quantité inconnuë n'a que trois dimensions; oubien à telle, $z^4 \infty *. apzz. aaqz. a^3 r$, si elle en a quatre; oubien en prenant a pour l'vnité, à telle, $z^3 \infty *. pz.q$, & à telle $z^4 \infty *. pzz. qz. r.$

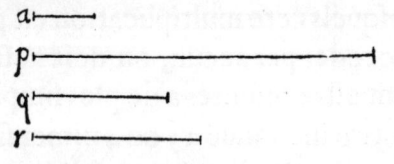

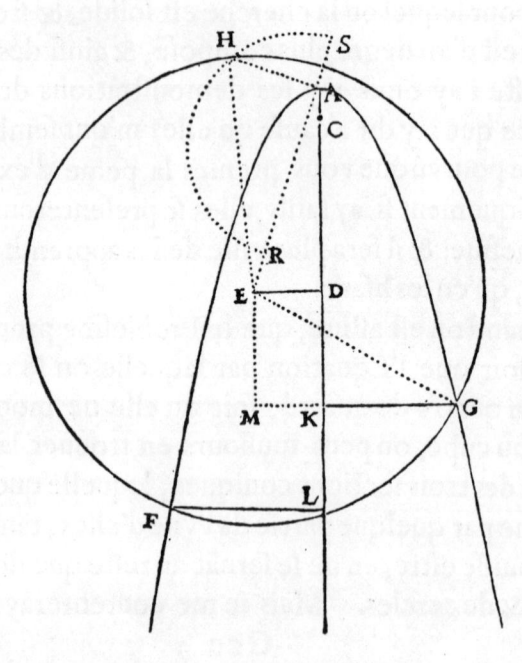

Aprés

Now, when it is clear that the proposed problem is solid, whether the equation upon which its solution depends is of the fourth degree or only of the third, its roots can always be found by any one of the three conic sections, or even by some part of one of them, however small, together with only circles and straight lines. I shall content myself with giving here a general rule for finding them all by means of a parabola, since that is in some respects the simplest of these curves.

First, remove the second term of the proposed equation, if this is not already zero, thus reducing it to the form $z^3 = \pm apz \pm a^2q$, if the given equation is of the third degree, or $z^4 = \pm apz^2 \pm a^2qz \pm a^3r$, if it is of the fourth degree. By choosing a as the unit, the former may be written

GEOMETRY

$z^3 = \pm pz \pm q$ and the latter $z^4 = \pm pz^2 \pm qz \pm r$. Suppose that the parabola FAG (pages 194-198) is already described; let ACDKL be its axis, a, or 1 which equals 2AC, its latus rectum (C being within the parabola), and A its vertex. Lay off CD equal to $\frac{1}{2}p$ so that the points D and A lie on the same side of C if the equation contains $+p$ and on opposite sides if it contains $-p$. Then at the point D (or, if $p = 0$, at C), erect DE perpendicular to CD, so that DE is equal to $\frac{1}{2}q$, and about E as center with AE as radius describe the circle FG, if the given equation is a cubic, that is, if r is zero.

LIVRE TROISIESME. 391

Aprés cela supposant que la Parabole FAG est desia descrite, & que son aissieu est A C D K L, & que son costé droit est *a*, ou 1, dont A C est la moitié, & enfin que le point C est au dedans de cete Parabole, & que A en est le sommet; Il faut faire C D $\infty \frac{1}{2} p$, & la prendre du mesme costé, qu'est le point A au regard du point C, s'il y a $+p$ en l'Equation; mais s'il y a $-p$ il faut la prendre de l'autre coste. Et du point D, oubien, si la quantité

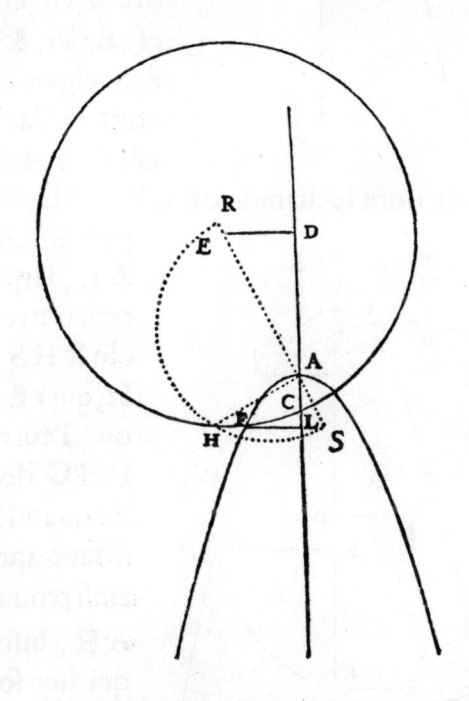

p estoit nulle, du point C il faut esleuer vne ligne a angles droits iusques a E, en sorte qu'elle soit esgale a $\frac{1}{2} q$. Et enfin du centre E il faut descrire le cercle F G, dont
le

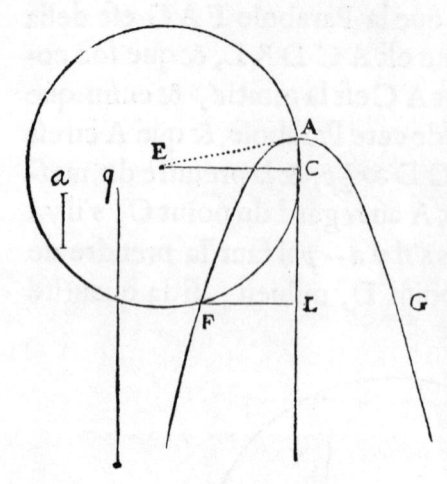

392 LA GEOMETRIE.

le demidiametre soit A E, si l'Equation n'est que cubique, en sorte que la quantité *r* soit nulle. Mais quand il y a + *r* il faut dans cete ligne A E prolongée, prendre d'vn costé A R esgale à *r*, & de l'autre A S esgale au costé droit de la Parabole qui est 1, & ayant descrit vn cercle dont le diametre soit R S, il faut faire A H perpẽdiculaire sur A E, laquelle A H rencontre ce cercle R H S au point H, qui est celuy par où l'autre cercle F H G doit passer. Et quand il y a -- *r* il faut aprés auoir ainsi trouué la ligne A H, inscrire A I, qui luy soit esgale, dans vn autre cercle, dont A E soit le diametre, & lors c'est par le point I, que

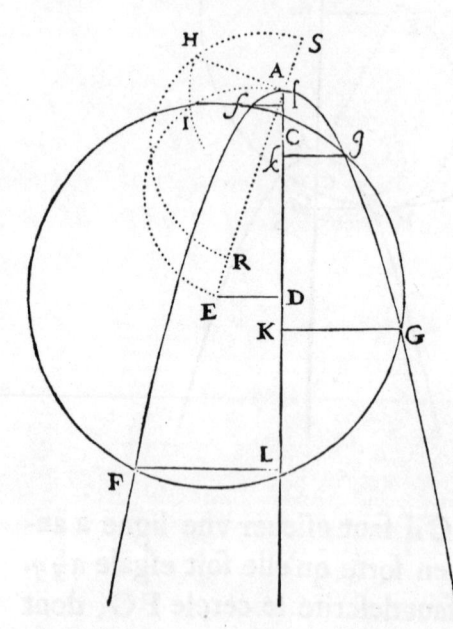

THIRD BOOK

If the equation contains $+r$, on one side of AE produced, lay off AR equal to r, and on the other side lay off AS equal to the latus rectum of the parabola, that is, to 1, and describe a circle on RS as diameter. Then if AH is drawn perpendicular to AE it will meet the circle RHS in the point H, through which the other circle FHG must pass.

If the equation contains $-r$, construct a circle upon AE as diameter and in it inscribe AI, a line equal to AH;[227] then the first circle must pass through the point I.

[227] That is, draw a chord equal to AH.

GEOMETRY

Now the circle FG can cut or touch the parabola in 1, 2, 3, or 4 points; and if perpendiculars are drawn from these points upon the axis they will represent all the roots of the equation, both true and false. If the quantity q is positive the true roots will be those perpendiculars, such as FL, on the same side of the parabola, as E,[228] the center of the circle; while the others, as GK, will be the false roots. On the other hand, if q is negative, the true roots will be those on the opposite side, and the false or negative roots[229] will be those on the same side as E, the center of the circle. If the circle neither cuts nor touches the parabola at any point, it is an indication that the equation has neither a true nor a false root, but that all the roots are imaginary.[230]

This rule is evidently as general and complete as could possibly be desired. Its demonstration is also very easy. If the line GK thus constructed be represented by z, then AK is z^2, since by the nature of the parabola, GK is the mean proportional between AK and the latus rectum, which is 1. Then if AC or $\frac{1}{2}$, and CD or $\frac{1}{2}p$, be subtracted from AK, the remainder is DK or EM, which is equal to $z^2 - \frac{1}{2}p - \frac{1}{2}$ of which the square is

$$z^4 - pz^2 - z^2 + \frac{1}{4}p^2 + \frac{1}{2}p + \frac{1}{4}.$$

And since $DE = KM = \frac{1}{2}q$, the whole line $GM = z + \frac{1}{2}q$, and the square of GM equals $z^2 + qz + \frac{1}{4}q^2$. Adding these two squares we have

$$z^4 - pz^2 + qz + \frac{1}{4}q^2 + \frac{1}{4}p^2 + \frac{1}{2}p + \frac{1}{4}$$

[228] That is, on the same side of the axis of the parabola.

[229] "Les fausses ou moindres que rien." This is the first time Descartes has directly used this synonym.

[230] It may be noted that Descartes considers the cubic as a quartic having zero as one of its roots. Therefore, the circle always cuts the parabola at the vertex. It must then cut it in another point, since the cubic must have one real root. It may or may not cut it in two other points. It may cut it in two coincident points at the vertex, in which case the equation reduces to a quadratic.

LIVRE TROISIESME. 393

que doit passer F I G le premier cercle cherché. Or ce cercle F G peut coupper, ou toucher la Parabole en 1, ou 2, ou 3, ou 4 poins, desquels tirant des perpendiculaires sur laissieu, on a toutes les racines de l'Equation tant vrayes, que fausses. A sçauoir si la quantité q est marquée du signe $+$, les vrayes racines seront celles de ces perpendiculaires, qui se trouueront du mesme costé de la parabole, que E le centre du cercle, comme F L; & les autres, comme G K, seront fausses : Mais au contraire si cete quantité q est marquée du signe $-$ les vrayes seront celles de l'autre costé; & les fausses, ou moindres que rien seront du costé où est E le centre du cercle. Et enfin si ce cercle ne couppe, ny ne touche la Parabole en aucun point, cela tesmoigne qu'il n'y a aucune racine ny vraye ny fausse en l'Equation, & qu'elles sont toutes imaginaires. En sorte que cete reigle est la plus generale, & la plus accomplie qu'il soit possible de souhaiter.

Et la demonstration en est fort aysée. Car si la ligne G K, trouuée par cete construction, se nomme z, A K sera zz, a cause de la Parabole, en laquelle G K doit estre moyene proportionelle, entre A K, & le costé droit qui est 1. puis si de A K i'oste A C, qui est $\frac{1}{2}$, & C D qui est $\frac{1}{2}p$, il reste D K, ou E M, qui est $zz - \frac{1}{2}p - \frac{1}{2}$, dont le quarré est

$$z^4 - pzz - zz + \tfrac{1}{4}pp + \tfrac{1}{2}p + \tfrac{1}{4}.$$

& a cause que D E, ou K M est $\frac{1}{2}q$, la toute G M est $z + \frac{1}{2}q$, dont le quarré est $zz + qz + \tfrac{1}{4}qq$, & assemblant ces deux quarrés, on a

$$z^4 - pz + qz + \tfrac{1}{4}qq + \tfrac{1}{4}pp + \tfrac{1}{2}p + \tfrac{1}{4},$$

Ddd   pour

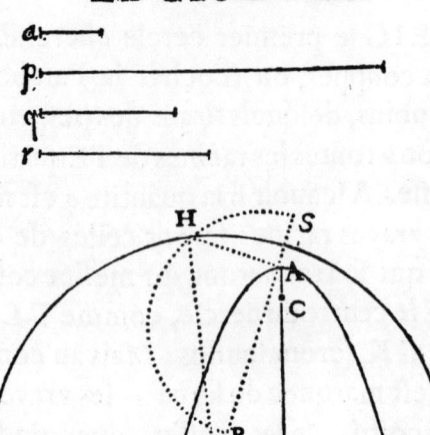

pour le quarré de la ligne G E, a cauſe qu'elle eſt la baze du triangle rectangle E M G.

Mais a cauſe que cete meſme ligne G E eſt le demi-diametre du cercle F G, elle ſe peut encore expliquer en d'autres termes, a ſçauoir E D eſtant $\frac{1}{2}q$, & A D eſtant $\frac{1}{2}p+\frac{1}{2}$, E A eſt $\sqrt{\frac{1}{4}qq+\frac{1}{4}pp+\frac{1}{2}p+\frac{1}{4}}$ a cauſe de l'angle droit A D E, puis H A eſtant moyene proportionelle entre A S qui eſt 1 & A R qui eſt r, elle eſt $\sqrt{r}$. & à cauſe de l'angle droit E A H, le quarré de H E, ou E G eſt $\frac{1}{4}qq+\frac{1}{4}pp+\frac{1}{2}p+\frac{1}{4}+r$: ſibienque il y a Equation entre

for the square of GE, since GE is the hypotenuse of the right triangle EMG.

But GE is the radius of the circle FG and can therefore be expressed in another way. For since $ED = \frac{1}{2}q$, and $AD = \frac{1}{2}p + \frac{1}{2}$, and ADE is a right angle, we have

$$EA = \sqrt{\frac{1}{4}q^2 + \frac{1}{4}p^2 + \frac{1}{2}p + \frac{1}{4}}.$$

Then, since HA is the mean proportional between AS or 1 and AR or r, $HA = \sqrt{r}$; and since EAH is a right angle, the square of HE or of EG is

$$\frac{1}{4}q^2 + \frac{1}{4}p^2 + \frac{1}{2}p + \frac{1}{4} + r,$$

and we can form an equation from this expression and the one already

obtained. This equation will be of the form $z^4 = pz^2 - qz + r$, and therefore the line GK, or z, is the root of this equation, which was to be proved. If you will apply this method in all the other cases, with the proper changes of sign, you will be convinced of its usefulness, without my writing anything further about it.

Let us apply it to the problem of finding two mean proportionals between the lines a and q. It is evident that if we represent one of the mean proportionals by z, then $a : z = z : \dfrac{z^2}{a} = \dfrac{z^2}{a} : \dfrac{z^3}{a^2}$. Thus we have an equation between q and $\dfrac{z^3}{a^2}$, namely, $z^3 = a^2 q$.

Describe the parabola FAG with its axis along AC, and with AC equal to $\frac{1}{2} a$, that is, to half the latus rectum. Then erect CE equal to $\frac{1}{2} q$ and perpendicular to AC at C, and describe the circle AF

LIVRE TROISIESME. 395

entre cete somme & la precedente. ce qui est le mesme que $z^4 \infty * pzz - qz + r$. & par consequent la ligne trouuee GK qui a esté nommée z est la racine de cete Equation. ainsi qu'il falloit demonstrer. Et si vous appliqués ce mesme calcul a tous les autres cas de cete reigle, en changeant les signes + & -- selon l'occasion, vous y trouuerés vostre conte en mesme sorte, sans qu'il soit besoin que ie m'y areste.

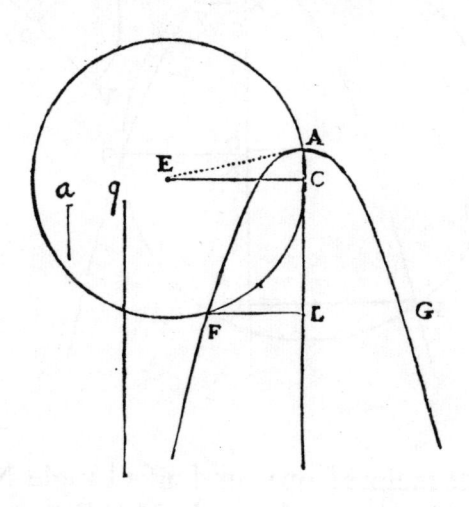

Si on veut donc suiuant cete reigle trouuer deux moyennes proportionelles entre les lignes a & q; chascun sçait que posant z pour l'vne, comme a est à z, ainsi z à $\frac{zz}{a}$, & $\frac{zz}{a}$ à $\frac{z^3}{aa}$; de façon qu'il y a Equation entre q & $\frac{z^3}{aa}$, c'est a dire, $z^3 \infty * * aaq$. Et la Parabole FAG estant

L'inuention de deux moyennes proportionelles.

Ddd 2 de-

descrite, auec la partie de son aissieu A C, qui est $\frac{1}{2}a$ la moitié du costé droit; il faut du point C esleuer la perpendiculaire C E esgale à $\frac{1}{2}q$, & du centre E, par A, descriuant le cercle A F, on trouue F L, & L A, pour les deux moyennes cherchées.

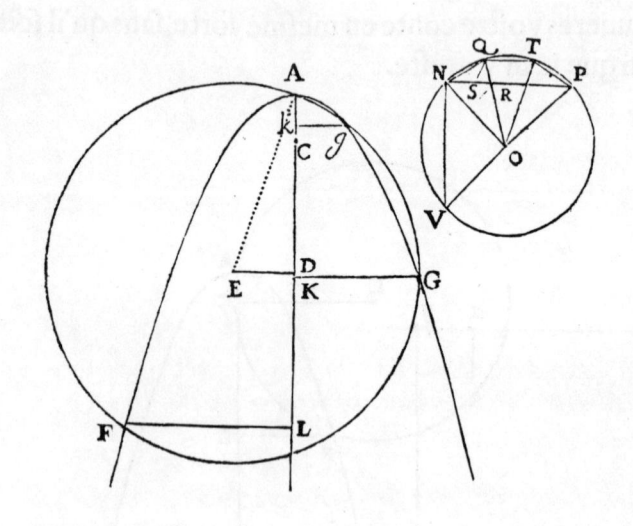

La façon de diuiser vn angle en trois. Tout de mesme si on veut diuiser l'angle N O P, oubien l'arc, ou portion de cercle N Q T P, en trois parties esgales; faisant N O ∞ 1, pour le rayon du cercle, & N P ∞ q, pour la subtendue de l'arc donné, & N Q ∞ z, pour la subtendue du tiers de cet arc; l'Equation vient,

$z^3 \infty *3z --q$. Car ayant tiré les lignes N Q, O Q, O T; & faisant Q S parallele a T O, on voit que comme N O est a N Q, ainsi N Q a Q R, & Q R a R S; en sorte que

about E as center, passing through A. Then FL and LA are the required mean proportionals.[231]

Again, let it be required to divide the angle NOP, or rather, the circular arc NQTP, into three equal parts. Let $NO = 1$ be the radius of the circle, $NP = q$ be the chord subtending the given arc, and $NQ = z$ be the chord subtending one-third of that arc; then the equation is $z^3 = 3z - q$. For, drawing NQ, OQ and OT, and drawing QS parallel to TO, it is obvious that NO is to NQ as NQ is to QR as QR is to RS. Since $NO = 1$ and $NQ = z$, then $QR = z^2$ and $RS = z^3$; and since NP or q lacks only RS or z^3 of being three times NQ or z, we have $q = 3z - z^3$ or $z^3 = 3z - q$.[232]

Describe the parabola FAG so that CA, one-half its latus rectum, shall be equal to $\frac{1}{2}$; take $CD = \frac{3}{2}$ and the perpendicular $DE = \frac{1}{2} q$; then describe the circle FAgG about E as center, passing through A. This circle cuts the parabola in three points, F, g, and G, besides the vertex, A. This shows that the given equation has three roots, namely, the two true roots, GK and gk, and one false root, FL.[233] The smaller

[231] This may be shown as follows: Draw FM $\perp$ to EC; let $FL = z$. From the nature of the parabola, $\overline{FL}^2 = a \cdot AL$; $AL = \frac{z^2}{a}$; $\overline{EC}^2 + \overline{CA}^2 = \overline{EA}^2$; $\overline{EM}^2 + \overline{FM}^2 = \overline{EF}^2$; $\overline{EA}^2 = \frac{q^2}{4} + \frac{a^2}{4}$; $\overline{EM}^2 = (EC - FL)^2 = \left(\frac{1}{2} q - z\right)^2$; $\overline{FM}^2 = \overline{CL}^2 = (AL - AC)^2 = \left(\frac{z^2}{a} - \frac{a}{2}\right)^2$; $\overline{EF}^2 = \frac{q^2}{4} - qz + z^2 + \frac{z^4}{a^2} - z^2 + \frac{a^2}{4}$. But $EF = EA$.

$$\therefore \frac{q^2}{4} + \frac{a^2}{4} = \frac{q^2}{4} - qz + z^2 + \frac{z^4}{a^2} - z^2 + \frac{a^2}{4},$$

whence $z^3 = a^2 q$.

[232] $\angle NOQ$ is measured by arc NQ;
$\angle QNS$ is measured by $\frac{1}{2}$ arc QP or arc NQ;
$\angle SQR = \angle QOT$ is measured by arc QT or NQ;
$\therefore \angle OQN = \angle NQR = \angle QSR$.
$\therefore NO : NQ = NQ : QR = QR : RS$.
$QR = z^2$; $RS = z^3$. Let OT cut NP at M.
$NP = 2NR + MR = 2NQ + MR$
$= 2NQ + MS - RS$
$= 2NQ + QT - RS$
$= 3NQ - RS$.
Or $q = 3z - z^3$.
Rabuel, p. 534.

[233] G and g being on the opposite side of the axis from E, and F being on the same side.

GEOMETRY

of the two roots, gk, must be taken as the length of the required line NQ, for the other root, GK, is equal to NV, the chord subtended by one-third the arc VNP,[234] which, together with the arc NQP constitutes the circle; and the false root, FL, is equal to the sum of QN and NV, as may easily be shown.[235]

It is unnecessary for me to give other examples here, for all problems that are only solid can be reduced to such forms as not to require this rule for their construction except when they involve the finding of two mean proportionals or the trisection of an angle. This will be obvious if it is noted that the most difficult of these problems can be

[234] For proof, see Rabuel, page 535.

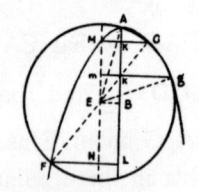

[235] Let $AB = b$; $EB = MR = mk = NL = c$; $AK = t$; $Ak = s$; $AL = r$; $KG = y$; $kg = z$, $FL = v$. Then $GM = y+c$, $gm = z+c$, $FN = v-c$, $\overline{GK}^2 = a \cdot AK$, $at = y^2$, $t = \dfrac{y^2}{a}$, $\overline{gk}^2 = a \cdot Ak$, $as = z^2$, $s = \dfrac{z^2}{a}$, $\overline{FL}^2 = a \cdot AL$, $ar = v^2$, $r = \dfrac{v^2}{a}$,

$$ME = AB - AK = b - \frac{y^2}{a}$$

$mE = b - \dfrac{z^2}{a}$ $\qquad$ $EN = \dfrac{v^2}{a} - b$ $\qquad$ $\overline{EG}^2 = \overline{EM}^2 + \overline{MG}^2$

$$\overline{EA}^2 = \overline{AB}^2 + \overline{BE}^2$$

$$\overline{EG}^2 = b^2 - \frac{2by^2}{a} + \frac{y^4}{a^2} + y^2 + 2cy + c^2$$

$2ab = \dfrac{y^3 + 2a^2c + a^2y}{y}$ $\qquad\qquad\qquad$ $2ab = \dfrac{z^3 + 2a^2c + a^2z}{z}$

$$\frac{y^3 + 2a^2c + a^2y}{y} = \frac{z^3 + 2a^2c + a^2z}{z}$$

$$2a^2c = z^2y + zy^2$$

Similarly,
$$2a^2c = v^2y - vy^2$$

$z^2y + zy^2 = v^2y - vy^2$ $\qquad\qquad\qquad$ $v^2 - z^2 = vy + zy$

$v - z = y$ $\qquad\qquad\qquad$ $v = y + z$ $\qquad\qquad\qquad$ $FL = KG + kg$

Rabuel, p. 540.

LIVRE TROISIESME. 397

que N O estant 1, & N Q estant z, Q R est zz, & R S est
z^3 : Et a cause qu'il s'en faut seulement R S, ou z^3, que la
ligne N P, qui est q, ne soit triple de N Q, qui est z, ou
à $q \infty 3 z -- z^3$ oubien,

$z^3 \infty * 3z -- q$.

 Puis la Parabole F A G estant descrite, & C A la moitié de son costé droit principal estant $\frac{1}{2}$, si on prent C D $\infty \frac{3}{2}$, & la perpendiculaire D E $\infty \frac{1}{2} q$, & que du centre E, par A, on descriue le cercle F A g G, il couppe cete Parabole aux trois poins F, g, & G, sans conter le point A qui en est le sommet. Ce qui monstre qu'il y a trois racines en cete Equation, à sçauoir les deux G K, & $g k$, qui sont vrayes; & la troisiesme qui est fausse, á sçauoir F L. Et de ces deux vrayes c'est $g k$ la plus petite qu'il faut prendre pour la ligne N Q qui estoit cherchée. Car l'autre G K, est esgale à N V, la subtendue de la troisiesme partie de l'arc N V P, qui auec l'autre arc N Q P acheue le cercle. Et la fausse F L est esgale a ces deux ensemble Q N & N V, ainsi qu'il est aysé a voir par le calcul.

 Il seroit superflus que ie m'arestasse a donner icy d'autres exemples; car tous les Problesmes qui ne sont que solides se peuuent reduire a tel point, qu'on n'a aucun besoin de cete reigle pour les construire, sinon entant qu'elle sert a trouuer deux moyennes proportionelles, oubien a diuiser vn angle en trois parties esgales. Ainsi que vous connoistrés en considerant, que leurs difficultés peuuent tousiours estre comprises en des Equations, qui ne montent que iusque au quarré de quarré, ou au cube : Et que toutes celles qui montent au quarré de quarré, se reduisent au quarré, par le moyen de quelques autres, qui ne

Que tous les problesmes solides se peuuent reduire a ces deux constructions.

Ddd 3   montent

398 **La Geometrie.**

montent que iusques au cube: Et enfin qu'on peut oster le second terme de celles cy. En sorte qu'il n'y en a point qui ne se puisse reduire a quelq; vne de ces trois formes.

$$z^3 \infty * - pz + q.$$
$$z^3 \infty * + pz + q.$$
$$z^3 \infty * + pz - q.$$

Or si on a $z^3 \infty * - pz + q$, la reigle dont Cardan attribue l'inuention a vn nommé Scipio Ferreus, nous apprent que la racine est,

$$\sqrt{C. + \tfrac{1}{2}q + \sqrt{\tfrac{1}{4}qq + \tfrac{1}{27}p^3}} + \sqrt{C. - \tfrac{1}{2}q + \sqrt{\tfrac{1}{4}qq + \tfrac{1}{27}p^3}}$$

Comme aussy lorsqu'on a $z^3 \infty * + pz + q$, & que le quarré de la moitié du dernier terme est plus grand que le cube du tiers de la quantité connuë du penultiesme, vne pareille reigle nous apprent que la racine est,

$$C. + \tfrac{1}{2}q + \sqrt{\tfrac{1}{4}qq - \tfrac{1}{27}p^3} + \sqrt{C. + \tfrac{1}{2}q - \sqrt{\tfrac{1}{4}qq - \tfrac{1}{27}p^3}}$$

D'où il paroist qu'on peut construire tous les Problesmes, dont les difficultés se reduisent a l'vne de ces deux formes, sans auoir besoin des sections coniques pour autre chose, que pour tirer les racines cubiques de quelques quantités données, c'est a dire, pour trouuer deux moyennes proportionelles entre ces quantités & l'vnité.

Puis si on a $z^3 \infty * + pz + q$, & que le quarré de la moitié du dernier terme ne soit point plus grand que le cube du tiers de la quantité connuë du penultiesme, en supposant le cercle NQPV, dont le demidiametre NO soit $\sqrt{\tfrac{1}{3}p}$, c'est a dire la moyenne proportionelle entre le tiers de la quantité donnée p & l'vnité; & supposant aussy la ligne NP iuscrite dans ce cercle qui soit $\tfrac{3q}{p}$

c'est

THIRD BOOK

expressed by equations of the third or fourth degree; that all equations of the fourth degree can be reduced to quadratic equations by means of other equations not exceeding the third degree; and finally, that the second terms of these equations can be removed; so that every such equation can be reduced to one of the following forms:

$$z^3 = -pz+q \qquad z^3 = +pz+q \qquad z^3 = +pz-q$$

Now, if we have $z^3 = -pz+q$, the rule, attributed by Cardan[236] to one Scipio Ferreus, gives us the root

$$\sqrt[3]{\frac{1}{2}q + \sqrt{\frac{1}{4}q^2 + \frac{1}{27}p^3}} - \sqrt[3]{-\frac{1}{2}q + \sqrt{\frac{1}{4}q^2 + \frac{1}{27}p^3}}.\text{[237]}$$

Similarly, when we have $z^3 = +pz+q$ where the square of half the last term is greater than the cube of one-third the coefficient of the next to the last term, the corresponding rule gives us the root

$$\sqrt[3]{\frac{1}{2}q + \sqrt{\frac{1}{4}q^2 - \frac{1}{27}p^3}} + \sqrt[3]{\frac{1}{2}q - \sqrt{\frac{1}{4}q^2 - \frac{1}{27}p^3}}.$$

It is now clear that all problems of which the equations can be reduced to either of these two forms can be constructed without the use of the conic sections except to extract the cube roots of certain known quantities, which process is equivalent to finding two mean proportionals between such a quantity and unity. Again, if we have $z^3 = +pz+q$, where the square of half the last term is not greater than the cube of one-third the coefficient of the next to the last term, describe the circle NQPV with radius NO equal to $\sqrt{\frac{1}{3}p}$, that is to the mean proportional between unity and one-third the known quantity p. Then take $NP = \frac{3q}{p}$, that is, such that NP is to q, the other known

---

[236] Cardan; Liber X, Cap. XI, fol. 29: "Scipio Ferreus Bononiensis iam annis ab hinc triginta fermè capitulum hoc inuenit, tradidit uero Anthonio Mariæ Florido Veneto, qui cū in certamen cū Nicolao Tartalea Brixellense aliquando uenisset, occasionem dedit, ut Nocolaus inuenerit & ipse, qui cum nobis rogantibus tradidisser, suppressa demonstratione, freti hoc auxilio, demonstrationem quæliuimus, eamque in modos, quod diffcillimum fuit, redactam sic subjecimus."

See also Cantor, Vol. II (1), p. 444; Smith, Vol. II, p. 462.

[237] Descartes wrote this:

$$\sqrt{C. + \frac{1}{2}q + \sqrt{\frac{1}{4}qq + \frac{1}{27}p^3}} + \sqrt{C. \frac{1}{2}q + \sqrt{\frac{1}{4}qq + \frac{1}{27}p^3}}.$$

quantity, as 1 is to $\frac{1}{3}p$, and inscribe NP in the circle. Divide each of the two arcs NQP and NVP into three equal parts, and the required root is the sum of NQ, the chord subtending one-third the first arc, and NV, the chord subtending one-third of the second arc.[238]

Finally, suppose that we have $z^3 = pz - q$. Construct the circle NQPV whose radius NO is equal to $\sqrt{\frac{1}{3}p}$, and let NP, equal to $\frac{3q}{p}$, be inscribed in this circle; then NQ, the chord of one-third the arc NQP, will be the first of the required roots, and NV, the chord of one-third the other arc, will be the second.

An exception must be made in the case in which the square of half the last term is greater than the cube of one-third the coefficient of the next to the last term;[239] for then the line NP cannot be inscribed in the circle, since it is longer than the diameter. In this case, the two

[238] It may be noted that the equation $z^3 = 3z - q$ may be obtained from the equation $z^3 = 3z + q$ by transforming the latter into an equation whose roots have the opposite signs. Then the true roots of $z^3 = 3z - q$ are the false roots of $z^3 = 3z + q$ and vice-versa. Therefore FL = NQ + NP is now the true root.

[239] The so-called irreducible case.

LIVRE TROISIESME. 399

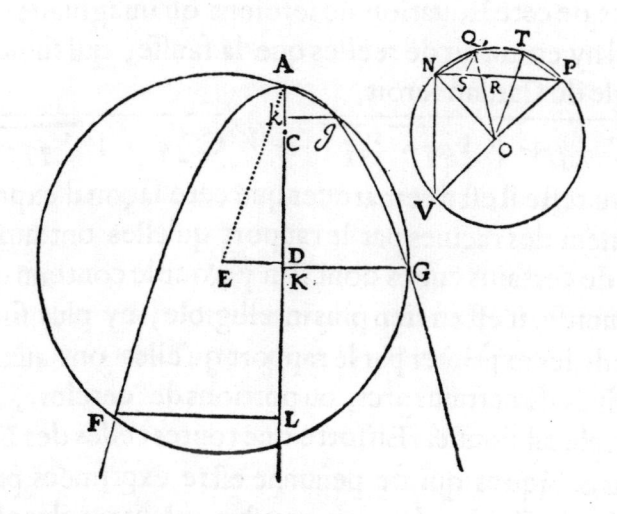

c'est a dire qui soit à l'autre quantité donnée q comme l'vnité est au tiers de p; il ne faut que diuiser chascun des deux arcs N Q P & N V P en trois parties esgales, & on aura N Q, la subtendue du tiers de l'vn, & N V la subtendue du tiers de l'autre, qui iointes ensemble composeront la racine cherchée.

Enfin si on a $z^3 \propto * p\, z - q$, en supposant derechef le cercle N Q P V, dont le rayon N O soit $\sqrt{\tfrac{1}{3}p}$, & l'inscrite NP soit $\tfrac{3p}{q}$, N Q la subtenduë du tiers de l'arc NQP sera l'vne des racines cherchées, & N V la subtendue du tiers de l'autre arc sera l'autre. Au moins si le quarré de la moitié du dernier terme, n'est point plus grand, que le cube du tiers de la quantité connuë du penultiesme. car s'il estoit plus grand, la ligne N P ne pourroit estre inscrite dans le cercle, a cause quelle seroit plus longue que son diametre: Ce qui seroit cause que les deux vrayes racines

400 LA GEOMETRIE.

cines de cete Equation ne feroient qu'imaginaires, & qu'il ny en auroit de reelles que la fauſſe, qui ſuiuant la reigle de Cardan ſeroit,

$$\sqrt{C.\tfrac{1}{2}q + \sqrt{\tfrac{1}{4}qq - \tfrac{1}{27}p^3}} + \sqrt{C.\tfrac{1}{2}q - \sqrt{\tfrac{1}{4}qq - \tfrac{1}{27}p^3}}.$$

La façon d'exprimer la valeur de toutes les racines des Equations cubiques: & enſuite de toutes celles qui ne montent que iuſquesau quarré de quarré.

Au reſte il eſt a remarquer que cete façon d'exprimer la valeur des racines par le rapport qu'elles ont aux coſtés de certains cubes dont il n'y a que le contenu qu'on connoiſſe, n'eſt en rien plus intelligible, ny plus ſimple, que de les exprimer par le rapport qu'elles ont aux ſubtenduës de certains arcs, ou portions de cercles, dont le triple eſt donné. En ſorte que toutes celles des Equations cubiques qui ne peuuent eſtre exprimées par les reigles de Cardan, le peuuent eſtre autant ou plus clairement par la façon icy propoſée.

Car ſi par exemple, on penſe connoiſtre la racine de cete Equation, $z^3 \infty * - qz + p$. a cauſe qu'on ſçait qu'elle eſt compoſée de deux lignes, dont l'vne eſt le coſté d'vn cube, duquel le contenu eſt $\tfrac{1}{2}q$, adiouſté au coſté d'vn quarré, duquel derechef le contenu eſt $\tfrac{1}{4}qq - \tfrac{1}{27}p^3$; Et l'autre eſt le coſté d'vn autre cube, dont le contenu eſt la difference, qui eſt entre $\tfrac{1}{2}q$, & le coſté de ce quarré dont le contenu eſt $\tfrac{1}{4}qq - \tfrac{1}{27}p^3$, qui eſt tout ce qu'on en apprent par la reigle de Cardan. Il ny a point de doute qu'on ne connoiſſe autant ou plus diſtinctement la racine de celle cy, $z^3 \infty * + q - p$, en la conſiderant inſcrite dans vn cercle, dont le demidiametre eſt $\sqrt{\tfrac{4}{3}p}$, & ſçachant qu'elle y eſt la ſubtenduë d'vn arc dont le triple a pour ſa ſubtendue $\tfrac{3q}{p}$. Meſme ces termes

roots that were true are merely imaginary, and the only real root is the one previously false, which according to Cardan's rule is

$$\sqrt[3]{\frac{1}{2}q+\sqrt{\frac{1}{4}q^2-\frac{1}{27}p^3}} + \sqrt[3]{\frac{1}{2}q-\sqrt{\frac{1}{4}q^2-\frac{1}{27}p^3}}.$$

Furthermore it should be remarked that this method of expressing the roots by means of the relations which they bear to the sides of certain cubes whose contents only are known[240] is in no respect clearer or simpler than the method of expressing them by means of the relations which they bear to the chords of certain arcs (or portions of circles), when arcs three times as long are known. And the roots of the cubic equations which cannot be solved by Cardan's method can be expressed as clearly as any others, or more clearly than the others, by the method given here.

For example, grant that we may consider a root of the equation $z^3 = -qz+p$ known, because we know that it is the sum of two lines of which one is the side of a cube whose volume is $\frac{1}{2}q$ increased by the side of a square whose area is $\frac{1}{4}q^2-\frac{1}{27}p^3$, and the other is the side of another cube whose volume is the difference between $\frac{1}{2}q$ and the side of a square whose area is $\frac{1}{4}q^2-\frac{1}{27}p^3$. This is as much knowledge of the roots as is furnished by Cardan's method. There is no doubt that the value of the root of the equation $z^3 = +qz-p$ is quite as well known and as clearly conceived when it is considered as the length of a chord inscribed in a circle of radius $\sqrt{\frac{1}{3}p}$ and subtending an arc that is one-third the arc subtended by a chord of length $\frac{3q}{p}$.

[240] Descartes here makes use of the geometrical conception of finding the cube root of a given quantity.

Indeed, these terms are much less complicated than the others, and they might be made even more concise by the use of some particular symbol to express such chords,[241] just as the symbol $\sqrt[3]{}$ [242] is used to represent the side of a cube.

By methods similar to those already explained, we can express the roots of any biquadratic equation, and there seems to me nothing further to be desired in the matter; for by their very nature these roots cannot be expressed in simpler terms, nor can they be determined by any constuction that is at the same time easier and more general.

It is true that I have not yet stated my grounds for daring to declare a thing possible or impossible, but if it is remembered that in the method I use all problems which present themselves to geometers reduce to a single type, namely, to the question of finding the values of the roots of an equation, it will be clear that a list can be made of all the ways of finding the roots, and that it will then be easy to prove our method the simplest and most general. Solid problems in particular cannot, as I have already said, be constructed without the use of a curve more complex than the circle. This follows at once from the fact that they all reduce to two constructions, namely, to one in which two mean pro-

[241] This is another indication of the tendency of Descartes's age toward symbolism. This suggestion was never adopted.

[242] In Descartes's notation, ⌐ C.

mes sont beaucoup moins embarassés que les autres, & ils se trouueront beaucoup plus cours si on veut vser de quelque chiffre particulier pour exprimer ces subtenduës, ainsi qu'on fait du chiffre $\sqrt{C}$. pour exprimer le costé des cubes.

Et on peut aussy en suite de cecy exprimer les racines de toutes les Equations qui montent iusques au quarré de quarré, par les reigles cy dessus expliquées. En sorte que ie ne sçache rien de plus a desirer en cete matiere. Car enfin la nature de ces racines ne permet pas qu'on les exprime en termes plus simples, ny qu'on les determine par aucune construction qui soit ensemble plus generale & plus facile.

Il est vray que ie n'ay pas encore dit sur quelles raisons ie me fonde, pour oser ainsi assurer, si vne chose est possible, ou ne l'est pas. Mais si on prent garde comment, par la methode dont ieme sers, tout ce qui tombe sous la consideration des Geometres, se reduist a vn mesme genre de Problesmes, qui est de chercher la valeur des racines de quelque Equation ; on iugera bien qu'il n'est pas malaysé de faire vn denombrement de toutes les voyes par lesquelles on les peut trouuer, qui soit suffisant pour demonstrer qu'on a choisi la plus generale, & la plus simple. Et particulierement pour ce qui est des Problesmes solides, que iay dit ne pouuoir estre construis, sans qu'on y employe quelque ligne plus composée que la circulaire, c'est chose qu'on peut assés trouuer, de ce qu'ils se reduisent tous a deux constructions ; en l'vne desquelles il faut auoir tout ensemble les deux poins, qui determinent deux moyenes proportionelles entre deux

Pourquoy les problesmes solides ne peuuent estre construits sans les sections coniques, ny ceux qui sont plus composés sans quelques autres lignes plus composées.

Eee lignes

402 LA GEOMETRIE.

lignes données; & en l'autre les deux poins, qui diuisent en trois parties esgales vn arc donné: Car d'autant que la courbure du cercle ne depend, que d'vn simple rapport de toutes ses parties, au point qui en est le centre ; on ne peut aussy s'en seruir qu a determiner vn seul point entre deux extremes, comme a trouuer vne moyenne proportionelle entre deux lignes droites données, ou diuiser en deux vn arc donné : Au lieu que la courbure des sections coniques, dependant tousiours de deux diuerses choses, peut aussy seruir a determiner deux poins differens.

Mais pour cete mesme raison il est impossible, qu'aucun des Problesmes qui sont d'vn degré plus composés que les solides, & qui presupposent l'inuention de quatre moyennes proportionelles, ou la diuision d'vn angle en cinq parties esgales, puissent estre construits par aucune des sections coniques. C'est pourquoy ie croyray faire en cecy tout le mieux qui se puisse, si ie donne vne reigle generale pour les construire, en y employant la ligne courbe qui se descrit par l'intersectiõ d'vne Parabole & d'vne ligne droite en la façon cy dessus expliquée. car i'ose asfurer qu'il ny en a point de plus simple en la nature, qui puisse seruir a ce mesme effect ; & vous auès vû comme elle suit immediatement les sections coniques, en cete question tant cherchée par les anciens, dont la solution enseigne par ordre toutes les lignes courbes, qui doiuent estre receuës en Geometrie.

Facon generale pour construire tous les problesmes reduits a

Vous sçaues desia comment, lorsqu'on cherche les quantités qui sont requises pour la construction de ces Problesmes, on les peut tousiours reduire a quelque Equation, qui ne monte que iusques au quarré de cube, ou

au

portionals are to be found between two given lines, and one in which two points are to be found which divide a given arc into three equal parts. Inasmuch as the curvature of a circle depends only upon a simple relation between the center and all points on the circumference, the circle can only be used to determine a single point between two extremes, as, for example, to find one mean proportional between two given lines or to bisect a given arc; while, on the other hand, since the curvature of the conic sections always depends upon two different things,[243] it can be used to determine two different points.

For a similar reason, it is impossible that any problem of degree more complex than the solid, involving the finding of four mean proportionals or the division of an angle into five equal parts, can be constructed by the use of one of the conic sections.

I therefore believe that I shall have accomplished all that is possible when I have given a general rule for constructing problems by means of the curve described by the intersection of a parabola and a straight line, as previously explained;[244] for I am convinced that there is nothing of a simpler nature that will serve this purpose. You have seen, too, that this curve directly follows the conic sections in that question to which the ancients devoted so much attention, and whose solution presents in order all the curves that should be received into geometry.

[243] As, for example, the distance of any point from the two foci. Descartes does not say "all points on the circumference," but "toutes ses parties."

[244] See page 84.

GEOMETRY

When quantities required for the construction of these problems are to be found, you already know how an equation can always be formed that is of no higher degree than the fifth or sixth. You also know how by increasing the roots of this equation we can make them all true, and at the same time have the coefficient of the third term greater than the square of half that of the second term. Also, if it is not higher than the fifth degree it can always be changed into an equation of the sixth degree in which every term is present.

Now to overcome all these difficulties by means of a single rule, I shall consider all these directions applied and the equation thereby reduced to the form:

$$y^6 - py^5 + qy^4 - ry^3 + sy^2 - ty + u = 0$$

in which q is greater than the square of $\tfrac{1}{2}p$.

Livre Troisiesme. 403

au surfolide. Puis vous sçaués aussy comment, en augmentant la valeur des racines de cete Equation, on peut tousiours faire qu'elles deuienent toutes vrayes; & auec cela que la quātité connuë du troisiesme terme soit plus grande que le quarré de la moitié de celle du second: Et enfin comment, si elle ne monte que iusques au surfolide, on la peut hausser iusques au quarré de cube; & faire que la place d'aucun de ses termes ne manque d'estre remplie. Or affin que toutes les difficultés, dont il est icy question, puissent estre resoluës par vne mesme reigle, ie desire qu'on face toutes ces choses, & par ce moyen qu'on les reduise tousiours a vne Equation de telle forme, *vne Equation qui n'a point plus de six dimésions.*

$$y^6 - py^5 + qy^4 - ry^3 + syy - ty + v \infty\, 0,$$

& en laquelle la quantité nommée *q* soit plus grande que le quarré de la moitié de celle qui est nommée *p*.

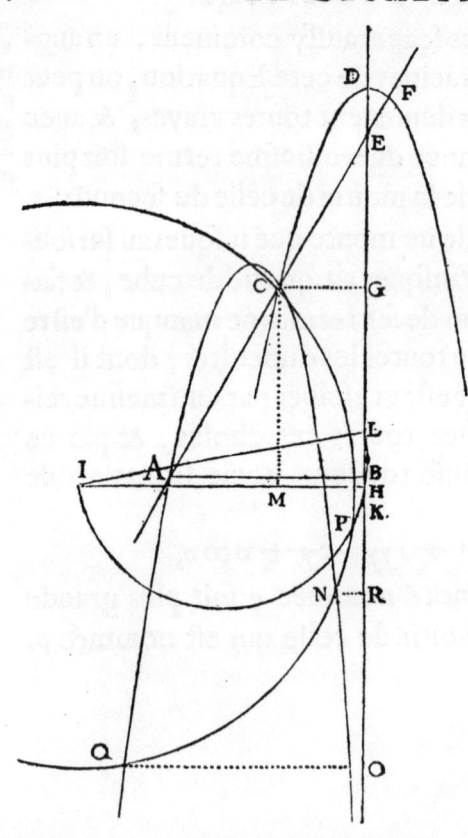

Puis ayant fait a ligne B K indefiniement longue des deux costés; & du point B ayant tiré la perpendiculaire A B, dontla longueur soit $\frac{1}{2}p$; il faut dans vn plan separé descrire vne Parabole, comme C D F dont le costé droit principal soit

$$\sqrt{\frac{s}{\sqrt{v}} + q - \frac{1}{4}pp,}$$

que ie nommeray *n* pour abreger. Aprés cela il faut poser le plan dans lequel est cete Parabole sur celuy ou sont les lignes A B & B K, en sorte que son aissieu D E se rencontre iustement au dessus de la ligne droite B K: Et ayant pris la partie de cet aissieu, qui est entre les poins E & D, esgale à $\frac{2\sqrt{v}}{pn}$, il faut appliquer sur ce point E vne longue reigle, en telle façon qu'estant aussy appliquée sur le point A du plan de dessous, elle demeure tousiours iointe a ces deux poins, pendant qu'on haussera ou baissera la Parabole

THIRD BOOK

Produce BK indefinitely in both directions, and at B draw AB perpendicular to BK and equal to $\frac{1}{2}p$. In a separate plane[245] describe the parabola CDF whose principal parameter is

$$\sqrt{\frac{t}{\sqrt{u}}+q-\frac{1}{4}p^2}$$

which we shall represent by n.

Now place the plane containing the parabola on that containing the lines AB and BK, in such a way that the axis DE of the parabola falls along the line BK. Take a point E such that $DE = \dfrac{2\sqrt{u}}{pn}$ and place a ruler so as to connect this point E and the point A of the lower plane. Hold the ruler so that it always connects these points, and slide the parabola up or down, keeping its axis always along BK. Then the

---

[245] This does not mean in a fixed plane intersecting the first, but, for example, on another piece of paper.

point C, the intersection of the parabola and the ruler, will describe the curve ACN, which is to be used in the construction of the proposed problem.

Having thus described the curve, take a point L in the line BK on the concave side of the parabola, and such that $BL = DE = \dfrac{2\sqrt{u}}{pn}$; then lay off on BK, toward B, LH equal to $\dfrac{t}{2n\sqrt{u}}$, and from H draw HI perpendicular to LH and on the same side as the curve ACN. Take HI equal to

$$\frac{r}{2n^2} + \frac{\sqrt{u}}{n^2} + \frac{pt}{4n^2\sqrt{u}}$$

which we may, for the sake of brevity, set equal to $\dfrac{m}{n^2}$. Join L and I, and describe the circle LPI on LI as diameter; then inscribe in this circle the line LP equal to $\sqrt{\dfrac{s + p\sqrt{u}}{n^2}}$. Finally, describe the circle PCN about I as center and passing through P. This circle will cut or touch the curve ACN in as many points as the equation has roots; and hence the perpendiculars CG, NR, QO, and so on, dropped from these points upon BK, will be the required roots. This rule never fails nor does it admit of any exceptions.

For if the quantity s were so large in proportion to the others, p, q, r, t, u, that the line LP was greater than the diameter of the circle

Livre Troisiesme. 405

bole tout le long de la ligne B K, sur laquelle son aissieu est appliqué au moyen dequoy l'intersection de cete Parabole, & de cete reigle, qui se fera au point C, descrira la ligne courbe A C N, qui est celle dont nous auons besoin de nous seruir pour la construction du Problesme proposé. Car aprés qu'elle est ainsi descrite, si on prent le point L en la ligne B K, du costé vers lequel est tourné le sommet de la Parabole, & qu'on face B L esgale à D E, c'est à dire à $\frac{2Vv}{pn}$: Puis du point L, vers B, qu'on prene en la mesme ligne B K, la ligne L H, esgale à $\frac{t}{2nVv}$; & que du point H ainsi trouué, on tire à angles droits, du costé qu'est la courbe A C N, la ligne H I, dont la longeur soit $\frac{r}{2nn}+\frac{Vv}{nn}+\frac{pt}{4nnVv}$, qui pour abreger sera nommée $\frac{m}{nn}$: Et aprés, ayant ioint les poins L & I, qu'on descriue le cercle L P I, dont I L soit le diametre; & qu'on inscriue en ce cercle la ligne L P dont la longeur soit $\sqrt{\frac{s\mp pVv}{nn}}$: Puis enfin du centre I, par le point P ainsi trouué, qu'on descriue le cercle P C N. Ce cercle couppera ou touchera la ligne courbe A C N, en autant de poins qu'il y aura de racines en l'Equation : En sorte que les perpendiculaires tirées de ces poins sur la ligne B K, comme C G, N R, Q O, & semblables, seront les racines cherchées. Sans qu'il y ait aucune exception ny aucun deffaut en cete reigle. Car si la quantité *s* estoit si grande, à proportion des autres *p*, *q*, *r*, *t*, & *v*, que la ligne L P se trouuast plus grande que le diametre du cer-

Eee 3 cle

406　La Geometrie.

cle I L, en sorte qu'elle n'y pust estre inscrite, il ny auroit aucune racine en l'Equation proposée qui ne fust imaginaire: Non plus que si le cercle I P estoit si petit, qu'il ne coupast la courbe A C N en aucun point. Et il la peut couper en six differens, ainsi qu'il peut y auoir six diuerses racines en l'Equation. Mais lorsqu'il la coupe en moins, cela tesmoigne qu'il y a quelques vnes de ces racines qui sont esgales entre elles, oubien qui ne sont qu'imaginaires.

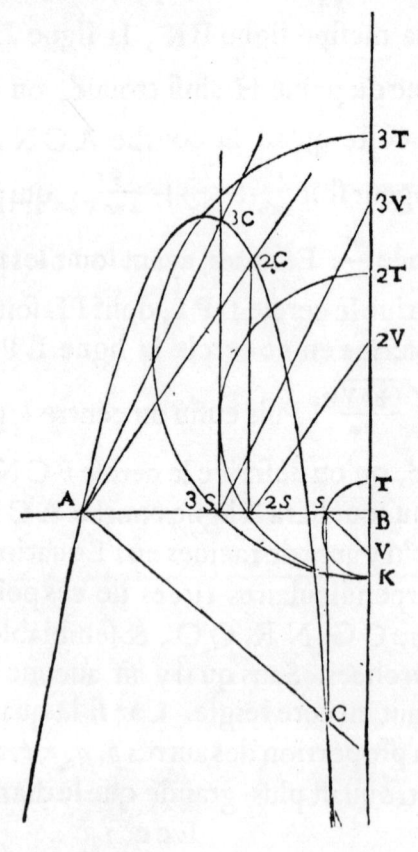

Que

THIRD BOOK

LI,[246] so that LP could not be inscribed in it, every root of the proposed equation would be imaginary; and the same would be true if the circle IP[247] were so small that it did not cut the curve ACN at any point. The circle IP will in general cut the curve ACN in six different points, so that the equation can have six distinct roots.[248] But if it cuts it in fewer points, this indicates that some of the roots are equal or else imaginary.

[246] That is, the circle IPL, of which the diameter is t, page 222.
[247] That is, the circle PCN.
[248] The points determining these roots must be points of intersection of the circle with the main branch of the curve obtained, that is, of the branch ACN.

If, however, this method of tracing the curve ACN by the translation of a parabola seems to you awkward, there are many other ways of describing it. We might take AB and BL as before (page 226), and BK equal to the latus rectum of the parabola, and describe the semicircle KST with its center in BK and cutting AB in some point S. Then from the point T where it ends, take TV toward K equal to BL and join S and V. Draw AC through A parallel to SV, and draw·SC through S parallel to BK; then C, the intersection of AC and SC will be one point of the required curve. In this way we can find as many points of the curve as may be desired.

Livre Troisiesme.

Que si la'façon de tracer la ligne A C N par le mouuement d'vne Parabole vous semble incommode, il est aysé de trouuer plusieurs autres moyens pour la descrire. Comme si ayant les mesmes quantités que deuant pour A B & B L; & la mesme pour B K, qu'on auoit posée pour le costé droit principal de la Parabole, on descrit le demicercle K S T dont le centre soit pris a discretion dans la ligne B K, en sorte qu'il couppe quelq; part la ligne A B, comme au point S, & que du point T, ou il finist, on prene vers K la ligne T V, esgale à B L; puis ayant tiré la ligne S V, qu'on en tire vne autre, qui luy soit parallele, par le point A, comme A C; & qu'on en tire aussy vne autre par S, qui soit parallele a B K, comme S C; le point C, ou ces deux paralleles se rencontrent, sera l'vn de ceux de la ligne courbe cherchée. Et on en peut trouuer, en mesme sorte, autant d'autres qu'on en desire.

Or

LA GEOMETRIE.

Or la demonstration de tout cecy est assés facile. car appliquant la reigle A E auec la Parabole ED, sur le point C; comme il est certain qu'elles peuuent y estre appliquées ensemble, puisque ce point C est en la courbe A C N, qui est descrite par leur intersection; si C G se nomme y, G D sera $\frac{yy}{n}$, à cause que le costé droit, qui est n, est à C G, comme C G a G D. & ostant D E, qui est $\frac{2Vv}{pn}$, de G D, on a $\frac{yy}{n} - \frac{2Vv}{pn}$, pour G E. Puis à cause que A B est a B E, comme C G est a G E ; A B estant $\frac{1}{2}p$, B E est $\frac{py}{2n} - \frac{Vv}{ny}$.

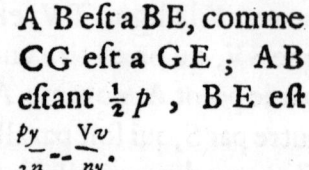

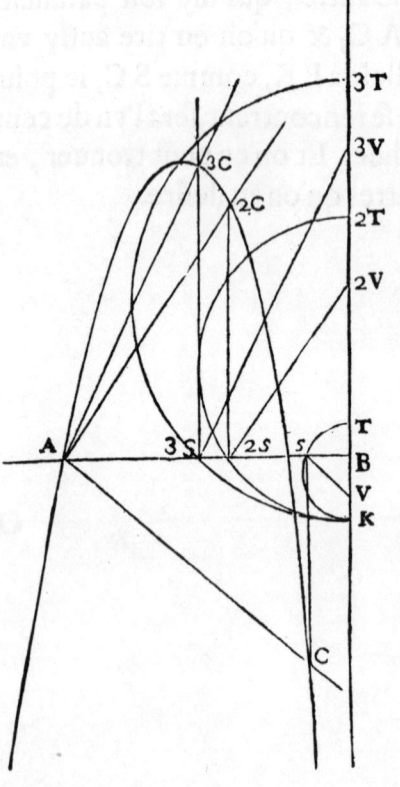

Et tout de mesme en supposant que le point C de la courbe à esté trouué par l'intersectiõ des lignes droites, S C parallele à B K, & A C parallele a S V. S B qui est esgale à C G, est y : & BK estant esgale au costé droit de la Parabole, que iay nommé n, B T est $\frac{yy}{n}$. car comme K B est a B S, ainsi B S est a B T. Et T V estant

The demonstration of all this is very simple. Place the ruler AE and the parabola FD so that both pass through the point C. This can always be done, since C lies on the curve ACN which is described by the intersection of the parabola and the ruler. If we let CG $= y$, GD will equal $\frac{y^2}{n}$, since the latus rectum n is to CG as CG is to GD. Then DE $= \frac{2\sqrt{u}}{pn}$, and subtracting DE from GD we have GE $= \frac{y^2}{n} - \frac{2\sqrt{u}}{pn}$. Since AB is to BE as CG is to GE, and AB is equal to $\frac{1}{2}p$, therefore BE $= \frac{py}{2n} - \frac{\sqrt{u}}{ny}$. Now let C be a point on the curve generated by the intersection of the line SC, which is parallel to BK, and AC, which is parallel to SV. Let SB $=$ CG $= y$, and BK $= n$, the latus rectum of the parabola. Then BT $= \frac{y^2}{n}$, for KB is to BS as BS is

to BT, and since $TV = BL = \dfrac{2\sqrt{u}}{pn}$ we have $BV = \dfrac{y^2}{n} - \dfrac{2\sqrt{u}}{pn}$. Also SB is to BV as AB is to BE, whence $BE = \dfrac{py}{2n} - \dfrac{\sqrt{u}}{ny}$ as before. It is evident, therefore, that one and the same curve is described by these two methods.

Furthermore, $BL = DE$, and therefore $DL = BE$; also $LH = \dfrac{t}{2n\sqrt{u}}$

and $$DL = \dfrac{py}{2n} - \dfrac{\sqrt{u}}{ny}$$

therefore $$DH = LH + DL = \dfrac{py}{2n} - \dfrac{\sqrt{u}}{ny} + \dfrac{t}{2n\sqrt{u}}.$$

Also, since $GD = \dfrac{y^2}{n}$,

$$GH = DH - GD = \dfrac{py}{2n} - \dfrac{\sqrt{u}}{ny} + \dfrac{t}{2n\sqrt{u}} - \dfrac{y^2}{n}$$

which may be written

$$GH = \dfrac{-y^3 + \dfrac{1}{2}py^2 + \dfrac{ty}{2\sqrt{u}} - \sqrt{u}}{ny}$$

and the square of GH is equal to

$$\dfrac{y^6 - py^5 + \left(\dfrac{1}{4}p^2 - \dfrac{t}{\sqrt{u}}\right)y^4 + \left(2\sqrt{u} + \dfrac{pt}{2\sqrt{u}}\right)y^3 + \left(\dfrac{t^2}{4u} - p\sqrt{u}\right)y^2 - ty + u}{n^2 y^2}$$

Whatever point of the curve is taken as C, whether toward N or toward Q, it will always be possible to express the square of the segment of BH between the point H and the foot of the perpendicular from C to BH in these same terms connected by these same signs.

Livre Troisiesme. 409

estant la mesme que BL, c'est a dire $\frac{2\sqrt{v}}{pn}$, BV est $\frac{yy}{n} - \frac{2\sqrt{v}}{pn}$: & comme SB est a BV, ainsi AB est à BE, qui est par consequent $\frac{py}{2n} - \frac{\sqrt{v}}{ny}$ comme deuant, d'où on voit que c'est vne mesme ligne courbe qui se descrit en ces deux façons.

Aprés cela, pourceque BL & DE sont esgales, DL & BE le sont aussy: de façon qu'adioustât LH, qui est $\frac{t}{2n\sqrt{v}}$, à DL, qui est $\frac{py}{2n} - \frac{\sqrt{v}}{ny}$, on à la toute DH, qui est $\frac{py}{2n} - \frac{\sqrt{v}}{ny} + \frac{t}{2n\sqrt{v}}$; & en ostant GD, qui est $\frac{yy}{n}$, on à GH, qui est $\frac{py}{2n} - \frac{\sqrt{v}}{ny} + \frac{t}{2n\sqrt{v}} - \frac{yy}{n}$. Ce que i'escris par ordre en cete sorte GH $\infty \frac{-y^3 + \frac{1}{2}pyy + \frac{ty}{2\sqrt{v}} - \sqrt{v}}{ny}$.

Et le quarré de GH est,

$$\frac{y^6 - py^5 \left\{\begin{matrix}- \frac{t}{\sqrt{v}} \\ + \frac{1}{4}pp\end{matrix}\right\} y^4 \left\{\begin{matrix}+ 2\sqrt{v} \\ + \frac{pt}{2\sqrt{v}}\end{matrix}\right\} y^3 \left\{\begin{matrix}- p\sqrt{v} \\ + \frac{tt}{4v}\end{matrix}\right\} yy - ty + v}{nn\,yy}$$

Et en quelque autre endroit de cete ligne courbe qu'on veuille imaginer le point C, comme vers N, ou vers Q, on trouuera tousiours que le quarré de là ligne droite, qui est entre le point H & celuy où tombe la perpendiculaire du point C sur BH, peut estre exprimée en ces mesmes termes, & auec les mesmes signes $+$ & $-$.

De plus IH estant $\frac{m}{nn}$, & LH estant $\frac{t}{2n\sqrt{v}}$, IL est $\sqrt{\frac{mm}{n^4} + \frac{tt}{2n\sqrt{v}}}$, à cause de l'angle droit IHL; & LP estāt

Fff $\qquad \sqrt{}$

410 LA GEOMETRIE.

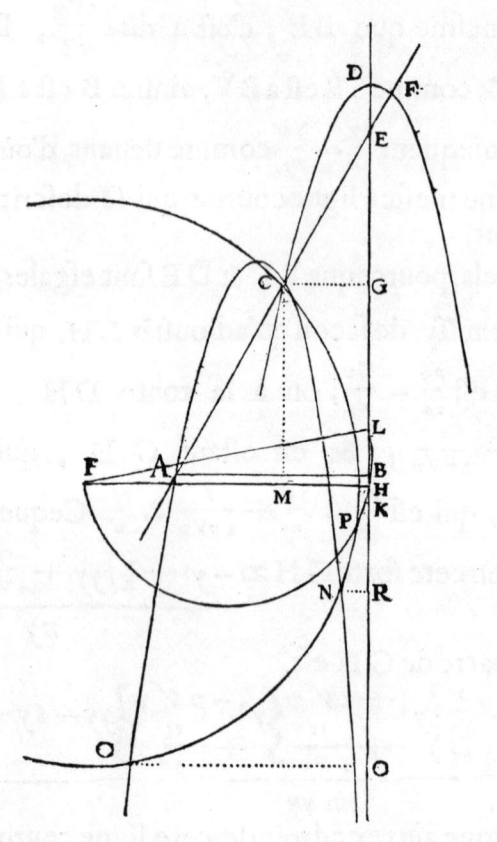

$$\sqrt{\frac{s}{nn} + \frac{p\sqrt{v}}{nn}},$$ I P ou I C est,

$$\sqrt{\frac{mm}{n^4} + \frac{tt}{4nnv} - \frac{s}{nn} - \frac{p\sqrt{v}}{nn}},$$ a cause auſſy de l'angle droit I P L. Puis ayant fait C M perpendiculaire ſur I H, I M eſt la difference qui eſt entre I H, & H M ou C G, c'eſt a dire entre $\frac{m}{nn}$, & y, en ſorte que ſon quarré eſt touſiours $\frac{mm}{n^4} - \frac{2my}{nn} + yy$, qui eſtant oſté du quarré

de

THIRD BOOK

Again, $IH = \dfrac{m}{n^2}$, $LH = \dfrac{t}{2n\sqrt{u}}$, whence

$$IL = \sqrt{\dfrac{m^2}{n^4} + \dfrac{t^2}{4n^2 u}},$$

since the angle IHL is a right angle; and since

$$LP = \sqrt{\dfrac{s}{n^2} + \dfrac{p\sqrt{u}}{n^2}}$$

and the angle IPL is a right angle,

$$IC = IP = \sqrt{\dfrac{m^2}{n^4} + \dfrac{t^2}{4n^2 u} - \dfrac{s}{n^2} - \dfrac{p\sqrt{u}}{n^2}}$$

Now draw CM perpendicular to IH, and

$$IM = HI - HM = HI - CG = \dfrac{m}{n^2} - y;$$

whence the square of IM is $\dfrac{m^2}{n^4} - \dfrac{2my}{n^2} + y^2$.

Taking this from the square of IC there remains the square of CM, or

$$\frac{t^2}{4n^2u} - \frac{s}{n^2} - \frac{p\sqrt{u}}{n^2} + \frac{2my}{n^2} - y^2,$$

and this is equal to the square of GH, previously found. This may be written

$$\frac{-n^2y^4 + 2my^3 - p\sqrt{u}\,y^2 - sy^2 + \frac{t^2}{4u}y^2}{n^2y^2}.$$

Now, putting

$$\frac{t}{\sqrt{u}}y^4 + qy^4 - \frac{1}{4}p^2y^4$$

for n^2y^4, and

$$ry^3 + 2\sqrt{u}\,y^3 + \frac{pt}{2\sqrt{u}}y^3$$

for $2my^3$, and multiplying both members by n^2y^2, we have

$$y^6 - py^5 + \left(\frac{1}{4}p^2 - \frac{t}{\sqrt{u}}\right)y^4 + \left(2\sqrt{u} + \frac{pt}{2\sqrt{u}}\right)y^3 + \left(\frac{t^2}{4u} - p\sqrt{u}\right)y^2 - ty + u$$

equals

$$\left(\frac{1}{4}p^2 - q - \frac{t}{\sqrt{u}}\right)y^4 + \left(r + 2\sqrt{u} + \frac{pt}{2\sqrt{u}}\right)y^3 + \left(\frac{t^2}{4u} - s - p\sqrt{u}\right)y^2,$$

or

$$y^6 - py^5 + qy^4 - ry^3 + sy^2 - ty + u = 0,$$

whence it appears that the lines CG, NR, QO, etc., are the roots of this equation.

If then it be desired to find four mean proportionals between the lines a and b, if we let x be the first, the equation is $x^5 - a^4b = 0$ or $x^6 - a^4bx = 0$. Let $y - a = x$, and we get

$$y^6 - 6ay^5 + 15a^2y^4 - 20a^3y^3 + 15a^4y^2 - (6a^5 + a^4b)y + a^6 + a^5b = 0.$$

Therefore, we must take AB $= 3a$, and BK, the latus rectum of the

Livre Troisiesme. 411

de I C, il reste $\frac{tt}{4nnv} - \frac{s}{nn} - \frac{pVv}{nn} + \frac{2my}{nn} - yy$.
pour le quarré de C M, qui est esgal au quarré de G H desia trouué. Oubien en faisant que cete somme soit diuisée comme l'autre par $nnyy$, on a

$$\frac{-nny^4 + 2my^3 - pV\overline{v}\,yy - syy + \frac{tt}{4v}yy}{nnyy}. \text{ Puis}$$

remettant $\frac{t}{Vv}y^4 + qy^4 - \frac{1}{4}ppy^4$, pour nny^4; & $ry^3 + 2V\overline{v}\,y^3 + \frac{pt}{2Vv}y^3$, pour $2my^3$: & multipliant l'vne & l'autre somme par $nnyy$, on a

$$y^6 - py^5 - \begin{Bmatrix}\tfrac{t}{Vv}\\+\tfrac{1}{4}pp\end{Bmatrix}y^4 + \begin{Bmatrix}2V\overline{v}\\+\tfrac{pt}{2Vv}\end{Bmatrix}y^3 - \begin{Bmatrix}pV\overline{v}\\+\tfrac{tt}{4v}\end{Bmatrix}yy - ty + v$$

esgal à

$$\begin{Bmatrix}-\tfrac{t}{Vv}\\-q\\+\tfrac{1}{4}pp\end{Bmatrix}y^4 + \begin{Bmatrix}+r\\+2V\overline{v}\\+\tfrac{pt}{2Vv}\end{Bmatrix}y^3 - \begin{Bmatrix}pV\overline{v}\\s\\+\tfrac{tt}{4v}\end{Bmatrix}yy$$

C'est a dire qu'on a,
$y^6 - py^5 + qy^4 - ry^3 + syy - ty + v \infty 0$.
D'où il paroist que les lignes C G, N R, Q O, & semblables sont les racines de cete Equation, qui est ce qu'il falloit demonstrer.

Ainsi donc si on veut trouuer quatre moyennes proportionnelles entre les lignes a & b, ayant posé x pour la premiere, l'Equation est $x^5 **** - a^4b \infty 0$ oubien $x^6 **** - a+b\,x^* \infty 0$. Et faisant $y - a \infty x$ il vient
$y^6 - 6ay^5 + 15aay^4 - 20a^3y^3 + 15a^4yy - \begin{Bmatrix}6a^5\\a_4\end{Bmatrix}y \begin{matrix}+a^6\\+a^5b\end{matrix} \infty 0$.
C'est pourquoy il faut prendre $3a$ pour la ligne A B, &
$\frac{\sqrt{6a^3 \mp aab}}{\sqrt{aa \mp ab}} + 6aa$ pour B K, ou le costé droit de la Pa-

Fff 2 rabole

rabole que iay nommé n. & $\frac{2a}{3n} \sqrt{aa + ab}$ pour D E ou B L. Et aprés auoir descrit la ligne courbe A C N sur la mesure de ces trois, il faut faire L H, $\infty \frac{6a^3 + aab}{2n\sqrt{aa+ab}}$

& H I $\infty \frac{10a^3}{nn} + \frac{aa}{nn}\sqrt{aa+ab} + \frac{18a^4 + 3a^3 b}{nn\sqrt{aa+ab}}$ & L P ∞

$\frac{\sqrt{15a^4 + 6a^3 \sqrt{aa+ab}}}{nn}$ Car le cercle qui ayant son centre au point I passera par le point P ainsi trouué, couppera la courbe aux deux poins C & N ; desquels ayant tiré les perdendiculaires N R & C G, si la moindre, N R, est ostée de la plus grande, C G, le reste sera, x, la premiere des quatre moyennes proportionelles cherchées.

Il est aysé en mesme façon de diuiser vn angle en cinq parties esgales, & d'inscrire vne figure d'vnze ou treze costés esgaux dans vn cercle, & de trouuer vne infinité d'autres exemples de cete reigle.

Toutefois il est a remarquer, qu'en plusieurs de ces exemples, il peut arriuer que le cercle couppe si obliquement la parabole du second genre; que le point de leur intersection soit difficile a reconnoistre: & ainsi que cete construction ne soit pas commode pour la pratique. A quoy il seroit aysé de remedier en composant d'autres regles, à l'imitation de celle cy , comme on en peut composer de mille sortes.

Mais mon dessein n'est pas de faire vn gros liure, & ie tasche plutost de comprendre beaucoup en peu de mots: comme on iugera peuteftre que iay fait, si on considere, qu'ayant reduit à vne mesme construction tous les

parabola must be

$$\sqrt{\frac{6a^3+a^2b}{\sqrt{a^2+ab}}+6a^2}$$

which I shall call n, and DE or BL will be

$$\frac{2a}{3n}\sqrt{a^2+ab}.$$

Then having described the curve ACN, we must have

$$LH = \frac{6a^3+a^2b}{2n\sqrt{a^2+ab}}$$

and

$$HI = \frac{10a^3}{n^2} + \frac{a^2}{n^2}\sqrt{a^2+ab} + \frac{18a^4+3a^3b}{2n^2\sqrt{a^2+ab}},$$

and

$$LP = \frac{a}{n}\sqrt{15a^2 + 6a\sqrt{a^2+ab}}.$$

For the circle about I as center will pass through the point P thus found, and cut the curve in the two points C and N. If we draw the perpendiculars NR and CG, and subtract NR, the smaller, from CG, the greater, the remainder will be x, the first of the four required mean proportionals.[249]

This method applies as well to the division of an angle into five equal parts, the inscription of a regular polygon of eleven or thirteen sides in a circle, and an infinity of other problems. It should be remarked, however, that in many of these problems it may happen that the circle cuts the parabola of the second class so obliquely[250] that it is hard to determine the exact point of intersection. In such cases this construction is not of practical value.[251] The difficulty could easily be overcome by forming other rules analogous to these, which might be done in a thousand different ways.

---

[249] The two roots of the above equation in y are NR and CG. But we know that a is one of the roots of this equation, and therefore NR, the shorter length, must be a, and CG must be y. Then $x = y - a = $ CG $-$ NR, the first of the required mean proportionals. Rabuel, p. 580.

[250] That is, makes so small an angle with it.

[251] This is especially noticeable when there are six real positive roots.

But it is not my purpose to write a large book. I am trying rather to include much in a few words, as will perhaps be inferred from what I have done, if it is considered that, while reducing to a single construction all the problems of one class, I have at the same time given a method of transforming them into an infinity of others, and thus of solving each in an infinite number of ways; that, furthermore, having constructed all plane problems by the cutting of a circle by a straight line, and all solid problems by the cutting of a circle by a parabola; and, finally, all that are but one degree more complex by cutting a circle by a curve but one degree higher than the parabola, it is only necessary to follow the same general method to construct all problems, more and more complex, ad infinitum; for in the case of a mathematical progression, whenever the first two or three terms are given, it is easy to find the rest.

I hope that posterity will judge me kindly, not only as to the things which I have explained, but also as to those which I have intentionally omitted so as to leave to others the pleasure of discovery.

[THE END]

Livre Troisiesme.

les Problesmes d'vn mesme genre, iay tout ensemble donné la façon de les reduire à vne infinité d'autres diuerses; & ainsi de resoudre chascun deux en vne infinité de façons. Puis outre cela qu'ayant construit tous ceux qui sont plans, en coupant d'vn cercle vne ligne droite; & tous ceux qui sont solides, en coupant aussy d'vn cercle vne Parabole; & enfin tous ceux qui sont d'vn degré plus composés, en coupant tout de mesme d'vn cercle vne ligne qui n'est que d'vn degré plus composée que la Parabole; il ne faut que suiure la mesme voye pour construire tous ceux qui sont plus composés a l'infini. Car en matiere de progressions Mathematiques, lorsqu'on a les deux ou trois premiers termes, il n'est pas malaysé de trouuer les autres. Et i'espere que nos neueux me sçauront gré, non seulement des choses que iay icy expliquées; mais aussy de celles que iay omises volontairement, affin de leur laisser le plaisir de les inuenter.

F I N.

PAr grace & priuilege du Roy tres chreſtien il eſt permis a l'Autheur du liure intitulé *Diſcours de la Methode &c. plus la Dioptrique, les Meteores, & la Geometrie &c.* de le faire imprimer en telle part que bon luy ſemblera dedans & dehors le royaume de France, & ce pendant le terme de dix annees conſequuutiues, a conter du iour qu'il ſera paracheué d'imprimer, ſans qu'aucun autre que le libraire qu'il aura choiſi le puiſſe imprimer, ou faire imprimer, en tout ny en partie, ſous quelque pretexte ou deguiſement que ce puiſſe eſtre; ny en vendre ou debiter d'autre impreſſion que de celle qui aura eſté faite par ſa permiſſion, a peine de mil liures d'amande, confiſcation de tous les exemplaires &c. Ainſi qu'il eſt plus amplement declaré dans les lettres donnees a Paris le 4 iour de May 1637. ſignees par le Roy en ſon conſeil *Ceberet* & ſeellees du grand ſceau de cire iaune ſur ſimple queuë.

l'Autheur a permis a Ian Maire marchand libraire a Leyde, d'imprimer le dit liure & de iouir du dit priuilege pour le tems & aux conditions entre eux accordeés.

Acheué d'imprimer le 8. iour de Iuin 1637.

By the grace and privilege of the very Christian King, it is permitted to the author of the book entitled *Discourse on Method*, etc., together with *Dioptrics, Meteorology, and Geometry*, etc., to have printed wherever he wishes, within or without the Kingdom of France, and during the period of ten consecutive years, beginning on the day when the printing is completed, without any publisher (except the one whom he selects) printing it, or causing it to be printed, under any pretext or disguise, or selling or delivering any other impression except that which has been allowed, under penalty of a fine of a thousand livres, the confiscation of all the copies, etc. This is more fully set forth in the letters given at Paris, on the fourth day of May, 1637, signed by the King and his counsel, Ceberet, and sealed with the great seal of yellow wax on a simple ribbon.

The author has given permission to Jan Maire, bookseller at Leyden, to print the said book and enjoy the said privilege for the time and under the conditions agreed upon between them.

The printing is completed the eighth day of June, 1637.

INDEX

The numbers refer to the pages of the present edition, not to those at the top of the facsimiles.

	PAGE
Abscissa	88
Adam, C.	10, 17
Agnesi, M. G.	2
Alembert, J. le R. d'	40
Angle, division of	219, 239
Apollonius	17-22, 26, 68, 72, 75, 96
Applicate	67
Arithmetic and geometry	2
Axes	95
Ball, W. W. R.	6
Beaune, F. de	2
Beman, W. W.	13, 26
Biquadratic equation	195 seq., 216 seq.
Boncompagni, B.	159
Bouquet, J. C.	55, 67, 71
Boyd, J. H.	55
Briot, C.	55, 67, 71
Cantor, M.	44, 91, 92, 160, 175, 179, 211
Cardan, H. (G., or J.)	159, 160, 211, 215
Catoptrics	115
Cavalieri, B.	26
Cissoid	44
Clairaut, A. C.	147
Class of curves	48, 56
Commandinus, F.	6, 17, 19
Complex curves	43, 48, 56
Conchoid	44, 55, 113
Conic sections	44
Coördinates, transformation of	51

	PAGE
Cousin, V.	10, 19, 63, 72, 112, 135
Cubic equation	195 seq., 208 seq.
Curved lines	40
D'Alembert, J. le R.	40
Diderot, D.	40
Dioptrics	115, 124, 135
Division	2
Enriques, F.	13
Equality, symbol of	6
Equating to zero	96
Equations	13, 34, 37, 156, 159, 192, 195
Equations, transformation of	163, 164, 166
Euclid	17, 19, 22
False (negative) roots	159, 200
Fermat, P.	25, 26, 112
Fibonacci, L.	159
Fink, K.	26
Focus	128
Fundamental theorem	160
Geometric curves	40, 48
Guisnée	156
Harriot, T.	160
Heath, T. L.	26, 44, 96, 155
Heiberg, J. L.	68
Horner's Method	179
Hultsch, F.	6, 19

INDEX

	PAGE
Hutton, C.	67
Imaginary roots	175, 187
Irreducible cubic	212
Kepler, J.	128
Klein, F.	13
Leibniz, G. W.	40
Lenses	124-147
Leonardo Pisano	159
L'Hospital, G. F. A., de	156
Loci, plane and solid	79
Mascheroni, L.	13
Mechanical curves	40, 91
Mean proportionals	47, 155, 219
Mersenne, Marin	10, 63
Mikami, Y.	179
Mirrors	127-136
Multiplication	2, 33
Negative numbers	63, 111
Normals	112
Order of curves	48
Ordinate	67, 88
Oresme, N.	26
Ovals	116-131, 143
Pappus	6, 17, 19, 21, 26, 40, 59, 63, 156, 188
Pappus, problem of	19, 21, 63
Parent, A.	147
Plato	6
Pliny	135
Polygon, regular	239
Problem solving	6
Ptolemy, C.	135
Quadratic equation	13, 34
Quadratrix	44

	PAGE
Rabuel, C.	2, 6, 9, 17, 33, 40, 47, 55, 56, 59, 68, 79, 88, 107, 111, 112, 120, 135, 191, 208, 239
Remainder Theorem	179
Riccati, V.	2
Roberval, G. P., de	26
Roots	5
Roots increased or diminished	163
Roots multiplied or divided	172
Rudolph, C.	159
Rule of Signs (equations)	160
Russell, B.	91
Saladino, G.	2
Scipio Ferreus	211
Signs, Rule of (equations)	160
Smith, D. E.	13, 26, 44, 92, 179, 211
Solid analytic geometry	147
Spirals	44
Steiner, J.	13
Stifel, M.	159
Supersolids (sursolids)	56, 80, 152
Symbolism	5, 6, 175, 180
Synthetic division	179
Tangents	112
Tannery, P.	10, 17, 21
Tartaglia, N.	211
Taylor, C.	44
Three-dimensional space	147
Transcendental curves	91
Transformation of roots	164, 166
True roots	159
Van Schooten, F.	2, 6, 9, 55, 147
Vieta, F.	10, 26, 43
Weber, H.	13
Wellstein, J.	13
Zeuthen, H. G.	17